Galileo Galilei and Motion
A reconstruction of 50 years of experiments and discoveries

Società Italiana di Fisica

Springer

Translated from the Italian by Christine Valerie Pennison - Pisa, Italy

Produced by the Editorial Staff of the Italian Physical Society under the supervision of Angela Oleandri

Data conversion and page setting: Marco D'Amico, Stampa Trentini, Argenta (Ferrara), Italy

Printing and binding: Compositori Industrie Grafiche, s.r.l, Bologna, Italy

Cover illustration: Simona Oleandri. The portrait of Galileo Galilei is an elaboration of the original drawing by Angelo Grilli, and is reproduced here by kind permission of the Artist.

Angelo Grilli

The Italian sculptor Angelo Grilli was born in Pavia in 1932 and dedicated himself to the plastic arts since his youth. He attended the *Scuola d'Arte* in Pavia and then the *Scuola Superiore d'Arte Cristiana* in Milan and *Accademia d'Arte Cignaroli* in Verona.
He is the author of many sculptures among which the War Memorial of Pavia, the bronze statue "La Grande Pace" in the archaeological area of Cadoneghe (Padua), the sculpture in the boardroom of the Cariplo Foundation in the City of London, the monumental fountain "Fontana delle Quattro Stagioni" in the historical center of the town of Alba (Cuneo).
To him we also due the bronze door and the magnificent absidal bas-relief of the Church "Sacra Famiglia" in Pavia and the "Annunciazione" of the Monumental Cemetery in Milan.
He is a worldwide famous medallist, having designed more than 100 models of striked medals.
His works are permanently exposed in international museums such as the Museo Vaticano in Rome, the Residenz Museum in Munich, the British Museum in London, and the Wroclaw Museum in Krakow.

Galileo Galilei and Motion

A reconstruction of 50 years of experiments and discoveries

Roberto Vergara Caffarelli

Roberto VERGARA CAFFARELLI
Dipartimento di Fisica
Università di Pisa
Largo Bruno Pontecorvo, 3
56127 Pisa, Italy

ISBN 978-88-7438-049-7, SIF, Italy
ISBN-13 978-3-642-04352-9, Springer, Berlin, Heidelberg, New York
ISBN-10 3-642-04352-6, Springer, Berlin, Heidelberg, New York
Library of Congress Control Number 2009934014

jointly published by:

Società Italiana di Fisica, Bologna
www.sif.it

Springer, Berlin, Heidelberg, New York
www.springer.com

printed in Italy on acid-free paper

SPIN 12652174

Table of Contents

Abbreviations:

G.G. *Le Opere di Galileo Galilei, Edizione Nazionale*, 3rd ed., voll. 1-XX, Florence, 1966.

G.G.N.M. Galileo Galilei's Notes on Motion, Joint Project of the Biblioteca Nazionale Centrale, Florence - Istituto e Museo di Storia della Scienza, Florence - Max Planck Institute for the History of Science, Berlin.

The following works are available on the internet:

The first edition of *Le Opere* (1890-1909) at the websites:
http://gallica.bnf.fr/
http://gallica2.bnf.fr/

The manuscript « Galileo Galilei's Notes on Motion», Shelf mark: Gal. 72 at the address:
http://www.mpiwg-berlin.mpg.de/Galileo_Prototype/MAIN.HTM?rigamenu=Ms.%20Galileiano%2072

Introduction

The subject of the great Pisan scientist's last research was the wonderful problem of percussion[1] and it concerns the dynamics of collisions.

After his trial in 1633, despite being sentenced to isolation and later becoming blind, Galileo, surprisingly, succeeded in developing a new field of research.

The loss of his most beloved daughter and of all hope of freedom, together with the worsening of his health, may have bowed him down but did not defeat him; on the contrary, writing his *Discorsi intorno a due Nuove Scienze* (Discourses on two New Sciences) and his research into the laws that govern collisions gave him the strength to overcome adversity.

He had not lost his creativity and in his work on the force of percussion we still find the best Galileo, clear, precise, psychologically aware, self-confident. If you read it today, if you did not already know it, you would find it difficult to imagine that the author was 75 years old.

It was then that he conceived a new machine on a par with all his other masterpieces, the pendulum and the inclined plane. *Galilei's machine*, as we shall call it from now on, to sanction the fact that his invention predates Atwood's[2], is extremely simple in construction, even banal like the others, but the use he made of it is a work of genius.

It is a piece of equipment in which two equal masses are balanced, suspended by a cord astride a pulley. With a few experiments, admirable in their simplicity, Galileo explores a field of physics that had remained obscure for over two thousand years, ever since Aristotle asked his students this question for the first time[3]:

---

[1] Galileo Galilei, *Le Opere*, Florence, 1968 (this is the national edition which from now on we shall indicate by G.G.) vol. VIII, *Discorsi e dimostrazioni matematiche intorno a due nuove scienze…*, pp. 321-346. It was published for the first time in the second edition of the works of Galileo, *Opere di Galileo Galilei* (Florence, 1718), with the title: *Giornata sesta del Galileo, Della forza della percossa. Da aggiugnersi a i Discorsi e alle Dimostrazioni mattematiche intorno alle due nuove scienze appartenenti alle meccaniche ed a i movimenti locali.*

[2] Atwood George (1745-1807) studied at Cambridge; in 1773 he started teaching at Trinity College where he gave lectures that were very popular; in 1776 he became a fellow of the Royal Society. In his most important work, *A Treatise on the Rectilinear Motion and Rotation of Bodies* (Cambridge, 1784), he described a machine for the study of uniformly accelerated motion, later built by Adams. In the same year he also wrote: *Analysis of a Course of Lectures on the Principles of Natural Philosophy.*

[3] It is the *quaestio* 19: «*Cur si quis super lignum magnam imponat securim, desuperque illi magnum adiiciat pondus, ligni quippiam quod curandum sit non dividit: si vero securim extollens percutiat, illud scindit, cum alioquin multo minus habeat ponderis id quod percutit, quam id quod superiacet & premit: an quia omnia cum motu fiunt: & grave ipsum, gravitatis magis assumit motum dum movetur, quam dum quiescit*», *Aristotelis Stagiritae quaestiones mechanicae Nicolao Leoniceno interprete*, in *Operum Aristotelis tomus tertius, Basileae MDXLII*, p. 555. I like to quote this rare edition by Filippo Melantone, that I am lucky enough to own, but for a modern edition see: Aristotele, *Problemi meccanici*, edited by M. E. Bottecchia Dehò, Rubbettino ed., 2000, Soveria Mannelli (Catanzaro).

> For if someone places a large axe on a piece of wood and adds a great weight on top of it, it will not split [...] if instead it is struck raising the axe, it is broken, even though that which strikes has much less weight than that which lies upon it and presses down; perhaps because all occurs with motion, and the body itself acquires more weight while it is in motion, than while it is still.

I shall outline Galileo's answer; just a few lines to explain what it is about.

Galileo observed that when two masses[4] are equal and are suspended from the ends of the cord, they are stationary, balancing each other. This is his first experiment: give one of them a push downwards. The two bodies move together in *uniform* motion, one rising and one descending, with the velocity imparted by the push. Thus Galileo shows the experimental validity of the principle of inertia even when the motion is vertical, because – he observes – the heaviness of one weight – with the cord that links it – cancels the heaviness of the other.

Then he rests one of the two weights on a bench, lifts the other to a preset height and lets it fall: the weight descends with growing velocity and when the cord becomes taut we have – as he calls it – a *wrenching*. The other weight, pulled by the cord, stops the first weight from continuing its accelerated motion: both, together, proceed with uniform motion, as in the previous experiment, to come to a halt only at the end of the available distance.

Then he studies a variant: he modifies the *wrenching* experiment adding another weight to the weight resting on the bench. Then, as before, he lifts the other weight and lets it fall: when the cord becomes taut again, the greater weight rises to a height which depends on the weight that has been added to it and on the maximum velocity reached in free fall by the lifted weight. Their motion, after the *wrenching*, is uniformly slowed up to the maximum height, and then accelerated in the opposite direction.

Calculating in the two experiments the velocity arrived at by the falling weight, immediately before the *wrenching*, and measuring the velocity of the two weights, immediately after the *wrenching*, we can verify that there is no change in the overall quantity of motion, *i.e.* the product of mass times velocity.

Galileo could not give the correct answer because, not being able to measure the maximum velocity reached before the *wrenching*, to estimate it he resorted to a theoretical result, which is not valid in this situation[5].

Galileo, finally, removed the bench and adds a small mass to one of the weights, lifts the greater of the two and leaves it free to descend from stationary. He observes an accelerated, but very slow, motion because there is only the weight of the added mass to move all the masses: this is the first clear evidence of the difference between inertial mass and gravitational mass, between mass and weight. In this final experiment Galileo, perhaps, managed to determine a more exact value of the constant of acceleration of gravity g.

---

[4] Galileo almost always writes «*peso*» (weight) or «*grave*» (heavy body), very rarely «*mole*» (mole) and I shall follow this terminology, to be consistent with the quotations from his texts, but I shall always write mass when I have to refer to the inertia of a body and not to its gravitational force. In this case the two equal masses are of 100 Tuscan pounds, equivalent to 33.95 kg.

[5] Galileo missed the fact that after the *wrenching* the mass in motion doubles, so that the velocity is reduced to a half. I shall show however, later on, that he had all the necessary notions available in order to arrive at the correct result.

It is difficult to travel back in time four centuries, freeing ourselves of all our knowledge, to appreciate the novelty of these simple experiments; I thought I could do so by re-reading carefully "the last day" that Galileo was unable to publish in 1638 with the *Discorsi intorno a due Nuove Scienze*, but it was not enough. So I reconstructed the three machines that Galileo described so well and I repeated his experiments on percussion. But I still did not feel totally sure that I had really established to what extent Galileo had managed to understand his own experiments and to re-elaborate them in the light of his theory of motion; so it was that I wrote this book.

1. Problems of chronology

1.1 *1599-1602: gravitational mass, inertial mass, collisions*

Galileo delivered the third and fourth days of the *Discorsi* (Discourses) to the publishers, Elzevier of Leiden, in June 1637, without being able to complete the last day devoted to the study of the force of percussion on which he had been working for two or three years. In the following years the elderly scientist found himself in conditions of extreme discomfort, deprived as he was of his sight, in an obvious state of depression and under close surveillance: the only people he was allowed to have close to him were the priest Marco Ambrogetti and sometimes his son Vincenzo, to whom he dictated his letters and his thoughts. From time to time, after 1639, after Ambrogetti's departure, Father Clemente Settimi of the *Scuole Pie* (Pious Schools) came to visit him, helping him in his reading; then the very young Vincenzo Viviani arrived and in the last three months Evangelista Torricelli too. This is the situation, which is well known through his correspondence in those years, and it is difficult to believe that such important results of his on the force of percussion could be the outcome of an extraordinary activity in old age; it is very probable, instead, that they are based on a body of theoretical and scientific knowledge obtained much earlier: the original ideas that can be glimpsed between the lines are not the anachronistic and strained interpretation of a modern reader but the elaboration of ideas that were already well formulated in the mind of the elderly scientist.

It may seem strange that after such a long time it is still necessary to carry out an investigation and examination to clarify the origin of much of his research and to follow its evolution and it may perhaps be useful to give an example immediately. In the famous letter that Galileo wrote in 1602 to Guidobaldo del Monte, in which he discusses the isochronism of the pendulum and the theory of chords, at the end, having arrived at the final greeting, he hints at the force of percussion:

> To Master Francesco[6] I shall be delighted to return his greeting, telling him that when I have an idle moment I will write to him to describe an experiment, that has already occurred to my imagination, to measure the moment of percussion: therefore with regard to his question, I judge what Your Excellency says on this matter to be excellent [...]

[6] Galileo was addressing someone called Francesco who was in the villa at Montebaroccio: he can only be Guidobaldo del Monte's eldest son.

Perhaps the experiment that had occurred to him is the one that he would then describe in the *Giornata aggiunta* (Added day)[7]: the experiment of the scales with two buckets one above the other, balanced by a counterweight. Galileo intended to use scales to measure the *moment of percussion*, making the water contained in the upper bucket fall into the lower bucket. The description of the experiment will be given elsewhere but the photograph (fig. 1.1) of its reconstruction in the *Laboratorio di Galileo Galilei*[8] (Galileo Galilei's laboratory) may give an idea of this equipment.

Nothing would be known of Francesco del Monte's question[9] if I had not had the luck to track down Galileo's answer to "Master Francesco's question" in a fragment. It is one of the many fragments which have survived by chance (or by miracle) and which were gathered together in the *Pensieri varj* (Various thoughts), published in Vol. XIV of the Albéri edition of *Le Opere di Galileo Galilei*[10] (The works of Galileo Galilei), which repeats what had been printed in the previous editions in Padua and Milan.

This document is of great importance in dating the writings on the force of percussion and shows that in 1602 Galileo was already clear about the distinction between resistance due to gravitational mass and resistance due to inertial mass[11]. It should immediately be pointed out that there are actually two handwritten versions of this thought: one – in the hand of Vincenzo Viviani – bears the annotation: «from an original note by Galileo, in his hand, amongst the things on percussion»[12], and another version which – in Antonio Favaro's opinion – is «another handwritten copy of the XVII century»[13].

---

7 G.G., vol. VIII, *Discorsi*, pp. 323-325. The experiment was meant to explain why: «the velocity of a weak moving body compensates the vigour of a strong resisting one that is slowly moved; but since we still notice in the operation of percussion the movement of the percussor intervene, joined to its velocity, against the movement of the resisting body and its having to be moved much or little; it was the first concept of the Academician to try to investigate what part it plays in the effect and operation of percussion, *v.g.*, by the weight of the hammer, and what is the greater and lesser velocity with which it is moved, trying, if possible, to find a measure which jointly measured and assigned one energy and the other...».

8 The *Laboratorio di Galileo Galilei* is a museum initiative in which the most important of Galilei's experiments are reconstructed and illustrated to visitors by scientific guides by means of equipment set up according to Galilei's writings. For more information it may be useful to consult the website: http://www.illaboratoriodigalileogalilei.it.

9 From the colon followed by "therefore" we can gather that the question concerned the force of percussion.

10 *Le Opere di Galileo Galilei, prima edizione completa*, Florence, 1855, pp. 329-338. The thoughts are numbered (22 in all) and the one that interests us is number 16 and is on pp. 332-333. The *pensiero* was first published in the 1744 Padua edition Vol. III, on p. 444; then in the 1811 Milan edition, Vol. X, on pp. 377-378; finally in the 1832 Milan edition, Vol. I, on pp. 248-249.

11 In the first case the motion can actually be achieved at constant velocity, after an initial acceleration phase, and in this way the external force is equal to the gravitational force and therefore depends on the object's gravitational mass; in the second case it is achieved with an impulsive force and the result inevitably depends on the object's inertial mass.

12 The copy, in Vincenzo Viviani's hand, «crossed through with transverse strokes», is quoted by Favaro (G.G, Vol. VIII, p. 343, in a note) as contained on f. 16r-t of the Ms. Galileiani Par. V, Tom. 4 (which Favaro called Codex B), now known as Ms. Gal. 74, cc. 16r-16v.

13 In the classification of the manuscripts by Vincenzo Antinori (G.G, Vol. VIII, p. 343, in a note) the *Pensieri varj* have the shelf mark Ms. Galileiani, Par. VI, Tom. 2, while the current shelf mark is: «Gal. 83 G.G. frammenti» and the thought is on c. 19r.

Fig. 1.1 The big scales with two buckets and a counterweight for the percussion experiment. (The scales were built to my specifications by the firm «Antolini Bilance s.r.l.» and are a gift that I received for the *Laboratorio di Galileo Galilei*, for which I am extremely grateful to Mr. Mario and Mr. Gabriele Antolini.)

Let us read it:

> In every moveable that is to be moved by force, it seems that there are two distinct species of resistance. One relates to that internal resistance which makes us say that a body weighing a thousand pounds [*libbre*] is harder to raise than one of a hundred; the other relates to the space through which motion must be made, as a stone requires greater force to be thrown one hundred paces [*passi*] than fifty, and so on. To this different resistance correspond proportionably the two different movers – the one that moves [a thing] by pressing without striking, and the other that acts by striking. The mover that operates without impact moves only a resistance which is less, though [it may be] only insensibly [less], than the power [*virtù*] or the pressing heaviness; but that will move it through an infinite distance, accompanying it always with its same force. That which moves by striking, moves any resistance, though [this can be] immense; but [moves it only] through a limited distance.
>
> Hence I consider these two propositions true: that the percussent moves an infinite resistance through a finite and limited interval, while the pressing [force] moves a finite and limited resistance through an infinite interval; hence to the percussent, the interval is proportionable

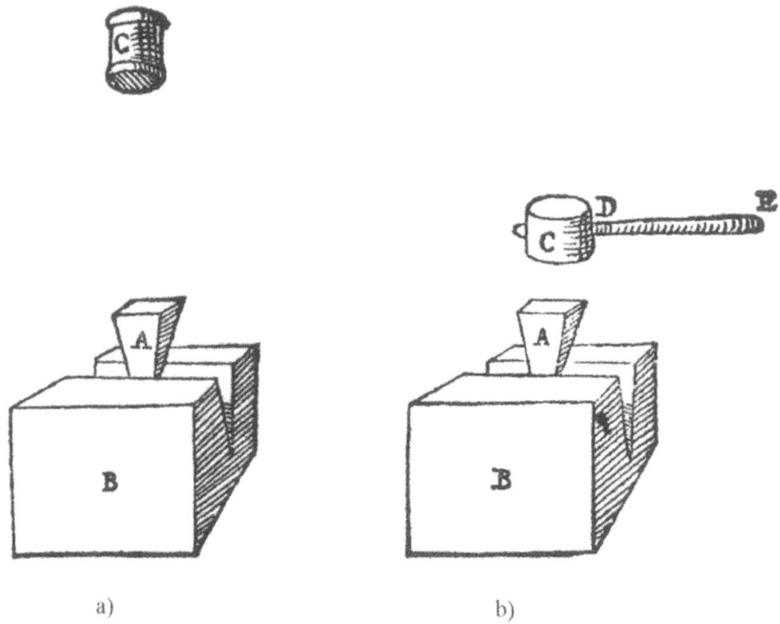

Fig. 1.2 *Le Mechaniche* (On Mechanics) 1581, Folio. 113v.

and not the resistance, while to the pressing [force] the resistance, and not the interval [is proportionable]. These things make me doubt whether *Francesco's question*[14] has an answer, as one that seeks to equate two things that are incommensurable; for such, I believe, are the actions of impact and of pressing. Thus, in this particular case [illustrated], any immense resistance that may exist in the wedge *BA* will be moved by any percussent *C*, but [only] through a limited interval as between point *B* and *A*, while the pressing [force] *D* will not drive just any resistance existing in the wedge *BA*, but only a limited resistance, and one not greater than the weight *D*. That, however, will be driven not [only] through the limited interval between points *B* and *A*, but *in infinitum*, provided that the resistance in the movable body *AB* remains always equal, as must be assumed, nothing to the contrary having been mentioned in the inquiry.

Since the figure is missing in both manuscript sources[15], the final part seems obscure; but that is not really so because we just have to turn to what Guidobaldo del Monte wrote about wedges

---

[14] The italics are mine.

[15] I owe this information to the kindness of Dr. Paola Pirolo, in charge of the manuscripts and rare books section of the *Biblioteca Nazionale Centrale di Firenze* and to the care of Dr. Susanna Pelle, of the *Servizio Riproduzione e Diritti* of that branch, who also pointed out to me the presence in the upper part of c. 19r of Gal. 83 of another text, published in G.G., Vol. VIII, *Frammenti di data incerta* at pp. 637-638, regarding the weight in water, a proximity that seems significant.

in his *Mechanicorum Liber*[16] (Book on Mechanics) in 1577 to understand what is being dealt with and to have an idea of the figure that used to accompany the original (fig. 1.2a, b). I use here, for the convenience of the reader, the fine and accurate translation by Filippo Pigafetta[17]:

> Let the wedge be *A*, that which must be split *B*, and that which strikes *C*; which rather strikes by itself, & moves; or rather by the power that holds it, & moves; that if by itself, first one must note, that the heavier it may be, so much greater will be the blow, & moreover the greater the distance between *A C*, then equally greater will be the blow: since every heavy object, while it moves, takes on more weight when moved, than staying still, & even more so, the greater distance from which it is moved.[...] But this is the second thing. Which is the reason why with this instrument great weights are moved, & they are split. So percussion is a most vigorous force, as shown by the nineteenth of Aristotle's mechanical questions: since if a very heavy weight is laid on the wedge, then the wedge shall do as nothing compared to percussion.

Galileo certainly bore Guidobaldo considerations in mind when he wrote at the end of *Le Mecaniche*[18]:

> We shall consider, therefore, the resistance to being moved that exists in the hammer at the point where it goes to strike, and how far it would be driven by the received force if it did not strike; and moreover what is the resistance to being moved of that which it strikes, and how much it is moved by a single stroke. And having found how far this great resistance goes forward under one stroke, by however much this is less than the distance through which the hammer would go by the impetus (*empito*) of what moves it, by so much is this resistance greater than that of the hammer; and so the wonder of the effect ceases in us, since it stems only from the term of natural arrangements and from what has already been said. Let there be added, for better comprehension, an example in particular terms. There is a hammer which, having four of resistance, is moved by a force such that if were set free from this at the point where the stroke is made, it would go ten paces (*passi*) beyond if it met with no obstruction. But let it rather be opposed there by a great beam whose resistance is as four thousand; that is, one thousand times as great as that of the hammer (and yet not immovable, so that it would overcome the resistance of the hammer beyond all proportion). Now the percussion being made on this, it will indeed be driven forward, but by thousandth part of ten paces (*passi*), in which the hammer would be moved.

The distance travelled by the hammer depends on its velocity when thrown; how far «a large beam» moves forward after the blow is a measurement of the velocity that it has acquired at

---

[16] *Guidubaldi e Marchionibus Montis Mechanicorum Liber*, Pesaro, 1577, f. 118r-118v.

[17] *Le Mechaniche dell'Illustriss. Sig. Guido Ubaldo de' Marchesi Del Monte*, Venice, 1581, f. 113v-114r. The figures in the two texts are the same.

[18] G.G., Vol. II, *Le Mecaniche*, pp. 189-190. For the dating of the text see: GALILEO GALILEI, *Le Mecaniche, edizione critica e saggio introduttivo di Romano Gatto*, Florence, 2002, where the editor maintains with sound arguments that the final version of the treatise dates to before 1599.

the moment of the blow: the resistances, four for the hammer and four thousand for the beam are obviously proportional respectively to the masses of the hammer and of «the great beam»[19]; Galileo is describing the collision between two bodies (the hammer striking the beam) and he knows their masses. From the two velocities before the collision he derives a velocity after the collision. It is surprising to discover that in this passage the theory of the force of percussion has a dynamic structure analogous to that used by Galileo almost forty years later in the *Giornata aggiunta*. Galileo is aware of having presented the matter in a colloquial and rather informal way and so he adds:

> I know that this will give rise in some to difficulties and objections, which however there are means to remove with little trouble, and these we willingly leave among the mechanical problems which we will be appended at the end of this discourse.

It is the right approach and it is worth examining it. Let us imagine that the beam, before being struck by the hammer, is held suspended at a certain height from the ground by two cords, and that the cords are released at exactly the same moment as the hammer blow. The beam will perform a parabola analogous to the parabola that the hammer would follow if it were thrown from the same height with the velocity and the horizontal direction that it has when striking the beam. Let us compare the two trajectories. Starting from the same height the hammer and the beam take the same time to reach the ground so the distances reached (which Galileo fixed at $L_H = 10$ paces for the hammer and $L_B = 1/100$ of a pace for the beam) are also a measurement of their velocities v_H and v_B. Galileo's data are consistent if the collision is completely anelastic: considering that the mass of the hammer is $m_H = 4$ units and the mass of the beam is $m_B = 4000$ units, we obtain $m_H v_H = (m_H + m_B)v_B$. By multiplying the relationship by the time t in which the hammer and the beam are in the air, the relationship becomes $m_H L_H = (m_H + m_B)L_B$ and therefore, again measuring in paces, we obtain $L_B = 40/4004$, practically Galileo's result. One could object that it is not possible to have a completely analestic[20] collision with a hammer but in order to do so one simply has to to exchange an axe for the hammer, assuming that the blow is sufficiently heavy to make the axe remain attached to the beam.

The experiments with collisions that Galileo actually carried out will have been more practical than the experiments of the hammer and the beam,[21] which he presented in order to

---

[19] We have just read in *pensiero n°* 16 that for Galileo there are: «two distinct kinds of resistance; one that concerns that internal resistance, because of which we say that it is more difficult to lift a stone of 1000 pounds, than one of a hundred: the other that concerns the space through which the motion must be made; and so a stone requires greater force to be thrown one hundred paces away than fifty ». In percussion we are dealing with the second case, in which two forces have to be considered however: the force (of the arm) that impresses great velocity on the hammer and the force (due to the hammer's collision) that impresses a much smaller velocity on the beam.

[20] If instead the collision is perfectly elastic the distance is halved: $L_B = 2m_H L_H/(m_B - m_H) = 100/4995$ by the distance measured in paces; if instead the masses were equal we would find: $L_H = 0$ and L_B indefinite.

[21] In another fragment of the *Giornata aggiunta* (G.G., Vol. VIII, p. 345) which I believe to be contemporary to *Le Mecaniche*, he describes another experiment with beam and hammer thus: «if with a very small hammer we strike, with uniform blows, against the head of a very great beam lying on the ground, after very many blows it will finally be seen that the beam has moved a perceptible distance, an obvious indication that each blow has

conform to Aristotelian tradition, but what matters is that it is established that he followed the correct path right from the beginning. The problem of percussion, both here and later, is always tackled as a dynamic problem and not a static one, as Galileo explains to Francesco del Monte who asked him if it were possible to establish a comparison between the force of percussion and the pressure of the overlying weight which performs the same effect as the blow. He replies in fact that the question «cannot be explained, as one that tries to make equal things that cannot be proportionate, as I believe is true of the actions of percussion and pressure».

Nevertheless the question attracted Galileo's interest however and he was able to find a suitable experiment to illustrate this lack of proportionality. A trace of this is preserved by Evangelista Torricelli; indeed, in the third of his *Lezioni Accademiche* (Academic Lessons)[22] devoted to percussion and given in the summer of 1642, a few months after Galileo's death, Torricelli recalled an experiment that the great scientist had carried out while still living at Padua. The experiment was made with bows of *different strengths*: taking the weaker bow, he tied to the centre of the bowstring a thread one *braccio* (0.58302 m) in length to which was attached a lead ball weighing two ounces (0.0566 kg). Letting the ball fall, he observed how much the bow bent and how much the string was pulled down; he then hung from that string a motionless weight heavy enough to bend the bow in the same way: that weight was ten pounds (3.395 kg). Moving on to a stronger bow, he repeated the experiment and he realised that the motionless weight that had the same effect as the two-ounce ball of lead let drop as before was twenty pounds. Torricelli concluded his description thus:

> Then taking ever stronger bows, he found that to match the force of that same ball of lead, and of that same drop, would need ever greater and greater weight, in agreement with the experiment on stronger and stronger bows. Then he said; if I take a very strong bow, then that lead ball, which is no more than two ounces, will have an effect equivalent to a thousand pounds of lead. Then taking a bow a thousand times more strong than that stronger one, that same ball will have an effect equivalent to a million pounds of lead; a most obvious sign, that the force of that little weight and of that *braccio* of fall, is infinite.

In his conclusion Torricelli shows that he has not understood that with this experiment Galileo wanted to prove the impossibility of a comparison between percussion and pressure, a point of view that he continued to maintain to the last, above all in the *Giornata aggiunta*.

There is not the faintest trace of the experiment so clearly described by Torricelli in Galileo's writings and this is one of the many indications of the destruction, through theft or neglect, of many of his papers.

In *Le "Opere" di Galileo Galilei, Edizione Nazionale* (The "Works" of Galileo Galilei, National Edition) *pensiero* (thought) n° 16 which Antonio Favaro placed amongst the *Frammenti di data*

worked separately, for its own part, in moving the beam; since if the first blow was not party to that effect then all the later blows, as if they were the first, would achieve nothing, which is contrary to the experiment, the sense and demonstration that shall be given *etc.*».

[22] *Lezioni Accademiche d'Evangelista Torricelli*, Florence, 1715, pp. 20-21; also in *Opere di Evangelista Torricelli*, Faenza, 1919, pp. 22-23, and in *Opere scelte di Evangelista Torricelli*, Turin, 1975, pp. 372-373.

incerta (Fragments of uncertain date) at the end of Vol. VIII does not appear with the others. There is an explanation for this omission. Favaro realised that at the end of the *Giornata sesta*[23] *del Galileo, Della forza della percossa* (Sixth day of Galileo, On the force of percussion), published for the first time in Florence in 1718, there is an identical text, muddled up with others on the same subject, with some minimal variants in spelling but with a significant difference: instead of the name «*Francesco*» we find «*Sagredo*».

We can imagine why: the editors obtained from Viviani's heirs a certain quantity of unpublished writings copied from the originals and concerning percussion; when they came to put together the fragments that make up the *Giornata aggiunta* that «*Francesco*», must have struck them as a blunder perhaps due to the text being copied in haste: hence the correction to «*Sagredo*», who is one of the interlocutors in the *Discorsi* also present in the other fragments.

We have seen that the 22 thoughts appear for the first time later on, in the third volume of his *Opere*[24] published in Padua in 1744; so this volume contains two versions, on page 210, where we find the Florentine addition of the *Giornata sesta* with the *Sagredo* correction and on p. 444, with the name *Francesco*. All later editions have adopted what was done at Padua. Even Favaro chose to present the *Giornata sesta* from the Florentine edition, preceding it with this warning[25]:

> No manuscript has come down to us of the Day devoted to the force of percussion and so we have been forced to republish it based on the Florentine edition of 1718 already quoted. In this edition, at the beginning of the Day, another text follows on (p. 339, line 30 – p. 342, line 33, in our new edition), which is in dialogue form, but which is still not well connected to the previous part, as also noted in the Florence edition; then followed (pp. 343–346) by a series of notes or fragments, also regarding the subject of percussion. We, while reproducing all these writings faithfully from the original edition (keeping the order in which the fragments are arranged, although it could have been done better), have nevertheless corrected the obvious mistakes [...] We were helped in correcting some printing errors by having found, in Volume IV (cc. 16r –17r) of part V of the Galilei Manuscripts (which we call codex B), two texts regarding this Day (p. 334, line 33 – p. 335, line 18, and p. 343, line 1 – p. 344, line 7), transcribed, in Viviani's hand, from «Galileo's original», or rather, one of them, from the original «in his hand», as Viviani informs us. We have gathered together at the foot of the page the variants presented in Viviani's copies, as also those offered for the second of them, extracted from another XVII century copy and, for the most part from fragments (p. 344, line 8 – p. 346 line 19) from a modern copy which, to tell the truth, is very imprecise.

[23] *Giornata Sesta* is referred to indifferently as Sixth day or Added day.

[24] In the foreword, at the beginning of the first volume of the Padua edition (first unnumbered sheet with the title "For the readers") it is written: «... they are taken from manuscripts found in Florence in the care of Galileo's heirs, or rather those of Viviani, who had collected all the writings of his Master to make of them a complete Edition. In these same manuscripts the *Pensieri varj*, as we have called them, were found, and *Frammenti* placed at the end of the third Volume».

[25] G.G., Vol. VIII, *Introduzione*, pp. 30-31.

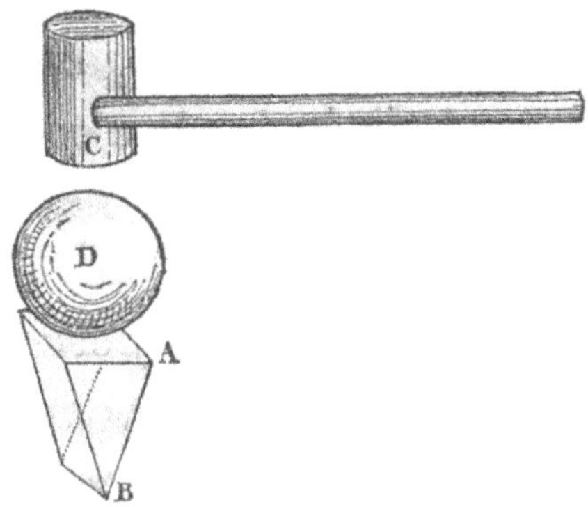

Fig. 1.3 Redrawn from *Le Opere*, Florence, 1718; Vol. II, p. 708.

The drawing (fig. 1.3) that accompanies the fragment in the Florentine edition of *Le Opere*, although very similar to the one in Guidobaldo's *Mechaniche*, was certainly not done by Galileo, because it brings together inappropriately the two cases of percussion and of pressure. Favaro, who missed this inconsistency, presented it without comment in the *Edizione Nazionale*, even though he knew it did not exist in the surviving documents. Favaro did not trust the documents that he had available and did not understand the importance of that name: *Francesco*, which he nevertheless points out in a note as present in the manuscripts without however wondering why. He eliminated from the *Frammenti di data incerta* the *pensiero* with the name «Francesco» and kept in the *Giornata aggiunta* the reply with the 1718 «Sagredo» substitution; in so doing, he transposed definitively the dating of an important text 35 years ahead. The reconstruction of these events, which shifts some outstanding deliberations by Galileo on the force of percussion back to his Paduan period, is the first evidence in favour of the hypothesis that the *Giornata aggiunta* is the result of very old experiments and knowledge.

1.2 *Difficulty in dating the discoveries*

It is a matter of fact that the precise chronology of his studies and discoveries has not yet been firmly established, especially given Galileo's way of proceeding which let some decades pass before publishing what he had discovered, making it difficult to determine "when" and "how".

Therefore if we wish to establish with certainty when and how Galileo's ideas were born and evolved we have to select the most important documents from amongst those that we know how to date, trying to connect them to each other in order to reconstruct the development of his thought over time.

Some progress was made with Stillman Drake's investigations into the papers of Ms. Gal. 72, preserved at the *Biblioteca Nazionale Centrale* in Florence[26]. The papers contain autographic

[26] *Galileo notes on motion arranged in probable order of composition and presented in reduced facsimile by Stillman Drake*, Supplement of the Annali dell'Istituto e Museo di Storia della Scienza, year 1979 – issue 2.

writings by Galileo with annotations, theorems and many calculations, not always included in the editing of the *Dialogo* (Dialogue) and the *Discorsi* (Discourses) and only partly published in the *Edizione Nazionale delle Opere*, while all those that mainly contain calculations and diagrams remained unpublished.

Drake recognised the results of experiments in many of the folios and he succeeded, by means of an intelligent dating operation by means of the watermarks[27], in giving a certain chronological order to the papers. This is how Drake describes his discovery:

> This unpublished material includes at least one group of notes which cannot satisfactorily be accounted for except as representing a series of experiments designed to test a fundamental assumption, which led to a new, important discovery. In these documents precise empirical data are given numerically, comparisons are made with calculated values derived from theory, a source of discrepancy from still another expected result is noted, a new experiment is designed to eliminate this, and further empirical data are recorded[28].

Many science historians have studied the Ms. Gal. 72 over the last 40 years, seeking the interconnections between the contents of some pages, above all from the oldest ones of the Paduan period, and carrying out experiments to find an objective confirmation of their theoretical analyses.

The effort to assign precise dates to Galileo's discoveries is understandable: it is the only way we can hope to understand how Galileo succeeded in organising his knowledge of motion, in overcoming the contradictions presented to him by his own experiments, and finally in applying his laws to solving the dynamic problems that he set himself.

Stillman Drake has devoted around a hundred publications to Galileo, and two of his books are particularly well known, *Galileo at work: his scientific biography* and *Galileo Pioneer Scientist*, which present significant suggestions and intuition on how Galileo carried out his experiments; however it is not always possible to concur with his conclusions. One of the weak points of his reconstructions is his attribution of the value of 169/180 of a millimetre (about 0.94 mm) to the *punctus* (point), a unit introduced by Galileo in Folios 116v and 166r of Ms. Gal. 72. When he then examined other papers, Drake used this equivalence to translate into corresponding metric units every number that appears to be a not otherwise identifiable measure of length.

He determined the value in millimetres of the *punctus* by measuring the divisions of the linear scale of the *geometrical and military compass*, an instrument that can almost certainly be traced back to Galileo, preserved at the *Istituto e Museo di Storia della Scienza* in Florence[29]. Drake then measured some lines of folio 166r, which had lengths given in *puncti*, arriving at a value of 174/180 of a

---

[27] Comparing, when possible, the watermarks and the countermarks of the papers used for the notes with those of the letters sent by Galileo, it is possible to arrive at a reliable date. Drake found no less than 20 different watermarks in about 50 folios which he believed could be attributed to the Paduan period, because many are present in letters written in the years 1602-1610. It is reasonable to deduce from this variety that his purchases of paper were always in small quantities. The watermarks of the Florentine papers are completely different from those from Padua.

[28] STILLMAN DRAKE, *Galileo's Experimental Confirmation of Horizontal Inertia: Unpublished Manuscripts*, Isis, Vol. 64 (Sept., 1973) p. 292, reprinted in *Essays on Galileo and the History and Philosophy of Science*, Toronto, 1999, p. 148.

[29] STILLMAN DRAKE, Isis, Vol. 64, Sept. 1973 *Op. cit.*, p. 296: «Thomas Settle, who was in Florence when I found this reference, kindly measured for me the units on Galileo's own instrument, preserved at the Science Museum there, and found that 180 points measure 169 millimetres».

millimetre. From the compatibility of these measurements he became convinced that he was right, without considering that in the drawing on folio 166r Galileo might have reduced a larger drawing in scale – for example in the ratio 1 : 2.5 – using his compass as a ruler.

Other scholars, including D. K. Hill and R. H. Naylor, have taken the measurements of the Florentine compass and found similar values: in conclusion, all the scholars who have concerned themselves so far with these papers (Thomas B. Settle, Roland H. Naylor, James Maclachlan, David K. Hill, Winifred L. Wisan, J. Renn, P. Damerow, S. Rieger, A. J. Hahn and obviously Stillman Drake himself) have accepted and kept this measurement of the *punto* uncritically.

Instead I believe that I have shown[30] that the *punctus* (point) is none other than the Latin translation of *picciolo*, a minute subdivision of the Florentine *braccio*, traditionally divided into 20 *soldi*, each of which is divided into 12 *piccioli*, in use until the reform promulgated by Grand Duke Peter Leopold on 11 July 1782, when the *braccio a terra* ("arm's length of land", equivalent to 0.55063 m) used in geographical and astronomical measurements was abolished, keeping only the *braccio da panno* ("arm's length of cloth" equivalent to 0.58302 m) as the fundamental unit of measurement of the Grand Duchy, in order to unify the various local units of measure, and the *denaro* was introduced[31] instead of the Florentine *picciolo*.

In those cases in which time does not come into play, Drake's hypothesis only leads to a contraction of the geometrical dimensions, with the *punctus* reduced from 2.29 mm (or from 2.43 mm for the *braccio da panno*) to 0.94 mm, a change of scale which does not lead to major differences in the interpretation of the papers. Instead when time intervenes explicitly in the experiment, his choice upsets the results, as occurs on f. 107v, fundamental for our understanding of Galileo's famous assertion (immediately recognised as wrong), that a body starting from stationary travels «100 *braccia* in 5 seconds».

In this book I present a reconstruction, for the most part original, of the great Pisan scientist's scientific journey in his studies on motion.

However my enquiries have spread well beyond the original purpose and has led to some surprising results. I repeated the experiments with water carried out in the period 1585-1592 which suggest that the discovery of the phenomenon of surface tension, the effect of wetting and the measurement of the adhesion of water to solid surfaces should be dated back to this period. I reconstructed the succession of the discoveries and experiments that lead him to the law of uniformly accelerated motion, identifying the probable reason why Galileo kept his writings on motion unpublished for thirty years. I built for the first time his last piece of experimental equipment which I have named *Galilei's machine* and I have shown how Galileo was able to use it to measure with a good degree of accuracy the acceleration constant *g* in experiments with vertical falls, with which he clearly shows the difference between inertial mass and gravitational mass. Finally I carried out, with his machine, the experiments on percussion, following the indications given, that he had not been able to include in the first edition of the *Discorsi* of which only a *Frammento di una giornata aggiunta* (Fragment of an added day) remains.

---

30 For the value of the *punctus* see the Author's paper *How long is Galileo's punctus?* at the web address: http://www.illaboratoriodigalileogalilei.it/ in the part devoted to *Scritti e Pubblicazioni di Galileo.*

31 As can be seen in the *TAVOLE DI RAGGUAGLIO per la riduzione dei pesi e misure che si usano in diversi luoghi del Granducato di Toscana al peso e misura veglianti in Firenze* (Tables for the conversion of weights and measures used in different places of the Granduchy of Tuscany to those in use in Florence) Florence, 1782.

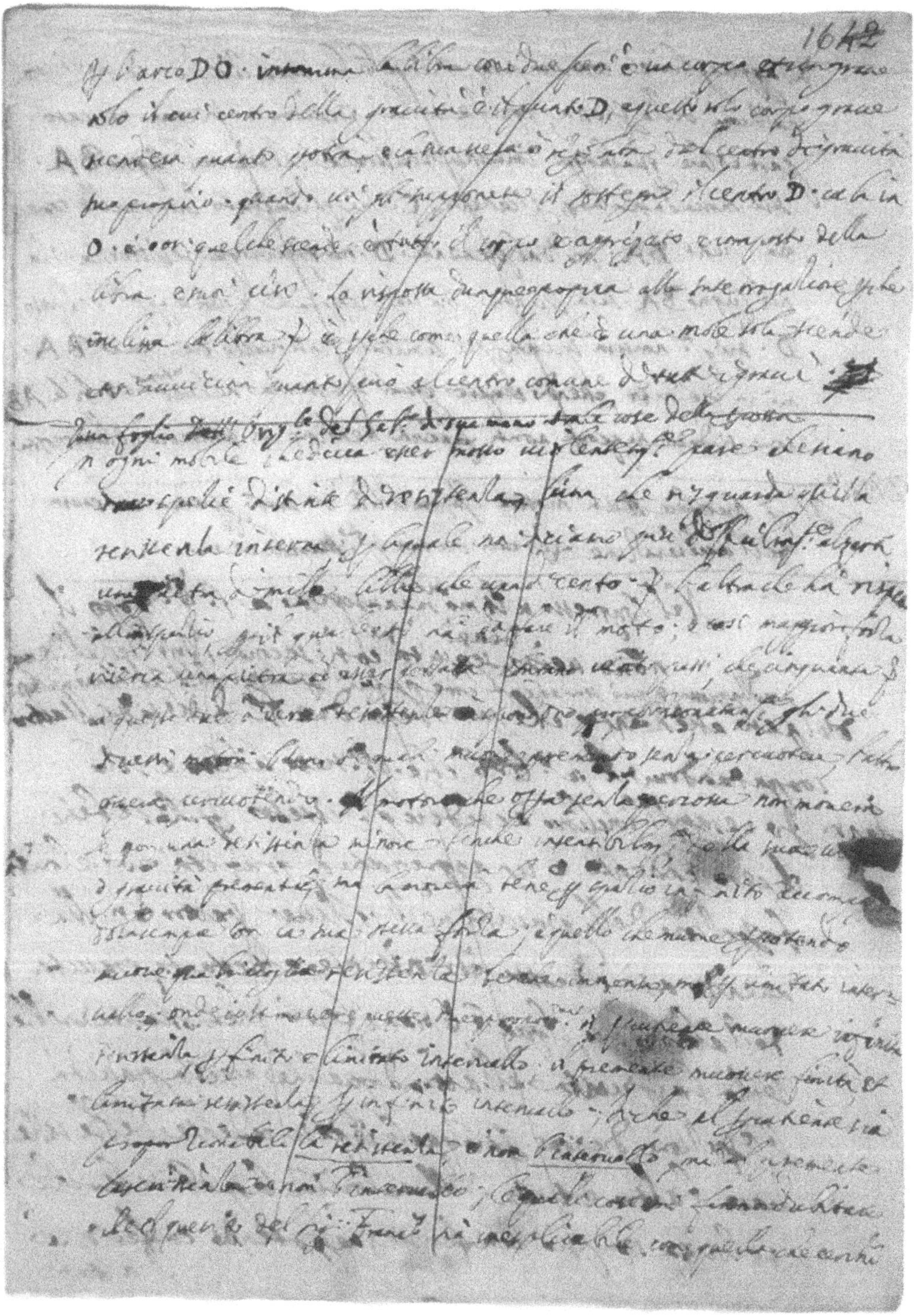

Pensiero no. 16 in Viviani'hands: Ms. Gal. 74, Folio 16r.

2. Around 1590: The dynamics of the *De motu*

Almost all scholars[32] agree in their belief that Galileo wrote the *De motu* (On motion) while teaching at the University of Pisa (1589-1592). It is therefore one of his oldest scientific writings, preserved in the *Biblioteca Nazionale Centrale* in Florence with the shelf mark Ms. Gal. 71, which remained unpublished and virtually unknown until being partially published by Eugenio Albèri in the Florentine edition of 1854 with the title *Sermones de motu gravium* (On the motion of heavy bodies), which was followed by Antonio Favaro's unabridged edition in 1890, included in the first volume of *Le "Opere"*. The Ms. Gal. 71 brings together various writings, which in the Edizione Nazionale are arranged in the following order: a *Trattato* (Treatise) divided into 23 chapters, followed by a *Saggio* (Essay) in 12 short chapters and a *Dialogo* (Dialogue) with two speakers, Alessandro and Domenico. In these writings, which seem to be later elaborations of common themes in an order which is the opposite of that published, the author critically examines many arguments connected with local motion, in the context of a well-established Aristotelian tradition and in the light of recent studies by Tartaglia, Cardano, Benedetti, Buonamici and Borro.

The first text, the *Trattato*, which is the one usually referred to when the *De motu* is quoted is certainly the most interesting of the three, because it contains some discoveries of extraordinary importance, such as the isochronism of the pendulum, the discovery of the phenomena of the surface of water (cohesion, adhesion and surface tension), the fundamental law of the inclined plane, the theorem of chords and the original versions of the principle of inertia and of the principle of action and reaction. The first 13 chapters of the *Trattato* concern the movement of a body in water; in the remaining 10 chapters violent motion is mainly discussed.

Extracting a passage from the *De motu*, we start immediately with the discovery of the isochronism of the oscillations of a pendulum because it certainly predates the writing of the *De motu*, where it is referred to indirectly, and in doing so we are proceeding according to the tradition introduced by Galileo's first biographer, Vincenzo Viviani.

---

[32] Michele Camerota, *Gli scritti* De motu antiquiora *di Galileo Galilei: il Ms Gal 71. Un'analisi storico-critica*, Cagliari, 1992. Following Camerota's presentation, we distinguish the main writings in Ms. Gal. 71 with the names: *Trattato* (G.G., Vol. I, pp. 251-340), *Saggio* (G.G., Vol. I, pp. 344-366) *Dialogo* (G.G., Vol. I, pp. 367-408). On pp. 341-343 there is a *reworking* of the first two chapters of the *Trattato*, while on pp. 409-417 there are some notes and on pp. 418-419 the so-called *plan of the work*.

2.1 *The pendulum, an exact measurer of time*

Some historians[33] have claimed that Galileo discovered the relationship between the length of the pendulum and the frequency of the oscillations very late, since he only wrote about it in the *Discorsi*[34]. This legalistic criterion of the date of publication that they have adopted thus excludes their taking into consideration any clue that may lead to the discovery being backdated to before 1637: just to give an example, the repeated statements in the *Dialogo*[35] on the length of the movement in seconds: «a hundred *braccia* in five seconds»[36].

Traditionally the discovery of the pendulum is attributed to the period when Galileo was studying at Pisa, that is to say before he finally abandoned his studies in 1585. The importance of establishing when Galileo began to use the pendulum as an instrument for measuring time has led us to reread the available documents carefully, starting with the oldest, from the manuscript of the *De motu*, where we find a first clue, which we think it would be interesting to illustrate.

[33] For example, CORNÉLIS DE WAARD, in his *Correspondence du P. Marin Mersenne*, Vol. IV, Paris, 1955, pp. 444-455, attributes the discovery to this author, quoting some passages from *Harmonicorum Libri*, T. I (Paris, 1636) Lib. II, prop. 26, p. 19 and *Harmonie Universelle*, T. I (Paris, 1636), *Livre* II *des Mouvements*, prop. 14, p. 135. De Waard, in an appendix devoted to the question, claims: «[*Galilée*] *ne semble avoir connu le rapport trouvé par Mersenne qu'après la publication des ouvrages du Minime*»; therefore he concludes: *«c'est à Mersenne qui revient l'honneur d'avoir énoncé et publié le premier la relation exacte entre la longuer du funépendule et la durée de son oscillation»*. ROBERT LENOBLE, in his *Mersenne ou la naissance du mécanicism*, Paris, 1943, on p. 466 writes: «*Mersenne trouve par lui-même la formule correcte* [of the law of falling]... *La loi de Galilée aurait donc pu s'appeler la loi de Mersenne*». Lenoble may not have known about the 1604 letter to Paolo Sarpi in which the law of falling is enunciated and the use of the pendulum is obvious, but he could not have known that Mersenne had read Galileo's law in the *Dialogo sopra i massimi sistemi del mondo*. But the whole of chapter 20 is devoted to this question.

[34] G.G., Vol. VIII, *Discorsi*, pp. 139-140. In a letter dated 5 June 1637, refering to a treatise he is writing, Galileo describes to Lorenzo Realio a "counter of time" that uses "a pendulum of solid and heavy material" and informs him that «the lengths of such pendulums maintain between them duplicate proportion of the lengths of the times».

[35] For the sake of brevity I indicate simply by *Dialogo* the 1632 treatise: *Dialogo di Galileo Galilei... Dove ne i congressi di quattro giornate si discorre sopra i due Massimi Sistemi del Mondo, Tolemaico, e Copernicano, proponendo indeterminatamente le ragioni Filosofiche e Naturali tanto per l'una, quanto per l'altra parte* (Dialogue concerning the Two Chief World Systems – Ptolemaic and Copernican). The *Dialogo* was published in G.G., Vol. VII.

[36] G.G., Vol. VII, *Dialogo*, see for example on p. 250 and on p. 251, and the following calculations on p. 252. In the *Dialogo* Galileo wants to make clear the difference between those who know how to measure time with a pendulum and those who do not. Salviati always speaks of seconds (26 times), while Sagredo makes precise references to time only twice and always using the beats of a pulse: on p. 46 «... in less than ten pulse beats it shall pass more than two hundred *braccia* high» [he should have written "more than four hundred *braccia*"] and on p. 180 «... let the time a stone takes to fall from the top of a tree be two pulse beats».

Starting from a suggestion by Cardano[37], later taken up by Buonamici in an immense treatise[38] (published in 1591 probably after Galileo's *De motu*), Galileo describes an experiment which provides indirect proof of the discovery of the isochronism of the oscillations of a pendulum[39]. This is what he found[40]:

> And the same thing is again evident, if someone projects, with the same hand, at the same moment, together, 2 pieces, one of wood, the other of iron; the iron or lead will be moved on a longer distance: which presumably indicates that, the motive force hangs on more penetratingly in the iron and is kept for a longer time in it than in the wood. The same thing is evident if two weights, one of wood, the other of lead, are suspended from two equal threads and, when they have received an impetus from an equal distance from the perpendicular, they are released; of the two, the lead will certainly be moved back and forth for a longer interval of time.

Notice the accuracy of the description, which presupposes a meticulous preparation of the experiment: 1) same length of cord, 2) simultaneous start, 3) same initial amplitude.

If we repeat the comparison between the two pendulums today we cannot fail to spot an equally obvious fact, even if Galileo does not mention it. After a certain number of oscillations we see, as he states, that the amplitude of the wooden pendulum has diminished compared to the lead pendulum, which keeps its initial pattern of movement for longer, but *we also see* (figs. 2.1, 2.2) that the frequencies of the two pendulums remain virtually unchanged. Galileo cannot have failed to notice it, especially because it is a very short experiment, which he will have repeated several times to be sure of what he was claiming.

---

[37] HIERONYMI CARDANI ... *DE SUBTILITATE ... PARISIIS 1550, liber II*, ff. 50v-51-51v; *idem, Lugduni*, 1558, pp. 96-97; *idem, OPERUM, LUGDUNI, 1663, Tomus Tertius, DE SUBTILITATE*, p. 394. His text is given later.

[38] FRANCISCI BONAMICI ... *DE MOTU LIBRI X ... FLORENTIAE, MDXCI*, p. 222 «the lead weight hanging [from a cord] when it is moved away from the perpendicular does not return to it but, after having passed beyond it for a certain distance, it is propelled many times one way and the other until, when the impetus has diminished and the space is reduced, finally it always returns to the perpendicular ... The lead goes and returns from the perpendicular and towards the perpendicular in a way which is truly no different, whether the impetus has been transmitted by he who holds it, or by the air which much more easily presses from every side. That motion, in fact, is [*directed*] towards places not solely according to nature and yet not totally against nature». In his treatise there are analogies and arguments that can also be found in Galileo, and some authors who had written against the Aristotelian ideas of motion are mentioned, *e.g.* on p. 505: «Philoponus and, after him, also Albert [*of Saxony*], St. Thomas and many others believed that in truth he who first gives the movement imparts a force not to the air but to the moveable, for example to the stone that, according to the greater or lesser force that is imparted, so it will move for a greater space and at a greater speed».

[39] The first treatise of the *De motu* was translated and annotated by I. E. Drabkin and published in the collection *On motion and on mechanics* (Madison, 1960). Here, on p. 108, corresponding to the passage from Galileo, there is the note: «Here and in the corresponding memorandum (413.1) we have the earliest reference attesting Galileo's interest in the pendulum».

[40] G.G., Vol. I, *De motu*, p. 335.

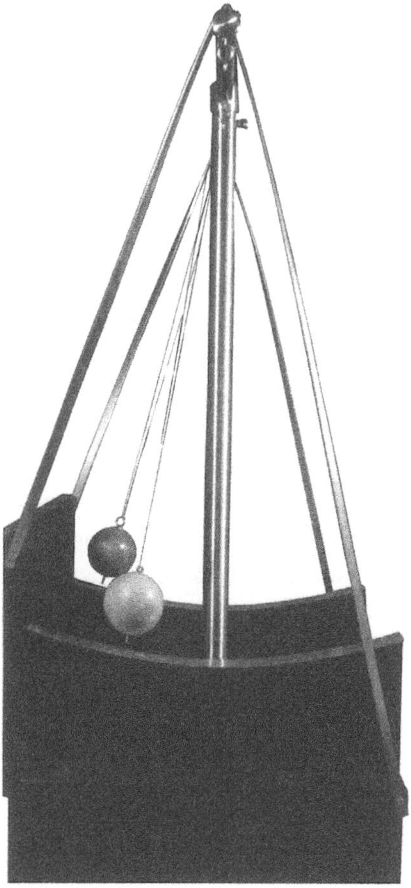

Fig. 2.1 Pendulums of wood and bronze. Seen from the side.

Fig. 2.2 Pendulums of wood and bronze. Seen from the front.

Indeed he feels that the discovery of the different behaviour of the amplitudes is so important, that in a series of notes that sum up the subject matter dealt with in the *De motu*, he includes another reminder on this question[41]:

> That a contrary force is impressed more strongly in heavier things is evident from the things which, after being suspended by a thread, are put into a motion of going back and forth: for the heavier they are, the longer they will be moved.

[41] G.G, Vol. I, *De motu*, p. 413.

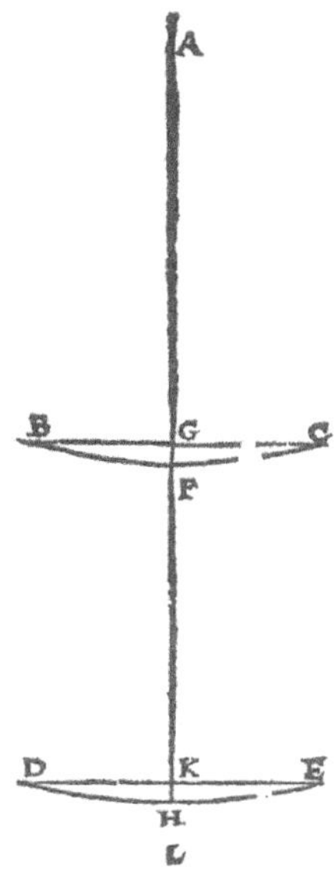

Fig. 2.3 *De subtilitate.* (See footnote 43.)

For Galileo the movement of the pendulum is special because there is a mass that repeatedly moves closer to and farther from the centre of the world; a motion that is natural when it descends and violent when it rises again; in his experiment the movement of the lead pendulum becomes progressively faster[42] than the movement of the wooden one because in the same time as the other it travels a greater distance: and the greater the power he imparts to the pendulum the greater this advantage.

Cardano, in his own way, had tried to explain the motion of a pendulum and the length of the oscillations related to the length of the cord in his *De subtilitate*[43] (On subtlety):

> But given that heavy bodies move with such difficulty along a direction equidistant from the horizon, why is it that they are so easily moved when they are suspended, so that a ring hanging from a thread seems to move by itself, and indeed, for this reason, shows the appearance of a magic spell?
> The cause is that all the force remains whole in the push: he who pushes forward, in reality, does two things, he supports and pushes; on the contrary, with the weight hanging, since it is now supported by another, all the force applied remains intact in the push.

[42] The Aristotelian definition of velocity applies perfectly to the comparison between the two pendulums: the one which travels more distance in the same time is the faster. For the two pendulums oscillating synchronously the different relationships between the amplitudes shows visually the progressive slowing of the lighter pendulum compared to the other.

[43] HIERONYMI CARDANI, *DE SUBTILITATE, op. cit.* in note 37, p. 21. The figure is on Folio 51r in the 1550 edition, on page 97 in the 1558 edition and on page 394 in the 1663 edition.

> And yet, when [*the weight*] is pushed it returns to the centre with about as much force as that with which it left it: so when with that force it is moved away from the centre, for example, the distance of a *braccio*, it will be necessary for it to move away just as far on the opposite side, and so returning continuously and alternatingly a little at a time it will come to a stop. So since with regard to the ring this motion is just a little helped even by a hidden impetus by spirits, it increases to such a point by itself that in appearance you would believe that it had been a force.
> So when the motion of the ring is pushed a little more, moving alone as it does (as we have said), it seems that there is a spirit contained in the ring which moves the ring.
> On the other hand this motion is even easier with a longer cord, as clearly demonstrated (fig. 2.3). Indeed, let the ring be in F &, suspended in A, move along BC; & again suspended in A be placed in G and move along DHE, which let be equal to BCF, & [*let*] L [*be*] the centre of the earth: it is obvious that as long as it is in F it will move against the natural movement along FG & as long as it is in H along HK, but HK is shorter than FG, as we have shown in the first [*book*] on Circles.
> So, given that the moving power is the same, & that which is moved [is] the same, & in F a greater distance from the centre is travelled than in H, that is to say it rises higher, *it will travel that distance in a longer time*: so, *if they have to move in equal times, a smaller thrust is required in H than in F*, & therefore the higher it is hung because of that the moveable moves more easily and with less effort.

I put the two phrases in italics in order to highlight two mistaken statements by Cardano, first when he states that the shorter pendulum takes a longer time, then when he thinks it is possible to obtain equal periods by diminishing the amplitude of the longer pendulum, and it is obvious that he has not observed how the periods depend exclusively on the lengths of the cord[44].

Galileo had read the second book of Cardano's *De subtilitate* which contains this passage and which has the title *De elementis, & eorum motibus, & actionibus* (On the elements and their motions and actions): indeed, he quotes it twice in one of his youthful works, before the *De motu*, which has the same title as Cardano's work, *Tractatus de elementis*[45] (Treatise on the elements); and it is difficult to believe that he had not read the text on the motion of a ring and that he had not noticed the drawing of pendular motion that illustrates the mistaken argument on the relationship between the length of the cord and period.

The *De motu* was written before he went to Padua, and the experiment with two pendulums in iron and wood is a strong argument in favour of the truth of Viviani's account of Galileo's discovery of isochronism when he was still a student and observed in the Cathedral the oscilla-

---

[44] In the conclusion of this passage, notice Cardano's interest for the occult and the esoteric to which his father had initiated him: «Since, therefore, the cord is long, the movement begins either due to a careless gesture of the hands, or to the air, or to the spirits themselves, whose force also descends along the cord. So certainly due to the ease of its movement & and for the many causes that can move it, it is not at all strange that the ring [*hanging*] at the beginning of the cord moves when the fingers are kept still, since once made to move it would be difficult for it to find the beginning of stillness since (as I have said) the hanging heavy body moves so tenaciously, and in this way seems to move by enchantment».

[45] G.G., Vol. I, *Juvenilia*, pp. 122 and 160.

tions of a lamp (or even of several lamps suspended at different heights). Galileo would describe the old experiment thus in the *Discorsi*[46]:

> Ultimately, I took two balls, one of lead and one of cork, the former being at least a hundred times as heavy as the latter, and I attached them to equal thin strings four or five *braccia* long, tied high above. Removed from the vertical, these were set going at the same moment, and falling along the circumferences of the circles, described by the equal strings that were the radii, they passed the vertical and returned by the same path. Repeating their going and comings a good hundred times by themselves, they sensibly showed that the heavy one kept time with the light one so well that in a hundred oscillations, nor in a thousand, does it get ahead in time even by a moment, but the two travel with equal pace.

When did Galileo begin to use the pendulum to measure time? I think at once, from his first experiments when he started to study the motion of bodies descending in water. When he carried out experiments with two spheres of different density it was not enough for him to verify that the denser sphere was also the fastest, he also had to verify whether it is true that their velocities were proportional to the amount by which their densities differ from that of water, and to do that he had to measure precisely the distance travelled by each one in a time span that had to be equal for both. He could do this accurately by counting a whole number of oscillations of the pendulum: a few oscillations for experiments that last a few seconds. He could do it by counting the beats of his pulse but with difficulty because his hands would be busy as he proceeded with the experiment. Perhaps he could do it by counting beats mentally with the tempo of music. It is an open question and everyone can shape their own opinion after considering in the next paragraph his experiments on motion in water and later his experiments on an inclined plane.

If I am not able to prove, beyond all shadow of doubt, that Galileo made use of a pendulum in his Pisan experiments to measure short time intervals, I can however show that by 7 September 1612 Galileo had already conceived his precise «measurer of time» that could work without great difficulty for hours and hours. The apparatus had probably not yet been built but it had been designed in detail and it would have been completely possible to construct it, as we shall see later; if it remained unknown it is because it is necessary to reflect on certain facts and draw the due consequences.

The date is that of a document kept at the *Archivio di Stato* of Florence[47], a memorandum by Galileo for Belisario Vinta, which the Secretary of State then transmitted to Orso d'Elci, the Grand Duke's ambassador to Madrid. It was written in such a way that officially it was Cosimo II de' Medici who was offering the King of Spain a way of «measuring longitude at any hour of the night and at almost any time of the year». In the letter Galileo's wish becomes an order from the Grand Duke: for the proposer «When it shall please Your Majesty to lend an ear to this business the said Galilei will be commanded to provide in a separate paper minute information of all the details concerning this equipment».

---

[46] G.G., Vol. VIII, *Discorsi*, pp. 128-129.

[47] G.G., Vol. XI, pp. 392-393; it bears the old shelf mark "Filza Medicea 4943".

But at the court of Philip III the offer was dropped at that time; negotiations began again in April 1616 and were finally abandoned in 1620.

The negotiation never reached a point at which it was necessary to go into detail and Galileo had no need to reveal how it was possible to observe the exact time of the occultation of Jupiter's satellites, overcoming the difficulties caused by the pitching of a ship. The point is fundamental because the difference in longitude between the position of a ship at sea and its point of departure is obtained by comparing the time of occultation observed on the ship with the time of the same occultation given in the «ephemerides of the aspects of these stars, calculated day by day and hour by hour [*in the meridian of the point of departure*], so that every night and in every place the longitude may be known[48]». Galileo's offer was an extremely demanding one for him because, once it was accepted, he would have had to keep the ephemerides up to date[49]:

> [...] while I from year to year shall provide, in writing or printed, the constitutions and aspects of these new stars, which are to be followed continuously from hour to hour; it is sufficient that they find only one of these constitutions in that night in which they wish to discover the longitude, and at once they shall know it, merely by knowing the count of the hours after their setting of the Sun.

If the time is measured accurately then, «by the supreme precision of the aforesaid celestial observations, all the particular places of the world will be adjusted so that there will absolutely not be an error of four miles[50] [*equivalent to 3000 braccia that are about 6607 m*] in any maximum distance[51]». He maintained a similar reserve with the Tuscan ambassador to whom he wrote only that he had «also found means to do them [*the observations*] on board ship, correcting the disturbance of the agitation of the waters[52]».

After his trial in 1633, while he was finishing writing the *Discorsi*, Galileo decided to turn to a new sponsor and on 15 August 1636 he wrote to the States General of the United Provinces of the Netherlands[53]. Now aged 73, this time he could no longer involve the Grand Duke in the negotiations and he was strictly controlled in his relations with the outside world. He realised that he had to trust the people he was dealing with and from the beginning he explained what his procedure consisted of. Every night the four satellites:

> [...] shining with the illumination of the Sun, are eclipsed as they enter into the cone of Jupiter's shadow; and because of their small size, the immersion in the darkness occurs in

[48] G.G., Vol. XII, p. 293.

[49] G.G., Vol. XII, p. 326.

[50] The Italian mile is equal to 1/60 of a degree and so Galileo claimed to be able to determine longitude with an accuracy of 1/15 of a degree. If the imprecision in determining the time of the occultation is of half a minute, the error is of 1/8 of a degree, about 14 km.

[51] G.G., Vol. XII, p. 268.

[52] G.G., Vol. XII, p. 292.

[53] G.G., Vol. XVI, pp. 463-471.

a time of about one minute of an hour; similarly a few hours later, leaving the shadow in another very short time, they recover their splendour: from which it is manifest that the observers of such eclipses cannot differ one from another about the time of the accurate observation, of a minute of an hour. In addition to their eclipses there are secondarily the applications of their bodies to Jupiter's body; where the exact moment when they seem to touch Jupiter's disc can be observed, as also, on the contrary, their separation from that same disc becomes observable; and such conjunctions and separations become observable without an error of half a minute of an hour, through the velocity of their motion and the very small moment that passes between touching and not touching.

The error is twice the error indicated twenty years earlier but probably the method of counting the time is the same[54]:

From this most true and stable principle I draw the structure of my numerator of time, using not a weight hanging from a thread but a pendulum of solid and heavy material, such as brass or copper. I make this pendulum in the shape of a sector of a circle of twelve or fifteen degrees, with a semidiameter of two or three palms' width; and the larger it is the less tedious it is to tend to it. I make this sector greater in the semidiameter in the middle, reducing it towards the outer edges, where I make it end in a rather cutting line, to avoid as much as possible the impediment of the air, which alone hinders it. This is perforated in the centre, and through it passes an iron rod like those on which steelyard balances turn; this rod, ending in the lower part in an angle, and resting on two supports of bronze, so that they shall be less worn away by the long movement of the sector, when this sector is moved many degrees from the perpendicular state (when it is well balanced), before it stops will swing to and fro a great number of vibrations; which for them to continue according to our need should be given a strong impulse by the person tending it, reducing it to wide vibrations: and having, once, measured with patience the numeration of the vibrations made in a natural day, with the revolution of a fixed star, we shall have the number of the vibrations of an hour, of a minute and of other lesser parts. Again, having made this experiment with a pendulum of any length, one can increase it or reduce it, so that each vibration lasts the time of a second; although the lengths of such pendulums maintain between themselves the duplicate proportion of that of the times, as for example: Having set that a pendulum of a length of four palms' width makes a thousand vibrations in a given time, if we wanted the length of another pendulum that in the same time made a duplicate number of vibrations, it is necessary that the length of the pendulum be the fourth part of the length of the other; and so, as can be seen by experiment, the multitude of vibrations of the pendulums with unequal lengths is the subduplicate of those lengths.

To avoid tedium for the person who must perpetually stand by numbering the vibrations, there is a rather convenient expedient, in this way: in other words by making a very small and slim stylus protrude from the middle of the circumference of the sector, which in passing strikes a bristle fixed at one of its ends, and making this bristle rest on the teeth of a

[54] G.G., Vol. XVII, pp. 101-103.

wheel as light as a sheet of paper, placed in the horizontal plane close to the pendulum, and having around it teeth like those of a saw; that is to say with one side placed square over the plane of the wheel, and the other inclined obliquely, carries out this office, which in striking the little bristle on the side perpendicular to the tooth, moves it, but then in returning this same bristle over the oblique side of the tooth does not otherwise move it, but is dragged over it and falls at the foot of the next tooth: and so in the passage of the pendulum the wheel will move the space of one of its teeth, but on the return of the pendulum it will not move at all; so its motion will be circular always in the same direction, and having marked the teeth with numbers, we shall see by our judgement the multitude of teeth passed, and in consequence the number of vibrations and the particles of time passed. Around the centre of this first wheel we can then fix another with a small number of teeth, which touches another greater toothed wheel, from the motion of which we could learn the number of the whole revolutions of the first wheel, arranging the multitude of teeth so that, for example, when the second wheel will have turned once, the other will have turned 20, 30 or 40 times or however many is desired. But to inform Your Lordships of this, since you have men most precise and ingenious in constructing clocks and other wondrous machines, is superfluous, because they themselves on this new foundation, of knowing that the pendulum, whether it moves through great or small spaces, makes it most equal reciprocations, will discover consequences more subtle than those that I can imagine. And since the failure of clocks consists mainly of our not yet being able to build what we call the clock time, so adjusted that it makes its vibrations equal; so in this most simple pendulum of mine, not subject to any alteration, is contained the way to keep the measurements of time always most equal.

2.2 *Natural motion (uniform velocity)*

With the pendulum, and above all with the inclined plane, of which we shall speak later, Galileo had all the experimental conditions he needed in order to carry out at Pisa those experiments that he would carry out during the twenty years spent at Padua; unfortunately however his imagination and his capacity for analysis were hampered by the Aristotelian vision of motion from which he had not yet completely freed himself, even if the young scholar did succeed in widening his horizon, at least in part, and created a research method, which would be recognised as distinctively his and innovative, a method that consisted of proceeding prudently and tenaciously with observations, reflections, hypotheses and experimental verification.

Later, at Padua, Galileo realised that the most favourable condition for studying the movement of a body is the condition where the medium interferes as little as possible, so that its nature of uniformly accelerated motion becomes obvious. Instead at Pisa his main aim was to study motion when it had stabilised in a state of constant velocity (limit velocity). This happens rapidly when the bodies move in a medium that has a sufficiently high density and the body has a specific weight which is not distant from that of the medium, a condition which can easily be obtained with water when the body is a sphere of wax mixed with sand or lead filings. We shall pay special attention to this initial phase of his experimental research, which has so far been neglected, bringing into focus the principles that guided him by reconstructing his fundamental Pisan experiments.

In the *De motu*[55] some ideas that are also in Giovanni Battista Benedetti's *Diversarum speculationum mathematicarum et physicarum liber* (Book on various speculations on mathematics and physics), published in Turin in 1585 can be recognised, where, in the chapter called *Discussione su alcune opinioni di Aristotele* (Discussions on some of Aristotle's opinions), Archimede's theory on the reduction of a body's weight due to the action of the medium it is immersed in plays a fundamental role.

Benedetti states that the relationship between the velocities with which a body moves in media of different density is proportional to the relationship between the weights that the body has in those media[56]; which theoretically is a fairly correct result if the velocities are those reached in the uniform motion phase, because the resistance opposed by the media has equal effect on the two velocities, (which however depend on the different viscosity of the media) and therefore does not affect the relationship.

We find a particularly interesting situation when he considers two bodies of the same material and of the same shape but of different size, for example two spheres of the same material but with different radius: Benedetti claims that the relationship between the velocities that the two bodies have in one medium is equal to the relationship between the velocities that they have in the other medium[57].

By similar reasoning Benedetti explains why the proportion between the velocities of two heterogeneous bodies, but of similar shape and equal size, in a given medium is equal to the proportion between their weights in the medium[58].

Finally, after having discussed how the two bodies move in a plenum, Benedetti arrives at his famous theorem on motion in a vacuum, entitled *Perché nel vuoto i corpi della stessa materia si muovono con uguale velocità* (Why in a vacuum bodies of the same material move with equal velocity)[59]. This is his demonstration:

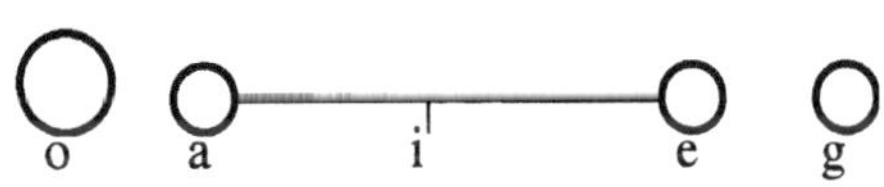

Fig. 2.4

[55] As has already been said, many scholars hold the opinion that the *Trattato*, which in *Le Opere* precedes the other parts, is the most complete and almost certainly the last chronologically of the writings that make up the collection that Vincenzo Viviani called *De motu antiquiora*. From now on the *Trattato* will simply be indicated by *De motu*, without further specification.

[56] GIOVANNI BATTISTA BENEDETTI, *Diversarum speculationum...*, p. 169: «*Velocitatem scilicet motus naturalis alicuius corporis gravis, in diversis mediis, proportionatam esse ponderi eiusdem corporis in iisdem mediis*».

[57] GIOVANNI BATTISTA BENEDETTI, *Diversarum speculationum...*, pp. 173-174: «*Quod duo corpora inaequalia eiusdem materiae in diversis mediis eandem velocitatis proportionem retinebunt*».

[58] GIOVANNI BATTISTA BENEDETTI, *Diversarum speculationum...*, p. 170: «*proportionem velocitatum, duorum corporum hetereogeneorum, sed similium figura, & magnitudine aequalium, in uno solo medio, aequalem esse proportioni ponderum ipsorum*».

[59] GIOVANNI BATTISTA BENEDETTI, *Diversarum speculationum...*, pp. 174-175: «*Quod in vacuo corpora eiusdem materiae aequali velocitate moverentur*».

> Let two bodies, *o* and *g*, be homogeneous, and *g* be the half of *o*. Then let two other bodies, *a* and *e*, be homogeneous like the first two, and let each of them be equal to *g*, and with our imagination we understand that both are placed at the ends of some line, and let the middle point of that line be *i* (fig. 2.4). It is clear that the point *i* will have as much weight as the centre of *o*, and therefore *i* by virtue of the bodies *a* and *e*, will move in a vacuum with a velocity equal to that of the centre of *o*: then when the said bodies *a* and *e* become disconnected from the said line, not for that reason would they change their velocity in any way, and each of them too would be as swift as *g*: thus *g* is as swift as *o*.

It is clear that the statement is correct with regard to the existence of vacuum, denied by Aristotle and all his followers, but it is wrong with regard to motion in vacuum, which is supposed uniform[60]. Benedetti's argument is also present in the *De motu* but Galileo avoids speaking of a vacuum[61] and in his demonstration he considers the motion of bodies in a medium, which is certainly water: indeed natural motion at constant velocity, which Benedetti and Galileo talk about, is rarely observed in air, when the bodies are very light compared to their size, such as small pieces of cork, balls of cotton, etc., or had begun to descend from far away, such as drops of water or hailstones etc.

It follows that Benedetti is trusting to imagination when he talks of constant velocity in air or vacuum, while his considerations on motion in water are probably due to practical observations.

Did Galileo know of Benedetti's *Diversarum speculationum mathematicarum et physicarum liber*? Some historians believe it to be probable because of the presence in the *De motu* of arguments treated in a similar style, all concerning natural motion. We shall see however that some aspects of natural motion are dealt with by Galileo with a confidence that presupposes careful preliminary experimental research to support his convictions, the more so since he can use the pendulum to measure time, having discovered its isochronicity.

Galileo dedicates the first 13 chapters of the *De motu* to natural motion, for which he distinguishes five different cases, *i.e.*: a) how two bodies of the same specific weight and equal shape but different size move in the same medium; b) how the same body moves in different media; c) how two bodies of different specific weight but which have the same shape and size move; d) how two bodies with different specific weight but the same weight move; e) how two bodies with different specific weight which also differ in shape and weight move[62].

---

[60] The Aristotelian definition of velocity also holds for uniformly accelerated motion, but on the condition that it is specified that the bodies being compared start from stationary and that the time is measured from the beginning of the motion; but Benedetti never states this and so the velocity spoken of is always uniform velocity. See Galileo's masterful explanation to Simplicio in G.G., Vol. VII, *Dialogo*, pp. 48-50.

[61] G.G., Vol. I, *De motu*, p. 263: «*Dicimus ergo, mobilia eiusdem speciei (eiusdem autem speciei vocentur quae ex eadem materia, ut plumbo vel ligno etc., conflantur), quamvis mole differant, tamen eadem cum celeritate moveri, nec citius descendere maior lapis quam minor*». (We say, then, that mobiles of the same species (let those things be said to be of the same species that are constituted of the same material, such as lead or wood, *etc.*), though they may differ in size, are however moved with the same swiftness, and a larger stone does not go down more swiftly than a smaller one.) The demonstration follows on p. 265 of the *De motu*.

[62] G.G., Vol. I, *De motu*, pp. 262 and 266.

The discussion of the resistance offered by the medium is not specifically dealt with in the *Trattato*, but we should not suppose that the subject was ignored: we shall see later that some of the experiments on the resistance offered by water, which are discussed in the *Discorso... intorno alle cose che stanno in su l'acqua o che in quella si muovono* (Discourse... on bodies that stay atop water or move in it)[63], actually date back to his Pisan period.

Galileo extrapolates for air and vacuum the results he has obtained from experiments in water, giving the reader the sensation that much of what he claims is the outcome of a fantastic construction, when it is only a generalisation, with limits that Galileo is doubtless well aware of, as shown by this passage, later cancelled, from the *De motu*[64]:

> ALESSANDRO: But since, of the three media through which motion occurs, fire is most distant from us, while in air we can only make experiments on downward motion, indeed the things that we have available are all heavier than air; so our demonstrations will be verified in water: indeed we have some bodies that descend in water, as well as some that, immerged in water, move upwards. Nevertheless, those things that we shall demonstrate for water and for the things that move in it, are also true for the other two media, that is for air and fire. On the demonstrations then that I put forward, similar things were demonstrated by Archimedes, but adopting in his demonstrations other suppositions and other methods. All those things that are purely mathematical shall be shown by me with arguments that are more properly physical; which is better in the present circumstance.
>
> DOMENICO: I will most welcome being able to understand these things: and if demonstrations with drawings are necessary, here is a most clean stretch of fine sand, where all the drawings can be conveniently made with this stick[65].

The most important sentences are those where he alludes to experiments that in air can only be carried out incompletely «*in aëre non nisi de motu deorsum periculum facere possimus*» and declares explicitly that he will verify his statements in water «*ideo in medio aquae demonstrationes nostras verificabuntur*».

The discussion of the various cases is mainly appropriately circumscribed to bodies of the same shape and size, but of different weight, that move in the same medium; or to the same body moving in different media, and so only the reduction in weight due to Archimedes' principle of buoyancy, which is invalid only in vacuum, remains in play as the cause *in itself* of the differences[66]:

---

[63] G.G., Vol. IV, pp. 88-90 and later on pp. 509-510. We shall often indicate this work, following Favaro, as *Le Galleggianti* (Floating bodies).

[64] G.G., Vol. I, *De Motu*, p. 380, footnote.

[65] Remember that the two friends are walking alongside the river Arno outside Pisa. Domenico offering to write in the sand for Alessandro, reminds us of Archimedes, and in this way Galileo, personified by Alessandro, declares himself to be continuing in the steps of the master from Syracuse.

[66] G.G., Vol. I, *De Motu*, p. 281.

> For in a plenum a mobile is moved swiftly according to the excess of its own heaviness over the heaviness of the medium through which it is moved; and thus in a void it will be moved according to the excess of its heaviness over the heaviness of the void: since this is null, the excess of the heaviness of the mobile over the heaviness of the void will be the total heaviness of this same mobile; thus it will be moved swiftly according to its own total heaviness. But in no plenum will it be able to be moved as swiftly, since the excess of the heaviness of the mobile over the heaviness of the medium is less than the total heaviness of the mobile: thus the swiftness will also be less, than if it were moved according to its own total heaviness.

The theory of motion in vacuum is the least Galileian of theories that Galileo could uphold, but it is introduced to preserve the internal consistency of the *De motu* which forces him to extrapolate to air and vacuum what he has observed in water, hypothesising the existence of an analogous uniform motion which is reached after a much longer distance (or, more accurately, a much longer time), which makes his study almost impossible; in any case, in this phase of his studies the accelerated or decelerated motion is always limited in time and is followed by the uniform motion and he presents an explanation for this fact which seems satisfactory to him for motion in air too[67]:

> For if a stone goes down from a high tower, its swiftness seems always to be increased: yet this happens because the stone, in comparison with the medium through which it is carried, namely air, is very heavy; and since it goes away with an amount of impressed force [*virtute impressa*] as great as its heaviness, it assuredly goes away with a great impressed force, which the motion from the height of a tower is not sufficient to consume, so that the swiftness is always intensified all through the height of a single tower. Now if we were to take a certain heavy thing, whose heaviness would not so very far surpass the heaviness of air, assuredly we would then see with our own eyes that this thing, a little after the beginning of its motion, would always be moved uniformly, provided however that the air was very calm.

Galileo starts by discussing the motion of a body passing through media of different density, so that all the accidental effects remain the same, and shows that the relationship between the velocities is proportional to the relationship between the weights that the body has in the two media[68]:

> For it is clear that that the same mobile going down in different media, observes in the swiftness of its motions, the ratio to one another of the excesses of its own heaviness over the heavinesses of the media: thus if the heaviness of the mobile is **8**, but the heaviness of a size of one medium, equal to that of the mobile, is **6**, then the swiftness of this body will be **2**; if the heaviness of an amount of the other medium, equal to the size of the mobile, is **4**, then the swiftness of the mobile, in this medium, will be **4**. It is therefore evident that these

[67] G.G., Vol. I, *De motu*, pp. 406-407.

[68] G.G., Vol. I, *De motu*, p. 272. Note that units of measure of velocity are never indicated: Galileo writes «the velocity would be like 2» or «the velocity would be 4» because what matters is the relationship between velocities and not their absolute value. Later (G.G., Vol. I, *De motu*, p. 400) there is a similar discussion.

> swiftnesses will be to one another as **2** and **4**; and not as the thicknesses or the heavinesses of the media, which is what Aristotle wanted, which are to one another as **6** and **4**."

Even in the case of bodies of different type but equal volume that move in the same medium Galileo states that the velocity is proportional to the difference between their weight and that of an equal volume of the medium, because of the hydrostatic thrust which must be subtracted from the heaviness of the body.

Once again the accidental causes are equal for the two bodies and they do not create particular differences. Let us see how he expounds his reasoning[69],

> Similarly the answer to the other question is evident: namely, what ratio the speeds of mobiles equal in size, but unequal in heaviness, observe with one another in the same medium. For the speeds of such mobiles will be to one another as the excesses by which the heavinesses of the mobiles exceed the heaviness of the medium: thus, for example, if two mobiles are equal in size, but unequal in heaviness, the heaviness of one being **8**, and of the other **6**, but the heaviness of an amount of the medium, equal in size to the size of one of the two mobiles, is **4**, then the swiftness of the former mobile will be **4**, and that of the latter will be **2**. Hence these speeds will observe the ratio of **4** to **2**; and not that which is between the heavinesses, namely **8** to **6**.

This time we have direct confirmation that the medium is water, because the example is returned to later to clarify that all the specific weights, both of the two weights and the water, must be taken in the air[70].

In the last writing in the *De motu*, in the form of a dialogue, similar examples are given and it is particularly interesting to see the way that *Alessandro*, who in the dialogue represents Galileo, discusses the case of bodies of different density and volume[71]:

> ALESSANDRO: ... But, as has often been said above, it is necessary that you always understand and assume that the different mobiles of which we speak differ only in heaviness, though they are equal in size; so that you would not perchance say: Let there be, for example, a mobile [***a***] whose heaviness [in air] is **8**; and let the heaviness of an amount of water equal in size to the said mobile be **3**; then it is manifest, from the things that have been said, that the swiftness [in water] of the said mobile will be as **5**: but if you take another mobile, such as ***c***, whose size were twice that of ***a***, and whose heaviness [in air] were less than twice the heaviness of ***a***, namely **12**, and the heaviness of an amount of water equal in size to ***c*** were **6**, then the swiftness [in water] of ***c*** would be as **6**. However, it must not be said that ***c*** will go down faster than ***a***; because then the ratio would no longer hold good, since the mobiles differ in size. But if we want the ratio to hold good, let us take half of ***c***, so that its size is equal to the

[69] G.G., Vol. I, *De motu*, pp. 272-273.

[70] G.G., Vol. I, *De motu*, p. 275.

[71] G.G., Vol. I, *De motu*, pp. 402-403.

size of ***a***; then the heaviness of ***c*** [in air] will be **6**: but the heaviness [of an amount] of water [equal to] half [the size of ***c***] will be **3**, so that the speed of half of ***c*** will be **3**, as compared with the speed of ***a***, which will be **5**: therefore a will go down faster than the whole of ***c*** (for the whole is moved with the same swiftness as its half).

In this discourse ***a*** has volume V and weighs **8**; the mass of water of volume V weighs **3**; the density of ***a*** is therefore $\rho_a = 8/3$ and thus $\rho_a - \rho_{\text{Water}} = (5/3)\rho_{\text{Water}}$. Instead for ***c*** we have volume $2V$ and weight **12**, and knowing that the weight of the volume $2V$ of water is **6**, the density of ***c*** is $\rho_c = 2$ and therefore $\rho_c - \rho_{\text{Water}} = \rho_{\text{Water}}$. From all this it follows that the relationship between the velocity is $v_a / v_c = (\rho_a - \rho_{\text{Water}})/(\rho_c - \rho_{\text{Water}}) = 5/3$, as Galileo found.

For the motion in water however Alessandro's reasoning is somewhat forced when we find in the final affirmation: «*the whole is moved with the same swiftness as its half*». The motion which is discussed here is the uniform motion when the body has reached the limit velocity given by the relationship: $v_L^2 = \text{const}\ (\rho - \rho_{\text{Water}})\, V/S$, where V is the volume of the body and S is its cross-section perpendicular to the direction of the motion. The ratio between the limit velocities of a sphere A of volume V and of a sphere B of volume $V/2$ is $v_A/v_B = [2S_B/S_A]^{1/2} = 2^{1/3}$. If A is a cube and B is a parallelepiped with the same base and a height half that of the cube[72], we would have instead $v_A/v_B = 2^{1/2}$. To obtain an equal velocity it is necessary for the cross-sections of A and B to satisfy the relationship $S_B = S_A/2$.

The same difficulty is present in the *Dialogo*, when Alessandro claims[73]:

> Hence it is evident that when we reason on the subject of the swiftness or the slowness of mobiles, it is necessary to have in mind those mobiles whose difference depends solely on heaviness, although they are equal in size. Then when the ratio of the speeds to one another has been found, the same ratio will be observed between mobiles of the same kind, no matter how much they may differ in size: for a piece of lead whose heaviness is 10 pounds [10 libras = 3.395 kg] goes down with the same speed as a piece of lead whose heaviness is 100 pounds[74] [100 libras = 33.95 kg].

To prove it he asks Domenico to concede the following as evident:

> If there are two mobiles, one of which is moved more swiftly than the other, these mobiles joined together will be moved on the one hand more swiftly than the one which alone was moved more slowly, but more slowly than the one which was moved more swiftly[75].

---

[72] For the superimposed bricks see G.G., Vol. VII, *Esercitazioni filosofiche di Antonio Rocco*, p. 731: «... I imagined in my mind two bodies equal in size and weight, as would be, for example, two bricks...». The drawing that accompanies the text (on p. 732), like that in the *De motu*, shows the bricks side by side, but further on we read: «However can it be true that, since *A* and *B* are two pieces of lead, one laid on the other will not increase its heaviness?». From the whole context that follows on p. 733 we deduce that the experiment is in the air.

[73] G.G., Vol I, *De motu* p. 403 the argument also occurs in the *Trattato* on pp. 265-266. See however the experiment described at the end of the next paragraph, where two spheres of different size and almost equal density are compared. Their motion is similar, just as Galileo claims here.

[74] It would have been more correct for Galileo to write *pondus* (weight) rather than *gravitas* (heaviness).

[75] G.G., Vol I, *De Motu*, p. 404.

Indeed the slowness of one slows down the velocity of the other, but has its motion increased by it, so that the velocity of the two units will be intermediate. From this principle it immediately follows that when two bodies are of the same material but of different weight, it is impossible for the larger to move more swiftly than the lighter, because their union, which is greater than each of them separately, should have an intermediate velocity. The velocity does not depend on the quantity of material, and therefore on the weight to the bodies but depends on their *gravitas* (heaviness), that is to say their density. Here, as in a few other passages[76] of the *De motu*, Galileo introduced explicitly the *libbre* (pounds), that is to say he uses a unit of weight, in contrast to the values that he assigns to *gravitas*, for which he never indicates dimensions.

In this fundamental theorem Galileo once again disregards the resistance of the medium, but it may also be that he had verified that the medium opposes more or less the same resistance to bodies of equal density although of different dimensions and this can occur, as well as in air, also in water when the container is narrow enough.

After having expounded all the possible cases, this is his conclusion[77]:

> These, then, are the general rules of the ratios of the motions of mobiles, whether of the same species or not, whether in the same medium or in different media, whether moved upward or downward.

If his theory of uniform motion, especially because of the reference to density, is true for bodies that move in water, in the case of air and vacuum it is certainly lacking in experimental confirmation; however, given the impossibility of carrying out analogous experiments, Galileo takes for granted that it is valid everywhere[78]:

> I will bring forth the demonstrations [of motion] with water as the medium: and no one will deny that the things that are demonstrated of water are also true of the other media.

This generalisation is, therefore, a consequence of the confidence acquired with the experiments in water; experiments that he did not describe in the *De motu* but which may have been very different from the examples that he introduced in the various cases discussed.

2.3 *Early experiments in water*

Galileo's impossible example

It is very probable that some examples in the *De motu* may not correspond to experiments that were actually carried out but adapted and reformulated for the purposes of expounding the

[76] See for example: G.G., Vol I, *De motu*, p. 266, p. 313, p. 339.

[77] G.G., Vol I, *De motu*, p. 273.

[78] G.G., Vol I, *De motu*, p. 380: «*quae vero de aqua demonstrantur, de aliis quoque mediis vera esse nemo inficias ibit*».

text, and this possibility tempts us to try and verify them. It seems to us that the best way to proceed is to concentrate on one of the examples which has the best defined details: the one in which Galileo discusseed the velocity in water of two bodies of equal volume, which had heaviness (in air) of **8** and **6** respectively, while the heaviness (again in air) of a volume of water equal to that of the two bodies was **4**, so that the relationship between the density of the two bodies and the density of the water is known[79]: $\rho_A = 2\rho_{Water}$ and $\rho_B = 1.5\rho_{Water}$. Galileo's conclusion was: «Those velocities will keep, therefore, the proportion that there is between **4** and **2**».

Galileo normally considered spherical bodies and to obtain two equal spheres with those particular densities it is enough to resort to an expedient suggested by Galileo himself[80]:

> And if, on the other hand, we conceive in our mind, for example, an amount of wax of considerable size[81] floating on water, and we mix the wax with either sand or some other heavier thing, in such a way that in the end it comes to be heavier than water [...]

Let us observe that, at first sight, Galileo's statement that the limit velocity of the heavier sphere is double that of the lighter sphere appears correct, because for velocities that are not too

---

[79] There are no natural substances with these density values: the materials that come closest to them are ebony ($\rho_{Ebony} \approx 1.26\ \rho$ kg/dm^3), brick ($\rho_{Brick} \approx 1.8$ kg/dm^3) and silica glass ($\rho_{Glass} \approx 2.2\ \rho$ kg/dm^2). For Tartaglia the baked stone called brick or *quadrello* has a density about double that of water (*Ragionamenti de Nicolo Tartaglia sopra la sua travagliata inventione* (Reasoning of Nicolo Tartaglia on his tormented invention), unnumbered sheet N° 29, Venice, 1551). Tartaglia found that weighing the brick in air and then in water from dry the ratio is 41 to 16 «that would be more than double in heaviness»; but when he repeated the operation after it was soaked in water he found that the ratio had become 93 to 48 «that is less than double», «so because the variation was so great... I took the middle between these two results». It happened to me too to find small but significant differences when weighing wax spheres in air when they were perfectly dry and after having wetted them. When you try to vary the density of a sphere that weighs about 100 grams by quantities that are of the order of $1/10^4$, variations of 250 milligrams due to the dampness absorbed are a harmful distraction. When the sphere is then placed in water, at first many small air bubbles adhere to it making it lighter: you have to shake it, remove the bubbles and wait some time; finally it may weigh even up to 100 milligrams more.

[80] Galileo uses this expedient in G.G, Vol I, *De motu*, p. 264. We find a similar use of malleable wax in the *Discorso al Serenissimo Gran Duca di Toscana Intorno alle cose, che Stanno in su l'acqua, o che in quella si muovono,* Florence, 1612[2], p. 21 (G.G., Vol. IV, p. 83): «Anyone who wants quickly to see this [by] experience with some flexible material that is easily shaped to any figure can take some wax and, first making of it a ball or some other solid shape, add to it as much lead as just barely makes it sink, so that one grain less would not suffice to make it submerge». Another technique is indicated in the *Considerazioni sopra 'l discorso del Colombo*, (G.G., Vol. IV, p. 606): «Imagine a ball of very thin glass, which when full of wax weighs, *e.g.*, ten pounds and a drachm, but that such a size of water weighs only ten pounds; that ball, as heavier by a drachm than as much water will certainly sink»; later on p. 530: «if I take two shapes, *v.g.*, of wax, and I increase the weight of one of them by adding lead filings, these two bodies, although in air shall not have changed type of heaviness, being both heavy and descending, nevertheless they will have changed it in water, where one will sink to the bottom and the other from the bottom will rise to the top».

[81] G.G., Vol. IV, *Discorso intorno alle cose che stanno in su l'acqua...*, pp. 88-89: «Now wax is very suitable for this, since besides its receiving no sensible alteration from impregnation by water, it is tractable, and the same piece is very easily brought to any shape, while being very little less heavy than water, it can be brought to very nearly equal heaviness therewith by imbedding in it a few lead filings».

high and for Reynolds numbers that are not too great, of the order of $10^2 - 10^3$, the limit velocity is given by the expression[82]

$$v_L = (2/9)R^2(\rho - \rho_{Water})g/\eta_{Water},$$

from which, with the values of the two densities, $\rho_A = 2\rho_{Water}$ and $\rho_B = 1.5\rho_{Water}$, we immediately obtain

$$v_{LA} = 2v_{LB}.$$

But things go very wrong when, setting aside the relationship between the two velocities required by the theory of proportions, we go on to calculate the value of each of them individually. To have an idea of the limit velocity, let us suppose that the common radius of the two spheres is $R = 0.025$ m.

With the density of the example we obtain absurdly high values for the limit velocities of the two spheres, $v_{LA} = 1520\ ms^{-1}$ and $v_{LB} = 760\ ms^{-1}$, and for the corresponding Reynolds numbers[83], $Re_A = 8.48 \times 10^7$ and $Re_B = 4.24 \times 10^7$, and this result indicates that the two spheres cannot arrive at a regime of uniform velocity over the brief distance available[84]: it would take much more than the height of a glass jar!

The experiment on motion at uniform velocity, obviously, cannot be carried out with the values of the example, but this can easily be explained: in transferring the results of the experiments he had carried out into the *De motu* , Galileo may have increased the values for the densities of the bodies without changing the relationship $(\rho_A - \rho_{Water})/(\rho_B - \rho_{Water})$; because in the real experiment they were so close to those of water, to be credible, they would have required an accurate description of the experiments and of their inherent problems, while the relationship $(\rho_A - \rho_{Water})/(\rho_B - \rho_{Water})$ does not change if the densities of the two spheres are $\rho_A = 2\ kg/dm^3$ and $\rho_B = 1.5\ kg/dm^3$, respectively, or $\rho_A = 1.000002\ kg/dm^3$ and $\rho_B = 1.000001\ kg/dm^3$.

Galileo often enunciated general results illustrating a theory with some examples which he tries to make easy and obvious; for this reason he introduces whole numbers without stating explicitly that those numbers do not describe a real situation, even if, after all, in so doing he leads the reader to think that they are correct. Indeed we shall see that Galileo, in his search for

---

82 In the expression R is the radius of the sphere, ρ is its density, ρ_{Water} is the density of water, $g \approx 9.806\ ms^{-2}$ and η_{Water} is the viscosity coefficient of water which is $0.81 \cdot 10^{-3}\ kgs^{-1}m^{-1}$ at 25°C. The relationship can be used when the motion occurs without turbulence and the water opposes a resistance proportional to the velocity of the body. On p. 393 of the *De motu* Galileo wrote: «as the motion is to motion so the resistance of the medium is to the resistance; so the swifter and more impetuous the motion the more the medium resists, because it must be split more swiftly, the motion will always go in the same measure as the resistance: therefore, changing the proportion, the slower the motion, than the less shall be the resistance».

83 The Reynolds number for a sphere is given by the expression $Re = vd\rho/\eta$, with v the velocity of the sphere, d its diameter, ρ and η the density and the viscosity coefficient of water, which have a relationship at 25°C of approximately $\rho/\eta \approx 0.997\ 10^3/0.893\ 10^{-3} \approx 1.116\ 10^6\ sm^{-2}$.

84 I made two wax spheres with lead inside with these densities and when I placed them in water I saw that they immediately acquired great velocity.

a motion that soon becomes uniform had to greatly decrease the density of the material used, until he arrived at spheres of wax that were only minimally weighted down, with a density fairly close to that of water.

His laborious attempts to reduce the density to arrive at uniform motion and the partial success he finally arrived at must have aroused in Galileo a determination to do the same with experiments in air. It is probable that the young Pisan professor wondered how to dampen down acceleration in air quickly and that he had the idea of making use of the inclined plane, which he was acquainted with from his reading of Guidobaldo Dal Monte's *Mechanicorum Liber* and perhaps directly from Pappus of Alexandria's *Mathematicae Collectiones* (Mathematical Collections)[85].

Galileo thought that with this instrument he could reproduce a situation similar to that of water, inclining the plane slightly to arrive soon at uniform motion. It is no surprise that his study of the inclined plane is only present in the final version of the *De motu*, the most complete one, which has conventionally been called by the name *Trattato*.

The studies on motion in water that Galileo carried out in his early youth are essential to understanding the birth of his method and all the later development of his research depends on them; therefore we shall pay special attention to them, reconstructing his experiments, which are much more articulated and varied than they appear in the *De motu* itself.

Reconstruction of Galileo's experiment

To obtain a uniform velocity over a short distance such as that available in a glass jar, without reducing the dimensions of the spheres too much [86] ($\varnothing \leq 0.06$ m) and with limited values of the Reynolds numbers so as to guarantee a non turbulent motion ($Re \leq 10^3$), it is necessary that the limit velocity v_L to be arrived at be around 10^{-2} m/s, and this can only be obtained if the difference between the density of the weighted wax and that of water is extremely small:
10^{-5} kg/dm^3 < $(\rho_{Sphere} - \rho_{Water})$ < 10^{-4} kg/dm^3.

Let us see if this is possible with the means that Galileo had available. To weight the wax we can, following his indications, make use of sand «or something heavier» (lead filings, lead pellets, etc.), but first we have to overcome a difficulty that the young Pisan scientist must certainly also have encountered: how to make two or more spheres with the same volume and the necessary densities with beeswax and little bits of lead?

We can find an indication in a passage in the *De motu* that gives the method found by Galileo to appraise the percentage of the two metals in a mixture of gold and silver using a set of scales; the dialogue begins with a rather naive question from Domenico[87]:

[85] *Pappi Alexandrini Mathematicae Collectiones A Federico Commandino Urbinatae in Latinum Conversae, & Commentarijs Illustratae*, Bologna, 1558.

[86] G.G., Vol. IV, *Discorso intorno alle cose che stanno in su l'acqua ...*, p. 89: «Such material being prepared, make it for example into a ball the size of an orange or larger, and heavy enough to stay at the bottom, but so lightly that by the removal of a single grain of lead it will float, and then with that grain restored it will return to the bottom». All the spheres used in the reconstruction of Galileo's experiments had diameters between 0.056 m and 0.058 m.

[87] G.G., Vol. I, *De Motu*, p. 379.

DOMENICO: This is entirely true: but nevertheless I still do not understand for what reason, in the case of the pebble in water, one must only take into consideration an amount of water as great in size as the size of the pebble, and not all the water.

Alessandro answers as follows:

ALESSANDRO: I am, at last, unable to avoid demonstrating to you some theorems, from the comprehension of which you will understand most clearly not only what you are asking for, but also what ratio bodies have, both heavy ones and light ones, with regard to the swiftness or the slowness of their motion, as well as what the ratio is of the heavinesses and lightnesses of one and the same body, if we were to weigh it in different media: all these things had to be demonstrated when I tried to find the real reason by which we could, in a mixture of two metals, assign to each individual metal a very precise share. Of these theorems (though they are not different from those demonstrated by Archimedes) I will bring for every one to see demonstrations that are less mathematical and more physical; I will make use of assumptions that are clearer and more obvious to the senses than those that Archimedes has taken.

DOMENICO: Are you asserting, then, that you also found out the true reason by which Archimedes discovered the goldsmith's fraud in the golden crown? Haven't the same things been written by many authors, and in particular by Vitruvius?

ALESSANDRO: I could demonstrate that that popular method of those who talk of a bowl full of water, etc., is most unreliable; by contrast, the one I have discovered[88] is very accurate,

---

88 The method Galileo followed is certainly original and there are no clues that might lead us to believe that he had read the *Ragionamenti de Nicolo Tartaglia sopra la sua travagliata inventione,* where the procedures to determine the densities of some very common materials are described, weighing them in air and in well water from dry (I indicate its density here by ρ_0). Tartaglia found $2\rho_0$ for brick, $3.5\rho_0$ for marble, $6.3\rho_0$ for iron and tin, $6.5\rho_0$ for copper, $10\rho_0$ for lead and silver, $17\rho_0$ for gold. This is an example of his method: «I weighed two cooked stones [*bricks*]..., and then I tied them with a fairly long string attached to the hooks of the scales, & this I did so that the said hooks should not enter into the water where they were to be weighed, & so carefully I weighed them again in a pot of fresh water». Tartaglia demonstrated four propositions and I quote here the first and last statements. The first: «The proportion in size of every two heavy bodies, whether they are of a same kind or of different kinds, is like the difference of the weight of one of them in air to the weight of the same one in water, to the difference of the weight of the other in air to the weight of that same one in water». The fourth: «It is possible to find the proportion of the size & the proportion of the heaviness according to type of the two bodies of which one is of a nature heavier than water (as is iron) & the other of a nature lighter than water (as is wax)». At the conclusion of the IV proposition Tartaglia points out that it might serve in compounds to find the proportion in which the component substances are present: «So the proportion of their weights is known, according to the kind & the proportion of their corporal area, that is that their size is also known, as was proposed by the evidences of this proposition it is possible to declare of a body mixed of two bodies differing in heaviness, let us say of gold & of silver, how much there is of one therein, & how much of the other, which rule shall be much & much more certain & less false than that which Archimedes found, as Vitruvius and other authors tell, to discover the fraud of the maker of Hiero's golden crown because his way will not serve except (approximately) in a large mass of gold. But with this rule such a fraud can be known exactly in a ducat & less than a golden ducat if done with diligence and of the practice of this we shall speak more particularly another time ». Galileo did not know this text. He wrote in *La Bilancetta*: «But knowing that this method was totally false and lacking in the precision that is needed in mathematical things, made me several times wonder in what

and I think it is the same as that of Archimedes, both because it is so elegant, and because it rests on Archimedes' own demonstrations.

Since it is common knowledge that Galileo wrote the version that we know of *La Bilancetta* (Little scales) before the *De motu*, it is reasonable to think that the young Pisan scientist built his extremely precise hydrostatic scales[89], and examined the reduction in weight due to buoyancy, with a view to the experiments that he was carrying out regarding the motion of bodies in water[90]: *La bilancetta* is not, therefore, a piece of research in its own right and it is for this reason, as well as the fact that it is such a short text, that Alessandro (*i.e.* Galileo), did not keep the promise he made to Domenico and publish it, despite its undoubted interest. The link between the scales and the experiments in water, in which objects are needed with density very close to that of water, explains why Galileo sought such great precision in his hydrostatic scales, arrived at by taking «a ruler at least two *braccia* long, and the longer it is the more precise the instrument shall be» and then:

> [...] wrapping a most thin brass wire around it, which shall divide the space *ef* into many small equal parts [...] But here I must warn that a difficulty in counting arises: because, those wires being so very thin, as is required for precision, it is not possible to count them by sight, because between such small spaces the eye is dazzled. So, to count them with ease, I took a most sharp little stylus, which is made to run most slowly over the said wires; so that, thus, partly by hearing, partly by the hand finding impediment at each wire, these said wires will be easily numbered.

A simple piece of reasoning allows us to assess the precision: the pair of scales has symmetrical arms about 600 mm long and with a brass wire with a diameter of 0.6 mm one of the arms can be divided into 1000 parts (or into more parts if a thinner wire were used); the masses of the spheres are around 0.1 kg. So Galileo could distinguish with his scales, moving the counterweight by the width of the wire, a difference in mass of about 10^{-4} kg and arrive at a density of

way, by means of water, one could find exactly the mixture of two metals; and finally, after diligently re-examining what Archimedes shows in his books *Delle cose che stanno nell'aqqua* (On floating bodies) and in those *Delle cose che pesano ugualmente* (On things that weigh equally) a method occurred to me that most finely resolves our question: the method that I believe is the same as Archimedes used, since, as well as being most exact, still depends on demonstrations found by Archimedes himself». Galileo quotes two books: *Archimedis de iis quae vehuntur in aqua libri duo a Federico Commandino urbinate in pristinum nitorem restituti et commentariis illustrati* (Bologna, 1565) and *Guidiubaldi e marchionibus Montis in duos Archimedis aequeponderantium libros paraphrasi Scholijs illustrata* (Pesaro, 1588) (see the letter of 16 January 1588 in which Guidobaldo writes that as soon as the book is printed he will send Galileo a copy). There is no evidence however that he ever owned or read Tartaglia's book.

89 For the precision of his scales see: ROBERTO VERGARA CAFFARELLI, *Galileo e Pisa*, Pisa, 2004, pp. 23-25, in which comparing his measurements of the densities of gold, silver, diamond and copper with the XIX century measurements, the precision is shown to be about 4/°°.

90 G.G., Vol. I, *La Bilancetta*, pp. 215-220; *Tavola delle proporzioni delle gravità in specie de i metalli e delle gioie pesate in aria ed in acqua*, pp. 225-228. On pp. 216-217 we read: «solid bodies that sink in water, weigh less in the water than in the air by the amount that is the heaviness in air of so much water in size as it is solid ... placing, for example, a ball of gold in water, if that ball were of water, it would weigh nothing, because water in water does not move up or down. So it is that the gold [ball] weighs in [the water] that amount, by which the heaviness of the gold surpasses the heaviness of the water».

Fig. 2.5

the wax and sand mixture so close to the density of water that it is only 1/1000 greater.

In recreating the experiments I tried to put myself in the same conditions in which I imagine Galileo found himself, trying to identify the difficulties that the young Pisan scientist encountered, the methods he followed and the results he arrived at.

I always gave the conventional value of 1000 kg/m^3 to the absolute density of distilled water (of the type on sale commercially) regardless of temperature[91], while I determined the relative density of the spheres in air and water by the Galileian method with scales.

The measurements of the masses and absolute densities were carried out with the equipment shown in fig. 2.5, in which a pair of scales, built in the XIX century, is less precise than Galileo's but is visibly sensitive to masses of a hundredth of a gram.

---

[91] In my experiments the temperature was always around 25°C and at this temperature the density of the water is 0.997 kg/dm^3. Since in measuring the densities of bodies their volume is obtained by observing the reduction in weight when they are immersed in water, and since in this operation the value of the density of the water intervenes, we find that the differences $\rho - \rho_{Water}$, which are the only quantities in which the correction due to the temperature might be important, should be corrected with a not very relevant multiplying factor of 0.997. The recurring factor ρ/η is used instead with the values at 25°C.

To make a sphere I softened a piece of beeswax of about 0.1 kg, leaving it for a while in warm water (at about 45–50° C); then, working the soft wax with my hands, I tried, as far as possible, to arrive at a spherical shape. Only after my first attempts did I happen to read the method recommended by Galileo[92]:

> Make a ball of wax, about as large as a walnut, and make the surface as smooth as possible, which shall be done by shaping it lightly with a clear shiny glass; so it will hover with a little lead placed inside, such that when submerged under water it will descend, but with little force, to the bottom [...]

I then tried to put his instructions into practice, with results which proved disappointing due to my inexperience and also to my lack of patience.

To weigh down the wax spheres I used lead pellets, inserting 3.7 g and 0.1 g lead shot, until they no longer floated.

Important observation: the bodies I have used were not made of homogeneous matter because they are mainly made up of wax with lead pellets concentrated in a small area. From now on, even if it is unusual, I shall always indicate by the term *density* the relationship between the body's weight and volume even when it is made up of two substances distributed in a highly uneven way, for which the density should be defined locally: $\rho(\boldsymbol{r}) = dm(\boldsymbol{r})/dv(\boldsymbol{r})$, where $\boldsymbol{r}$ is the position vector and $v(\boldsymbol{r})$ the elementary volume at point $\boldsymbol{r}$.

In order to weigh the bodies I had two supports made: a heavier one in order to be able to immerse easily bodies less dense than water, essentially a brass plate pierced in the middle, held up by 8 nylon strings tied above to a ring. The other support is similar but has a thin aluminium plate instead of a brass one. On the scales the mass of the brass support in air was 0.109750 kg and in water 0.100690 kg; the mass of the aluminium support in air was 0.010450 kg and in water 0.006930 kg.

The photograph (fig. 2.6) shows the sphere that I have called *Z*, which has a mass in air of m_Z = 0.102190 kg. Submerged in water, the mass of the sphere together with the support was 0.010170 kg and therefore the sphere in water *weighed*[93] 0.003240 kg.

The mass of the sphere of water that has the volume of sphere *Z* is obtained by subtracting from the weight of *Z* in air the weight it has in water. We obtain m_{Water} = 0.098950 kg. Note that the volume of the sphere expressed in dm^3 has this same numerical value. Supposing that the displaced water has an exactly spherical shape we can calculate the theoretical diameter of *Z* which is 0.05739 m. For direct measurements with callipers the result, instead, varies between 0.055 m and 0.059 m depending where it is measured. The shape I managed to give to the wax is rather

---

92 G.G., Vol. IV, *Lettera a Tolomeo Nozzolini*, p. 304.

93 More correctly we should say that when the sphere is submerged in water with the aluminium support the scales are balanced with a counterweight of 0.007220 kg. From now on I shall continue to write "*weight*" in italics because I want to recall that in reality I am indicating the value of the mass with which I balanced the scales. I neglect, obviously, the floating effect due to air.

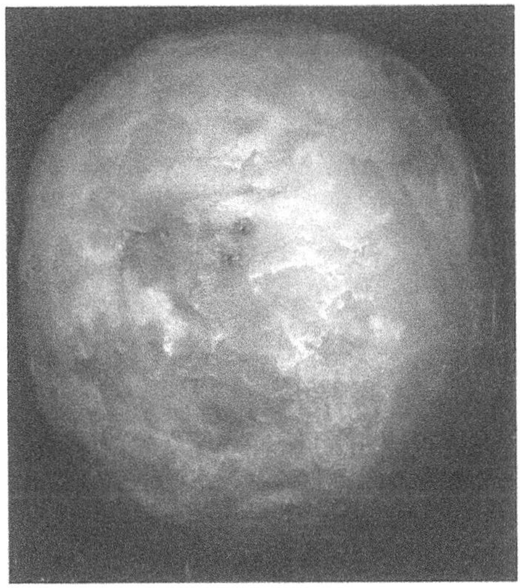

Fig. 2.6 Spere *Z*.

imperfect, certainly not comparable to what Galileo was capable of! The density of the weighted sphere is $\rho_Z = 0.102120/0.098950 = 1.032740$ kg/dm^3.

Introducing into the formula of the limit velocity $v_L = (2/9)R^2(\rho - \rho_{Water})g/\eta_{Water}$ the values of Z, we obtain too large a result, $v_L \approx 66$ ms^{-1}, but it is clear that even a tenth of this velocity would lead to a very turbulent motion. Now let us see what happens in practice in the container I have available.

The greatest limitation of the apparatus is the short distance available to be travelled, about 0.4 m, because in the glass cylinder in which the experiments are made[94] the level of the water must be slightly below the edge, so that the water will not overflow when the sphere enters, (on departure the sphere must be completely submerged); moreover the final part of the cylinder is hidden by the structure that holds it steady.

With my first attempts I formed an idea of how Galileo could have carried out his experiments, at least in its essential points: Galileo, after having prepared some wax spheres of equal volume, weighed them down by substituting some of the wax with lead so that they had different densities and then he let them descend in the water contained in a glass jar. To measure the distances travelled by each of them in successive and equal time intervals, he used the oscil-

[94] Its internal diameter is 0.14 m and the height is about 0.65 m.

lations of the pendulum[95]. Somehow[96] he marked the distance travelled in an oscillation and repeated the operation several times until he was certain of the point the sphere had reached. Then he doubled the number of oscillations and again established the point the sphere arrived at after that double time. He continued thus until he had no more space available. He found that the subdivision of the distance travelled tends to become uniform. If the motion was slow he may have found it preferable to fix first the positions of the sphere corresponding to an even number of oscillations and then to insert the positions corresponding to an odd number of oscillations, so as to have longer time intervals available for his operations.

In the course of my research I made several spheres more or less of the same size but of different densities, inserting into them lead instead of wax, I carried out several experiments and I finally came to appreciate the complexity of Galileo's experiments. What follows is a logical, but not chronological, presentation of what I found.

First I should describe the apparatus[97] (fig. 2.7). Not having much room available in my room in the Physics Department of Pisa University, I chose to apply a pendulum directly to the glass cylinder containing the water. A thin brass plate bent into a U shape was inserted at the top edge of the cylinder; on the outer side of the plate a small brass disc was fixed containing a ball bearing; the end of a steel rod bent into an L shape was inserted into the bearing and the pendulum oscillated with a period adjusted by a mass that could be made to slide along the rod (see fig. 2.7). The position of the mass of the pendulum was chosen so that a complete oscillation would take a second[98]. Diametrically opposite another brass plate bent into a U was fixed to the edge of the glass cylinder bearing a clip to keep a steel wire under tension with its other end fixed to the base holding the cylinder. Along this wire a certain number of PVC cylinders ran to fix the positions reached by the sphere during its descent.

Other distances from the edge of the cylinder were marked permanently with an adhesive tape that ran around the wall parallel to the top. The closest distance was about 0.10 m from the top and acted as the point of departure for the spheres; the other distances were at 0.19 m, 0.30 m and 0.39 m from the point of departure according to measurements with a stopwatch. The experiments were carried out as follows: I immersed the sphere taking it to the departure mark; I set the pendulum in motion; I tried to adjust the sphere's centre of gravity without letting go off it completely so it would not oscillate while descending; then, as the pendulum passed over the vertical, I let the

[95] Those who doubt that Galileo already used the pendulum may believe that he identified equal time intervals by counting rhythmically, as with the beats in music. From personal experience I know however that the contrary also happens: when you count the oscillations of a pendulum, it inevitably happens that you beat time internally, arriving – without intending to – at evidence of the isochronicity of a pendulum. Those who believe that in the experiments in the *De motu* Galileo marks time by counting rhythmically, give strong support to the fact that Galileo established in this same way the isochronicity of the oscillations of a pendulum, without even needing to make use of his wrist pulse.

[96] He could do it in several ways, for example marking the point with a piece of chalk or using something adhesive or sliding stretchy bands or strings tied around the cylinder.

[97] Like all of my equipment these too were created by Stefano Gennai.

[98] I timed 30 oscillations: 30.39 s - 30.22 s - 30.37 s - 30.37 s - 30.49 s. Although the period of the pendulum is on average $T = 1.0123$ s, for the sake of simplicity I approximate its duration to a second.

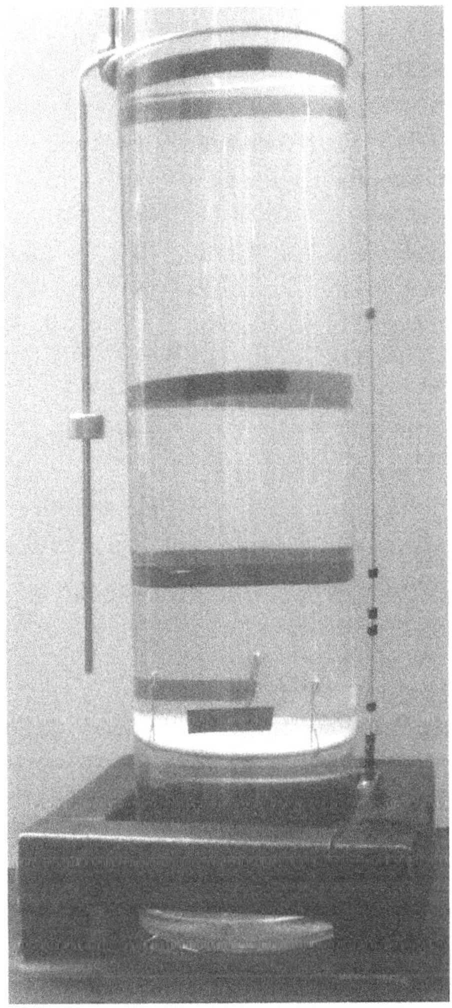

Fig. 2.7 The apparatus.

sphere go and followed its descent trying to position the small cylinders along the steel wire in the positions in which the sphere found itself at the moment when the pendulum was periodically parallel to the wire. I repeated the whole operation several times (many times!) until I was sure that it was well placed.

For sphere *Z* I obtained the following result:

distance travelled in 1 oscillation	0.152 m,
distance travelled in 2 oscillations	0.307 m.

The sphere has too great a velocity and there is no room to observe a third oscillation. To check the measurements I used a stopwatch to take the time taken by sphere *Z* to travel the distance of 0.30 m down to the third adhesive tape[99], finding on average 2.12 s, which is perfectly consistent with the time of 2 s needed to travel 0.307 m.

Amongst the other spheres that I made there is one, that I have called *K*, which has the following characteristics: on the scales it *weighed* in air 0.101580 kg and in water 0.001040 kg; the density was 0.101580/0.100540 = 1.010340 kg/dm^3; the diameter was 0.05765 m.

The measurements of the descent in water were

distance travelled in 1 oscillation	0.049 m,
distance travelled in 2 oscillations	0.132 m,
distance travelled in 3 oscillations	0.236 m,
distance travelled in 4 oscillations	0.332 m.

To check this I measured the time[100] taken by the sphere to descend 0.30 m obtaining 3.59 s, a time that is consistent with the previous data[101].

Following Galileo we must compare at this point the velocities of the two spheres that will be given by the distances travelled in the same time. The relationship between the distances travelled in the time of one oscillation is

$$v_Z / v_K = 0.152 / 0.049 = 3.1.$$

The relationship between the distances travelled in the time of two oscillations is

$$v_Z / v_K = 0.307/0.132 = 2.3.$$

The results should be compared with those of the relationship $(\rho_Z - \rho_{\text{Water}}) / (\rho_K - \rho_{\text{Water}})$

$$(\rho_Z - \rho_{\text{Water}}) / (\rho_K - \rho_{\text{Water}}) = 0.03274/0.01034 = 3.2.$$

The agreement is acceptable, bearing in mind the various circumstances that I shall discuss later on. Naturally no-one can say whether Galileo began with spheres of this density, or even with spheres of greater density, but we shall soon see that Galileo created spheres with density even closer to that of water. Before moving on to this further refinement it is necessary however to explain how such a good result is obtained, even though we are far from the limit velocity.

The explanation that can be given today can only be technical: we have to resolve Newton's equation with the force in water due to the heaviness and a resisting force proportional to the velocity of the body.

---

99 The times were: 2.02 s - 2.12 s - 2.23 s - 2.18 s - 2.13 s - 2.09 s - 2.13 s - 2.09 s - 2.13 s - 2.06 s.

100 The times to descend 0.3 m were: 3.69 s - 3.44 s - 3.58 s - 3.64 s - 3.54 s - 3.75 s - 3.51 s - 3.71 s - 3.54 s - 3.51 s with an average of 3.59 s.

101 The average velocity in the second oscillation was 0.332 – 0.236 = 0.096 m/s and with this velocity the sphere would have arrived after 0.59 s at a distance of 0.293 m, very close to the 0.300 m of the direct measurement.

The detailed calculations are given in appendix A; here it is enough to remember that the exact solution is

$s(t) = v_L\ [t + \tau \exp(-t/\tau) - \tau]$,

with $\tau = 2r^2\rho/\ 9\eta$.

When $t/\tau << 1$ the solution can be approximated to the equation of a uniformly accelerated motion:

$s(t) = \alpha^T t^2/2$

with acceleration

$\alpha^T = v_L/\tau = g(\rho - \rho_{Water})/\rho$.

To compare the velocities of the two spheres when the motion is still accelerated it is necessary, according to Aristotle, to compare the distances travelled by them in the same time Δt.

$v_1/v_2 = \alpha_1^T\ /\ \alpha_2^T = (\rho_2/\rho_1)[(\rho_1 - \rho_{Water})/(\rho_2 - \rho_{Water})] \approx (\rho_1 - \rho_{Water})/(\rho_2 - \rho_{Water})$.

So I have proved that even when we are far from the limit velocity Galileo's relationship between spheres of equal sizes but different density holds, on condition that the velocities are obtained by measuring the distance travelled in equal times, which is one of the two ways used by Aristotle to define velocity.

Let us compare the predicted values with the measurements, applying the equation $x(t) = \alpha^T t^2/2$ to the sphere Z, for which we find $\tau \approx 206\ s^{-1}$ and $\alpha^T = 0.311\ ms^{-2}$:

distance travelled in 1 oscillation	0.155 m	is instead	0.152 m,
distance travelled in 2 oscillations	0.620 m	is instead	0.307 m.

For sphere K we find $\tau = 210$ s while $\alpha^T = 0.100\ ms^{-2}$ and now the differences compared to the theoretical prediction are greater:

distance travelled in 1 oscillation	0.050 m	is instead	0.043 m,
distance travelled in 2 oscillations	0.200 m	is instead	0.122 m,
distance travelled in 3 oscillations	0.450 m	is instead	0.222 m,
distance travelled in 4 oscillations	0.800 m	is instead	0.351 m.

These growing differences are due to the fact that the wall and the base of the cylinder have the effect of considerably reducing the velocity of the wax ball and it is not surprising that the average velocity already observed in the second passage does not reach even 60% of the theoretical value[102]. This effect of the side walls is well known and has been studied in the case of small values for the Reynolds number and very small dimensions for the bodies compared to the

[102] There is also a continuous reduction in acceleration according to the distance travelled, as can be clearly seen in the experiment with sphere K.

cross-section of the container[103] (so that in any case it is preferable for the distance travelled to be as much as possible along the axis of the cylinder). As well as the effect of the side walls the base also has a braking effect.

It is interesting to point out that during the descents, above all at low velocity, I have often observed that the sphere has an irregular motion and from the very beginning tends to move towards the wall of the container and then continue almost scraping down it. The failure to follow a straight line is due for the most part to the circulation of the water established inside the cylinder, caused by the system adopted to retrieve the sphere after every descent. Indeed, for this reason I placed a disc made of stainless steel mesh inside the glass cylinder, connected by three wires to an outer ring. By lowering (or raising) the outer ring along the cylinder, the disc rose (or descended) together with the sphere. When the disc was pulled up a vortex and convection motion is created and it is necessary to distance the operations in order to allow the water to become still again.

Other irregularities are mainly due to the figure not having a perfectly spherical shape; moreover, as I have already pointed out, because of the concentrated distribution of the small lead weights, it is necessary to find the right position for the sphere before letting it go if we wish to prevent it from oscillating as it proceeds.

Considering the small dimensions of my glass cylinder (diameter 0.14 m and usable height about 0.4 m) I have the impression that Galileo had an advantage over me; he certainly carried out his experiments with a container of greater height and probably with a wide base, as is suggested in this passage[104]:

> [...] to take with him a very deep vase filled with water some time when he goes sailing, having prepared in advance a ball of wax or some other material which would descend very slowly to the bottom – so that in a minute it would scarcely sink a yard [*braccio*] [...]

We can try to assess the density of the ball Galileo refers to with the motion equation.

Ignoring the braking effect of the wall and the base and using $\alpha^T = g(\rho - \rho_{Water})/\rho$, from $s = gt^2(\rho - \rho_{Water})/2\rho$, we obtain

$$\rho = 1.000031 \text{ kg/dm}^3.$$

In my attempts I never reached such densities and it is really difficult to arrive at such extreme values, because it is a question of inserting or removing minute quantities of lead or sand into or from a sphere; to arrive at these densities Galileo melted the wax completely and then mixed in minimal quantities of lead filings.

I succeeded in creating spheres with density lower than that of the spheres *Z* and *K*; one of these, which I have called *D*, has the following characteristics: the mass measured in air is m_D = 0.098570 kg while when it is submerged in water with the support it *weighs* 0.007220 kg. Sub-

[103] See, for example, JOHN HAPPEL & HOWARD BRENNER, *Low Reynolds number hydrodynamics*, The Hague/Boston/Lancaster, 1983, and the literature quoted therein.

[104] G.G., Vol. VII, *Dialogo sopra i due massimi sistemi*, p. 275.

tracting the support's contribution we find that D *weighs* 0.000290 kg in water, so its volume is 0.098280 dm³ and the diameter is 0.05727 m. The density is 0.098570/0.098280 = 1.002950 kg/dm³.

Sphere D has a motion in water which is completely different from that of the motion of spheres Z and K. Indeed, the slower motion allows us to observe a greater number of oscillations:

N°	$s(n)$	$s_{\text{Theoretical}}$	$s(n+1) - s(n)$
1	0.008	0.014	-
2	0.050	0.057	0.042
3	0.107	0.129	0.057
4	0.164	0.229	0.057
5	0.229	0.358	0.065
6	0.285	0.514	0.056
7	0.345	0.699	0.060

As a check, I measured the time taken to descend 0.190 m, finding on average[105] $t = 4.89$ s; I then measured the time taken to descend to 0.300 m, finding on average[106] $t = 6.56$ s.

The results given in the third column of the table were obtained by introducing into the theoretical solution

$$s(t) = v_L \{t + \tau [\exp(-t/\tau) - 1]\}$$

the values of v_L and τ given by $v_L = 2r^2g(\rho - \rho_0)/ 9\eta = 6.50\ \text{ms}^{-1}$ and $\tau = 2r^2\rho_0/ 9\eta = 225.4$ s.

The fourth column shows very clearly that sphere D arrives at a uniform motion already at the second oscillation; this fact can only be explained by considerable interaction with the wall of the cylinder.

We can compare the velocity reached by sphere D after the first oscillation with that of spheres Z and K:

$$v_Z / v_D = 10.4, \qquad (\rho_Z - \rho_{\text{Water}}) / (\rho_D - \rho_{\text{Water}}) = 11.1,$$
$$v_K / v_D = 5.6, \qquad (\rho_K - \rho_{\text{Water}}) / (\rho_D - \rho_{\text{Water}}) = 3.5.$$

Let us repeat the comparison of the distance travelled in two oscillations:

[105] The times observed were: 4.91 s - 4.89 s - 4.87 s - 4.99 - 4.89 s.

[106] The times observed were: 6.12 s - 6.96 s - 6.59 s - 6.56 - 6.57 s.

$v_Z / v_D = 5.6,$ $(\rho_Z - \rho_{Water}) / (\rho_D - \rho_{Water}) = 11.1,$
$v_K / v_D = 2.4,$ $(\rho_K - \rho_{Water}) / (\rho_D - \rho_{Water}) = 3.5.$

The final comparison is between spheres *K* and *D* on the distance travelled in three oscillations:

$v_K / v_D = 2.9,$ $(\rho_K - \rho_{Water}) / (\rho_D - \rho_{Water}) = 3.5.$

Galileo might claim that these results do not really call his theory into question. The measurements are indeed rather uncertain, not only because it is very difficult to let the sphere drop without imparting some velocity to it but also because it is difficult to establish the precise position of the sphere as the pendulum passes over the vertical; the motion then is still obviously accelerated.

I was not able to repeat the experiments with a container with a much greater cross-section in order to reduce the effect of the walls, I have however seen what happens if the sphere is smaller.

The sphere that I used, which I have called *H*, *weighs* in air 0.020780 kg and in water 0.000273 kg; its density is ρ_H = 1.013310 kg/dm^3, its diameter ∅ = 0.033960 m, its limit velocity is v_L = 9.37 ms^{-1} and τ = 71.5 s. I have observed its motion in water with the following result:

Sphere *H* [ρ_H = 1.013310 kg/dm^3]				
N°	$s(n)$	$s_{Theoretical}$	$s(n+1) - s(n)$	$a = 2s(n)/n^2$
1	0.041	0.065	0.041	0.082
2	0.132	0.260	0.091	0.066
3	0.228	0.580	0.096	0.050
4	0.318	1.029	0.090	0.040
5	0.409	1.600	0.091	0.033

In the third column the theoretical values have been calculated using the precise solution. It is interesting to observe that the motion of *H* is not very different from that of *K*, as can be seen in the following table, in which I have given the results for *K*, probably because the density of *H* and of *K* are not very different.

Sphere *K* [ρ_K = 1.010340 kg/dm^3]				
N°	$s(n)$	$s_{Theoretical}$	$s(n+1) - s(n)$	$a = 2s(n)/n^2$
1	0.049	0.051	0.049	0.086
2	0.132	0.202	0.083	0.061
3	0.236	0.454	0.104	0.049
4	0.332	0.806	0.96	0.043

The research should be extended to check whether the motion's independence from size and its dependence on density alone are not purely random, and if they were then we could also understand why Galileo claimed it with such confidence.

I do not know of a theory already available for the interpretation of these results and I am not aware that the behaviour in water or another liquid of spheres of large size with almost the same density as the medium that they move in has yet been studied, much less the effect that the walls and the base of the container have on their motion. Once again Galileo is the first to arrive at an exploration of unusual situations.

In conclusion, these experiments and the considerations that I shall set out later have made me certain that Galileo studied motion in water very carefully, but they have also left me a doubt: were his results better than those that I arrived at? I cannot exclude the possibility that Galileo may have hidden the difficulties he met with while studying uniform motion in water, just as he would do later with the problems of rolling spheres down the inclined plane, while, as we shall soon see, he would make known the most interesting part of his Pisan research only after twenty years because, to our great fortune, he was challenged to support his point of view against that of a group of impassioned Aristotelians.

2.4 *What did Galileo see while he studied motion in water?*

While reconstructing Galileo's experiments in water I came across some unexpected situations that prompted me to track them down by carefully re reading Galileo's early writings. Onc of these *discoveries* was so important for my research that I must explain how it happened. When I began to reconstruct Galileo's experiments I thought of using some wooden spheres of various sizes that are easily available on sale. So I bought a certain number of them and had them spray-painted and protected by a transparent paint to make them impermeable.

The wooden spheres were far from having the required density and to bring them closer to the density of water I decided to introduce a small brass cylinder of appropriate size inside each one of them, with the idea of then gradually increasing their density with some brass nails until they had a density slightly greater than that of water.

And so I started out. After adding every pin I put the sphere into the water to see if it still floated and I noted the resulting reduction in the part that remained above water. At a certain point, for one of these spheres, when it was still just floating, I thought of pushing it under the water to see how slowly it rose to the surface and instead I saw that it sank to the bottom. I had exceeded the density of water and the sphere had not sunk before only because held back by the surface tension of the water, thanks to my caution in immersing it in the water.

I had not thought at all of surface tension and it is an effect that can only be seen with spheres that have a density that is just greater than that of water[107].

[107] It was sufficient to remove a minute piece of the last brass nail used to weigh down the wooden sphere, which had deliberately not been hammered completely home, to see the sphere that before was sinking to the bottom float. Consider that the small nails used in the experiment weigh about 2/10 of a gram each.

The attempt to use wooden spheres did not have the success hoped for because they became impregnated with water due to the nails and to the fact that the paint was not very stable; so I decided to follow Galileo's example and use spheres made of wax.

When I took my first sphere of weighted wax[108], which I called *A*, I immediately wanted to verify the effect of surface tension: I put it into the water, immersing it slowly until I saw it float. A spherical cap, shiny and dry, jutted out of the water, around which the edge of the water reflected the light creating the appearance of a ring. It is the phenomenon that Galileo called *arginetti* (little ridges of water) and it is a sign that wax has a low wettability[109].

I also saw that if the sphere is pushed lightly downwards, without submerging it however, the sphere returns to its original position; if instead it is pushed under the surface of the water, it starts descending slowly, another phenomenon pointed out by Galileo[110], who was the first to describe the effect of *wettability*.

I have already quoted a passage from the *De motu* in which he speaks of wax descending in water when it is made heavier by mixing it with sand or other substances. Now let us read it in full[111]:

> And if, on the other hand, we conceive in our mind, for example, an amount of wax of considerable size floating on water, and we mix the wax with either sand or some other heavier thing, in such a way that in the end it comes to be heavier than water and it just barely begins to go down very slowly, who would ever believe, if we took a particle of such wax, say one hundredth of it, either that it would not go down or that it would go down a hundred times more slowly than the totality of the wax? Surely no one.

It is undeniable that in the *De motu* Galileo was making experiments with wax of a density barely greater than that of water; but he also experiments with wax which is barely less dense. He wrote again about wax rising slowly just half a page later. He is still dealing with bodies of the same material that descend (when they are denser than water) or rise (when they are less dense), moving with a velocity that depends only on the medium and not on the quantity of material. At a certain point he clarifies the matter better, observing that if the bodies are not made up of the same material there is a different outcome, and he gives an example[112]:

> [...] as, for example, if we understand two mobiles, such as a piece of wax and an inflated bladder, both of which are carried upward from deep water, but the wax more slowly than

---

108 Sphere *A* has a mass in air of m_A = 0.098980 kg, weighs in water 0.000180 kg, the density is ρ_A = 1.00182 kg/dm^3 and the diameter Ø = 0.057357 m.

109 On a plane that passes through the centre of the sphere and is perpendicular to that kind of circumference that marks the separation between the wax sphere, the water and the air, the straight lines tangent to the water and the sphere form an angle which is called the junction angle which must be less than 180° for the water not to wet the sphere completely and cause it to submerge.

110 This observation can be dated back to the *De motu*, even if it appears explicitly for the first time in G.G., Vol. IV, *Diversi fragmenti attenenti al trattato* ..., p. 23.

111 G.G., Vol. I, *De motu*, p. 264.

112 G.G., Vol. I, *De motu*, p. 265.

the bladder, we ask that it be conceded, that if they are combined, the combination will go up more slowly than the bladder alone, but more swiftly than the wax alone.

The experiments on descent were done as follows: with one hand the sphere was held just under the level of the water. Since the hand partly covered the sphere, if we were not careful, a minimum part of it could remain in contact with the surface of the water: when this happened, at the moment at which the sphere is let go, we could see it remain *suspended*. Galileo may also have become aware of the effect this way.

In his *Discorso intorno alle cose che stanno in su l'acqua o che in quella si muovono* in 1612, Galileo speaks extensively of the phenomenon of floating, giving an explanation which was incorrect, even though it was based on a perfectly reasonable interpretation of results[113]. I shall return to this matter later, but this seems to me the appropriate place to illustrate how I saw and calculated it in my experiments.

I studied the effect with sphere *A*; the photographs in figs. 2.8, 2.9 and 2.10 illustrate the phenomenon and allow us to assess the proportion of the part remaining above water. The photographs were taken from various angles: in fig 2.8 the view is from above, the clearly visible *little ridges* border a dry region which is approximately a circle of radius r_A; in fig. 2.9 the part above water is seen through the opening of the calipers previously used to measure its diameter (here the sphere is in a small cubic container full of water up to the edge); in fig. 2.10 the sphere is seen in profile.

We know that to support the mass of sphere *A* when it is totally immersed in water only requires 0.000180 kg because its volume of 0.09880 dm^3 has replaced 0.09880 kg of water (see footnote 108). The volume of the submerged part is given by the formula:

$$V^{SP} = (1/3)\,\pi\, R_A^3\{2 + [2 + (r_A/R_A)^2][1 - (r_A/R_A)^2]^{1/2}\}.$$

I measured with calipers the diameter of the cap that emerges from the water and I found $\varnothing_A = 2r_A = 0.01825$ m; the radius of the sphere was already determined by the volume occupied in water: $R_A = 0.028678$ m.

The mass of 0.098598 kg which is the part of *A* which is supported by buoyancy corresponds to the volume of the immersed part, $V^{SP} = 0.098598$ dm^3. This mass must be subtracted from the total mass of sphere *A* to determine the mass of *A* supported by the surface tension of the water and we find $m_\tau = 0.000382$ kg which corresponds to a weight $gm_\tau = 0.00375$ N. Dividing the weight by the length of the circumference of radius r_A, we obtain an estimate of the water's linear tension[114] given by $\tau_{Water} = gm_\tau/2\pi r_A = 0.0654$ N/m, which is not too far from the known value at a temperature of 20 °C; $\tau_{Water} = 0.0728$ N/m.

113 G.G., Vol. IV, *Diversi fragmenti attenenti al trattato* ..., pp. 20, 22, 23; and in almost every page of *Le Galleggianti*.

114 The surface tension of a liquid, measured in joule/m^2, is the work necessary to increase by one unit its free surface and can also be given as the relationship between force and length, Nm^{-1}. For water the surface tension diminishes with temperature, going from 0.0756 Nm^{-1} (at 0 °C) to 0.0728 Nm^{-1} (at 20 °C) up to 0.0662 Nm^{-1} (at 60 °C).

Fig. 2.8 *Arginetti* (the little ridges).

Fig. 2.9 The little ridges.

Fig. 2.10 The little ridges in cross-section.

If the wax ball was perfectly spherical the *little ridges* would have bordered a perfectly spherical sector and from the measurement of the radius of the circumference marked by the *little ridges* I presume that a precise result would be arrived at.

To conclude, I report another experiment suggested by Galileo and which he may have known from the time when he wrote the *De motu*, where we read this observation[115]:

> It is evident that the difficulty of cleaving the medium is not the cause why wood does not go down in water: for if [in this case] this difficulty were overcome by the form of the mobile, the wood would descend, if, for example, it was given the form of a cone or an arrow; and yet this floats no less than a flat board.

[115] G.G., Vol. I, *De motu*, p. 414.

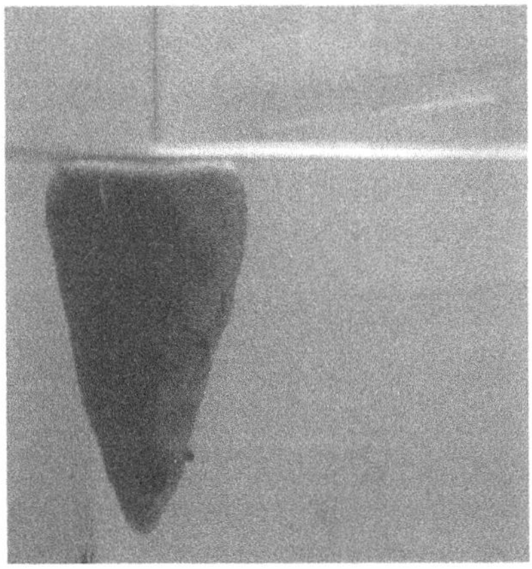

Fig. 2.11 Suspended cone.

Fig. 2.12 Suspended cone.

Fig. 2.13 Cone on the bottom with its image reflected by the side wall.

Galileo would discuss in *Le Galleggianti* the property possessed by slightly weighted wax, when it has the shape of a cone or a pyramid, of floating when the point faces downwards and submerging when turned the other way, which is the contrary to what is expected by all those who believe that it is the width that keeps bodies heavier than water afloat[116].

I built a wax cone which I weighted by pressing three pellets into the wax at the apex, two large ones and one small.

Characteristics of the cone: height H_{Cone} = 0.0906 m; average diameter of the base $\varnothing_{Cone}$ = 0.0448 m; *weight* in air m_C = 0.087230 kg and in water m_C = 0.000770 kg, density 1.008905 kg/dm³.

The photographs (figs. 2.11, 2.12, 2.13) clearly illustrate the phenomenon. Knowing that the value of the surface tension of water at 20 °C is τ = 0.0728 N/m and that our cone at the base has

[116] G.G., Vol IV; *Discorso intorno alle cose che stanno in su l'acqua…*, pp. 114–120.

a diameter of 0.0448 m, we can immediately calculate how far we can increase its height without sending it to the bottom: it is sufficient that the part of its mass which is not supported by buoyancy does not exceed the maximum limit of 0.00630 kg. The remaining weight, 0.08093 kg, is counterbalanced by the displaced water and so the immersed volume is 0.08093 dm^3. A volume of 0.0063 dm^3 stays out of the water, which corresponds to a cylinder with a diameter of 0.448 dm and height of 0.4 dm, which is what is glimpsed in the photograph in fig. 2.12.

With a cone that terminates in a cylindrical base a few millimetres high it is possible to assess precisely the volume that remains out of the water and with calculations similar to those already done for sphere A we can measure the surface tension with good approximation, because the body is supported by buoyancy for the submerged part and for the rest by the surface tension of the water. It would be even better if we gave the wax the shape of a perfect cylinder weighed down with a pellet placed exactly at the centre of the two flat sides, so that in water the cylinder is perfectly vertical and an upright section of it emerges, only the height of which needs to be measured.

Another fortuitous discovery

While these experiments were being carried out another remarkable effect occurred, which Galileo very probably also observed in his experiments with spheres with density slightly less than the density of the water.

The story of this further *discovery* will not take long to tell: while trying to make a sphere with a density even closer to the density of water I removed a few small pellets from a spare sphere, which had been weighted down too much. I measured the new density with scales, and it was less than that of water but I wanted to verify it in practice before starting to weigh it down again. I placed the sphere in water and I saw that it floated, but then – remembering the surface tension – I pushed it sharply downwards. The sphere descended until it came to a halt and then rose slowly. I was watching it rise: I expected that when it arrived at the surface it would emerge, instead to my surprise the sphere, when it arrived at the surface of the water, bounced back just as if it had banged into an elastic membrane; it descended, it stopped, it rose again and bounced back again, but with less force, and these bounces were repeated four or five times, until the sphere finally stopped, emerging from the surface of the water, perhaps slightly less than when it floated at the beginning.

This phenomenon allows the surface tension to be measured dynamically, based on the work of air-water separation done by the surface to stop the sphere, which has a known mass and a velocity which can be estimated at the moment of impact.

One of these spheres, which I have called G, has the following characteristics: in air it *weighs* 0.098420 kg and in water 0.098580 kg; its density is 0.9984 kg/dm^3; its diameter is 0.057314 m.

I measured the time required to let it rise to the surface departing from three different depths[117] and I saw that the average velocity is more or less the same: v_M = 0.021 m/s.

Observing the emergence of the sphere from the side through the opening of a pair of calipers after the first impact, I saw that, on the first rebound, at the moment in which the sphere

[117] The average time to rise from 0.43 m was 20.84 s; to rise from 0.39 m was 17.70 s, to rise from 0.30 m the time was 14.07. The average velocities are: 0.0206 m/s; 0.0220 m/s; 0.0213 m/s, respectively.

Fig. 2.14 The sphere protruding from the water.

reached the highest point, a breach opens in the surface of the water with a diameter of about 0.021 m, which I also photographed (fig. 2.14).

At the moment of greatest emersion there was a reduction $\Delta A = \pi r^2$ of the surface of the water and the consequent increase $\Delta U = \tau\pi r^2$ in potential energy[118], yielded by the sphere, which lost all its kinetic energy $mv^2/2$.

From the relationship $\tau\pi r^2 = mv^2/2$, with $m = 0.09842$ kg, $r = 0.010$ m, $v = 0.021$ m/s, we obtain $\tau = 0.069$ N/m to compare with the surface tension value at 25 °C which is $\tau = 0.0728$ N/m.

From a historical point of view these remarks have nothing to do with Galileo and can be considered a diversion; they are not totally superfluous however, because they serve to illustrate better the phenomena of *little ridges*, of surface tension, of bodies with greater density than water that float and finally the rather more interesting phenomenon of wettability, all discussed by Galileo.

Above all they serve to show that Galileo had good reasons to believe that it is not the water but rather the air that supports the sphere which is repulsed by the water. The spheres that are less dense than water do not emerge at once when they arrive at the surface from below, instead the surface layer of the water that borders on the air initially repulses the rising spheres; when instead these spheres are immersed in the water from above they float, staying considerably above the water. When a small weight is placed on the emerging cap of a sphere denser than water, the sphere descends slightly but is not submerged; when it is wetted with an extremely light layer

[118] The increase in potential energy is equal to the work done by the sphere to enlarge the circumference of the *little ridges* to the circumference of radius r against force $F(r) = 2\pi s\tau$. $U(r) = 2\pi\tau\,[\int s\,ds]_0^r = \pi r^2\tau$.

of water it sinks. The water separates the sphere from the air, therefore it is the air inside the *little ridges* which, by adhering to the sphere, increases its volume without increasing its weight and makes it float. This is the theory that Galileo expounded in the *Discorso intorno alle cose che stanno in su l'acqua*. Let us read what he writes[119]:

> Meanwhile, for better understanding of what I am saying, look at the accompanying diagram
>
> 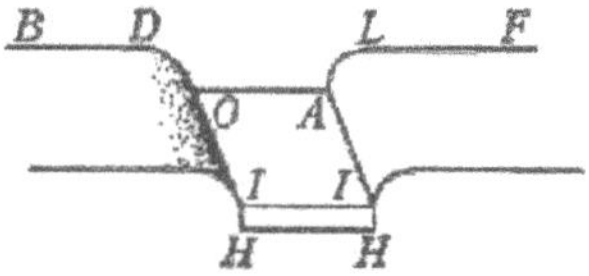
>
>
> in which the surface of the water extends along lines *FL* and *DB*, on which, if there be lightly placed a slice of material heavier than water, so that it does not submerge, this will not at all remain above, but will rather enter with its whole thickness into the water and will drop even farther.
>
> This is seen as the slice *AI-OI*, whose whole thickness goes down in the water, little ridges of water *LA* and *DO* remaining around it, while the surface of the water remains noticeable above the surface of the slide. See now whether it is true that the lamina fails to sink because its shape it unable to fend [aside] the corporeality of the water!
>
> But if the chip has already penetrated and vanquished the continuation of the water [level] and is by its nature heavier than water, what is the reason that it does not go on down, but stops suspended within that little cavity that it has made by its weight in the water? I reply: Because in [gradually] submerging until its [upper] surface arrives at the water level, it loses part of its weight, and it goes on then losing the rest of it, while that makes a ridge and a bank around it. It suffers this loss [of weight] by drawing down and making descend with it the air above itself by adherent contact, which air follows in to fill the cavity surrounded by the little ridges of water. Thus what in this case sinks into and becomes situated in water is not just the gold [here the printer put ferro for oro] lamina or ebony chip[120], but a composition of ebony [or gold]- and-air from which result a volume [solido] no longer heavier than water, as was the simple ebony or the simple gold. And if we attentively consider what and how much is the solid that in this experience enters in the water and opposes its heaviness, you will see that this consists of all that is found beneath the [general] surface of the water, being an aggregate and composition of an ebony chip and an almost equal amount of air, or a bulk composed of a lead lamina and ten or twelve times as much air. But, gentlemen my adversaries, in our question one seeks identity of material, and it is permitted only to alter the shape; therefore removed that air [if you object to it] which, joined with the chip, makes it into a different body, less heavy than water, and so put simply ebony in the water – for

---

[119] G.G., Vol. IV, *Discorso intorno alle cose che stannno in su l'acqua* ..., pp. 98-98, the part in italics is on p. 107 and is an addition contained in the 2nd edition printed the same year 1612.

[120] Here and in the following S. Drake used the word "chip" for the Italian word "tavoletta", which might perhaps be better translated as "board" or "block" to keep closer to the original meaning. (Note of the Author.)

certainly you will then see that the chip sink to the bottom; or, if that does not happen, you will have won the day. Now, to separate the air from the ebony, nothing more is needed than to wet the surface of this chip thinly with the same water, for water being thus interposed between the chip and the air, the other water around it will run [together] without hindrance and will receive within itself simple ebony alone, as it should do [by the wording of our question].

[...] Besides it is false that the chip would go to the bottom by virtue of new weight added by water, simply by thinly wetting it, since I can put ten or twenty little drops of water on the same chip when it is sustained on water, and those drops, provided that they do not join with the other surrounding water, will not weigh it down so that it sinks. But if I take the chip out and wipe away all water adhering to it, and wet its [whole] surface with just one small drop of water, putting it then back on the water, it will doubtless submerge, the rest of the water [now] running to cover it, the air above not retaining in after this interposition of the very thin veil of water that removes the air's contiguity with the ebony. Without resistance, the air separates itself and does not oppose at all the progress of the other water. Or rather, to say this better, the chip will freely descend because it finds itself already completely surrounded by and covered with water just as soon as its upper surface, veiled with water, arrives at the general level of the water.

[...] *For an ebony chip can be made that floats when placed on water, and even the addiction of a hundred grains of lead*[121] *placed upon it are insufficient to submerge it; yet, wetted, not only will it sink without that lead, but some cork or other light material attached to it does not suffice to keep it from going clear to the bottom* [...]

So why are the *Floating bodies* so often recalled along with the *De motu*, if they were written twenty years later? The answer is in the following paragraph.

2.5 *Bodies that stay atop water, or move in it*

To reconstruct Galileo's experiments in Pisa, of which nothing survives apart from a vague trace in some examples and observations scattered here and there, it is fundamental to recognise that there is a close relationship between what Galileo wrote on the movement of bodies in water in the *De motu* and some experimental results which he presented in 1612 in the *Discorso intorno alle cose che stanno in su l'acqua, o che in quella si muovono*. To do this we have to take a leap forward twenty years.

Galileo tells[122] us that in the summer of 1611, probably towards the end of June[123]:

[121] 100 *grani* (grains) = 4.9 g. The italics were used in the second edition of the *Discorso intorno...*, also in 1612 and indicates that this passage was added to the text of the first edition. (Note of the Author.)

[122] G.G., Vol. IV, *Diversi fragmenti attenenti al trattato...*, p. 33.

[123] G.G., Vol. XI, p. 133. On the first of July 1610 Lodovico Cigoli wrote to Galileo: «...they, when they meet with opposition ... either do not set out, or if they do they beat a cowardly retreat: nevertheless they are to be feared,

> [...] while discussing in a circle of gentlemen the first four qualities [*dry and wet, hot and cold*], a professor of philosophy said something that was rather trite for the Peripatetic schools, that condensing was caused by cold; and he adduced ice as evidence of this, claiming that it was no more than condensed water.

Instead Galileo, who was present, proposed as an explanation that water when it freezes increases in volume, harking back to Archimedes' theory of floating.

> The philosopher immediately denied that ice was less heavy than water, and asserted the contrary, [...] that ice was not caused to float on water by its lesser weight, since it was really heavier than water, but rather it was the fact of being so wide and spread out in shape that held it up, not being able to break through the resistance of the water.

Three days later that same philosopher challenged Galileo again, saying that he had found a man who would succeed, with arguments and experiments, in making him see with his own eyes the falsehood of his proposition. This man was Lodovico delle Colombe and Galileo engaged to confront him. According to Colombe's account[124], Galileo accepted the confrontation, setting some conditions that he left him, written in his own hand, as follows[125]:

> Since Master Lodovico delle Colombe holds the opinion that shape changes solid bodies with regard to sinking or not sinking, rising or not rising in the same medium, such as in water itself, so that a solid, for example, being of spherical shape it would sink, made into some other shape it would not sink but, on the contrary, since I Galileo Galilei consider this not to be true, but rather claiming that a solid body, made into a spherical shape or any other which sinks to the bottom, will also sink in any other shape, and therefore being contrary to the said Master Colombe, in this matter, I am content that we put it to the test. And since this test can be carried out in many ways, I am content that the Most Reverend Canon Nori[126], as our common friend, choose, between the experiments that we may propose, those

---

because they lay mines behind your back: and of these evil men, although they are to be found everywhere, I believe that where you are there are some who are greatly superior to these here in Rome, if not in number, at least in foul precision. So be on your guard with them, and make yourself clear to them, but in public: and when the dispute with that one comes, I pray you to keep me informed of what follows».

124 G.G., vol. IV, *Discorso apologetico di Lodovico delle Colombe d'intorno al discorso di Galileo Galilei circa le cose che stanno su l'acqua, o che in quella si muovono,* p. 318. Ludovico delle Colombe preceded the text with this explanation: «Some writings passed between Master Galileo and me, to establish the conventions and for greater clarity of what each one of us claimed; these writings, since he did not have them printed, and it seeming to me that in some matters he diversified from them in the assumptions of the book, I have decided to print them at the beginning of this work, so that from the truth of those writings it can be seen who argued more correctly».

125 G.G., Vol. IV, *Discorso apologetico...*, pp. 318-319.

126 See G.G., Vol. IV, p. 141, at the end of the *Discorso*: «I Francesco Nori, a Canon of Florence, having examined the present work, have not noticed anything in it contrary to Christian piety nor to good morals, and I judge it worthy to be printed. The last day of March 1612». The servite Agostino Vigiano, inquisitor in Florence, had already approved the work on 5 March. For Nori see also G.G., Vol. IV, p. 286: «We grant licence to the most Reverend Francesco Nori, Florentine Canon and Theologian, that he should examine the present work, and report whether

> that seem to him most apt to attest the truth; as I also bow to his judgement in deciding and settling any controversy that might arise between the parties in carrying out this test.

Ludovico delle Colombe continued his account of these events as follows:

> Then I added in my own hand under this writing: «Let the body be made of the same material and of the same weight, but of a different shape, to be chosen by Lodovico; and in the choice of bodies the most equal possible in density be chosen[127], in Master Galileo's judgement; and the shapes, chosen by Lodovico: and let the experiment be done four times, of the same matter, but of the same number of pieces of the same material as the times of the experiment.» By common consent Master Filippo Arrighetti was chosen as fellow judge to Master Nori. On the set day we appeared at the house of Master Filippo Salviati, one of the first gentlemen of our city and as rich in the wealth of the intellect as that of fortune, in the presence of the Most Illustrious and Excellent Lord D. Giovanni Medici[128], with a noble band of scholars, to hear us dispute together: but we could neither bring Master Galileo to debate, nor did he wish to make the experiment in appropriate size of shape and quantity of matter; and rather he decided (let each man judge the reason in his own way) to bring forth a treatise of his on the subject, hoping to make others believe through his discourse what he cannot show with sense; given that with alterations and additions, and taking away from the agreements and the truth it is easy with false assumptions and suppositions to remove the true conclusion.

Note the requirement immediately set by Galileo: «and in the choice of bodies the most equal possible in density be chosen, in Master Galileo's judgement». If the interpretation I have given is correct, this condition shows that Galileo wanted to play and win the challenge on the phenomenon of wettability: if the density of the body is almost equal to that of water, whatever its shape might be, the body sinks as soon as it is wetted and it is not the weight of the water which makes it sink, because it could bear much greater weight, but the fact that it has been deprived of contact with air. During the most heated phase of the dispute Galileo, prudently, made some notes that he would later gather together in a *dossier* which he has named *Diversi Frammenti attenenti al trattato delle cose che stanno su l'acqua* (Various fragments relative to the Discourse on bodies that stay atop water), and the summary of events in one of these fragments is instead very different than Ludovico delle Colombe's, because he refers to a first meeting, at which his adversary failed to appear[129]:

---

it has been purged of all those errors that militated against the Christian Faith and good morals. 26 August 1613. Piero Niccolini, Vicar of Florence».

[127] It could be interpreted as follows «the choice of the bodies in it [*i.e. in the water*] be made as equal in density as possible [*to water, as is the case with ice*] according to Master Galilei».

[128] Giovanni de' Medici had become hostile towards Galileo when he was still teaching at Pisa. Viviani tells us (G.G., Vol. XIX, *Racconto istorico di Vincenzio Viviani,* p. 606) that: «many would be philosophers, emulating him, stirred up by envy, were aroused against him; and using as an instrument to bring him down the opinion he gave of a certain machine, invented by an eminent person [*Giovanni de' Medici*], with the aim of emptying the harbour of Livorno, for which Galileo, with mechanical foundations and philosophical freedom, had foreseen a bad outcome (as indeed happened), were able with malicious impressions to provoke the hatred of that great personage».

[129] G.G., Vol. IV, *Diversi fragmenti attenenti al trattato …*, pp. 32-33.

> The match having been accepted by both parties, we agreed on a place and a time: which was not however kept by the other party; instead not only did he not appear on the chosen day[130],but neither for many days afterwards. But that would not have mattered: if this second philosopher, instead of meeting with me and making me see his reasonings and experiments, had not gone to many public places in the city to show to a great multitude of persons some balls and boards of his, first of box[131] and then of ebony, and to sing his triumph, saying that he had convinced me; and yet he had not even spoken to me. I, being forewarned of his constructions, knew every foundation of his before we were to meet; but, since the philosophical debate had already degenerated into a quarrelsome competition, and not being able in this respect to treat the dispute as would be appropriate, I judged it better, to avoid odious contestations, to propose in writing [...]

In *Le Galleggianti* the reconstruction of the facts proceeds more calmly, without any reference to Colombo's unsatisfactory behaviour. In any case, we learn that many days passed in negotiations and postponements, until September:

> On this conclusion over the course of many days many and many things were said, and several experiments produced, some of which Your Highness heard and saw.

The negotiation phase, for various reasons, dragged on throughout July and August: in the letters addressed to Galileo throughout the month of July we read words of regret for his illness[132], of hopes that he would return to good health and congratulations for his convalescence. It is clear that Galileo only began to concern himself again with the dispute in August; the missed meeting between Galileo and Colombe was fixed around the first half of August as Cigoli's letter indicates. If the date of the first meeting, when Colombe failed to appear, must be put before 15 August, the date of the meeting Colombe refers to, when Galileo did not «wish to make the experiment in appropriate size of shape and quantity of matter», must have been in early September.

Between one *dramatic scene* and another the end of September was arrived at, and a new character appeared on the scene: Maffeo Barberini, the future pope Urban VIII, was travelling from the Episcopal See of Spoleto to Bologna as Cardinal Legate for Paul V. Barberini broke his journey in Florence and was the guest of the Grand Duke, who one day arranged for him to find Galileo at his table, Barberini had known Galileo for some time and he had recently met him in Rome, during the scientist's famous journey to the Eternal City.

We know that during this luncheon the conversation turned to the dispute because Galileo left a brief account of it in a letter sent on 2 June 1612 to Cardinal Barberini, accompanying it with the gift of a copy of his treatise on *Le Galleggianti*:

---

130 On 23 August Ludovico Cigoli wrote to him from Rome: «I heard that you had to match with "Pippione" [*Ludovico delle Colombe*], at the house of Master Nori, where he then did not appear» (G.G., Vol. XI, p. 176).

131 Box (*Buxus sempervirens*) has a specific weight of around 1.25.

132 In a letter to Cristoph Grienberger dated 1 September he wrote that between June and July «he was abed sick».

Amongst the many favours that I have received from Your Most Illustrious and Reverend Lordship I clearly remember the favour that you did me at the table of the Most Serene Grand Duke my lord when you last passed here where, while a certain philosophical question was being debated, you supported my side against the Most Illustrious and Reverend Card. [*Ferdinando*] Gonzaga and others with opinions contrary to mine; and since I have agreed by instruction from his Serene Highness to put my reasons more clearly to paper, and then publish them in print, which has now been done, it occurred to me I should send a copy to Your Most Reverend Lordship and then entreat you, that when it is convenient you might deign to see, or hear, what I propose in this treatise, in which I believe you will see that you offered your patronage not only to your servant but, to no less a degree, to truth itself.

Antonio Favaro tried to arrange in chronological order the autograph texts that make up the *Diversi Fragmenti attenenti al trattato delle cose che stanno su l'acqua*: according to him, those that appear on pages 18-29, «for their content seem to us to belong to the, we might almost say, preliminary period of the dispute, which preceded the printing of Galileo's *Discorso.* [...] of these fragments some appeared to us almost to be notes that Galileo set down on paper while preparing for the oral dispute with his opponents». Immediately after these first papers Favaro placed a first brief version of the *Discorso* which occupies pages 30-54 of the *Diversi Frammenti.* Note that in the file put together by Galileo there is not the slightest reference to experiments.

Galileo, indeed, had decided to avoid the aggressiveness of Colombe and his supporters by setting out his reasoning in writing. This is confirmed in his letter dated 1 October 1611, to Lodovico Cardi da Cigoli[133] in which the first version is recalled, which was then included in the *Frammenti*:

I am obliged to answer two most welcome letters from Your Lordship; but because I am very busy with completing a work of 15 sheets, with regard to a certain contest which took place in the last few days between certain of these Peripatetic philosophers and myself, which I am doing for the G. Duke and perhaps it may be printed, I am forced to be very brief in my reply to you.

The final draft of the treatise on *Le Galleggianti*, begun perhaps in mid October, was already almost ready in December. On the 19th he informed Federico Cesi:

In answer to the last part of your letter, where you asked for special news of my health, I have nothing good to say at all with regard to the constitution of my body since for the past 2 months I have had continuous pain in kidneys and chest, and with other intermittent pains in legs, arms and other parts, and moreover, for the past 15 days, with a great flux of blood, which has almost emptied my veins and made me very weak. I have completely lost my taste and appetite, almost all my sleep; and all these ills I attribute to this contrary air, and in par-

[133] G.G., Vol. IV, *Diversi fragmenti attenenti al trattato* ..., pp. 213-214. According to Camerota, *op. cit.* p. 147, the first draft of *Le Galleggianti* was contained in G.G., Vol. IV, pp. 30-51, excluding what was written from p. 39 line 18 to p. 41 line 26.

ticular to one who does not totally escape it at night[134]. These things disturb my mind and bring melancholy, and the melancholy then increases them: however I move around, hobbling thus, doing something, and in a few days I shall send Your Excellency a Discourse on a certain dispute I had with some Peripatetic philosophers; and having done that, I wish to attend for a few days to replies to some letters, not neglecting in the meantime my heavenly observations, with some added exactness.

The letter confirms that Galileo continued making «heavenly observations with some added exactness» at the same time as drafting the treatise, and he was so enthusiastic about the results obtained that, straying slightly from his theme, he began the treatise on *Le Galleggianti* by giving the latest information on the times of the occultations of the four moons of Jupiter and on the great news of the observation of sunspots which convinced him that the Sun rotates[135]:

But because the high speed of their returns requires very scrupulous precision in calculations of their positions for past and for future times, especially if these times are several months or years, I am obliged to correct the tables of these movements with further and more exact observations than in the past and to bring them within the narrowest limits.
[...] but now that I have found a way to take those measures with no error greater than a few seconds of arc, I shall continue observations until Jupiter goes behind the Sun
[...] I add to these things the observation of some dark spots that are seen in the Sun's body, which, changing their position in that, offer a strong argument either that the Sun revolves, or perhaps that other stars similar to Venus and Mercury circulate around the Sun [...]

So Galileo wrote the treatise between mid October 1611 and mid February 1612[136], despite his dreadful state of health, which even prevented him from taking his leave of Cardinal Barberini, who mentioned his illness in the letter he wrote him from Bologna on 11 October[137]:

I greatly regret that you were not in a condition to see me when I left that city, not because I thought necessary any demonstration of your affection, which I know well, but because of the illness that overcame you.

At this point it seems almost inevitable that we must ask where Galileo found the time to develop the theoretical and experimental knowledge found in the *Discorso intorno alle cose che stanno in su l'acqua, o che in quella si muovono*.

We must exclude the possibility that he did it in parallel to drafting the *Discorso*, which took just over four months, during which time he reviewed and corrected the earlier demonstrations,

[134] Note the mention of astronomical observations, which he continued to make despite the bad state of health he found himself in.

[135] G.G., Vol. IV, *Discorso...*, , p. 64.

[136] The approval by the Florence inquisitor was dated 5 March 1612, but he must have received the manuscript some weeks earlier.

[137] G.G., Vol. XI, p. 216.

because we know that he spent part of that time sick, attending to correspondence, observing the moons of Jupiter and sunspots, taking care of ordinary daily affairs, visits, invitations to court, etc.

There is more: in an inventory of his manuscripts in 1818 two volumes are mentioned bearing the numbers XV and XVI, according to a list attributed to Viviani but which is believed to have been drawn up by Galileo himself. The description of volume XVI presents a *Trattato del moto* (Treatise on motion) and the *Aggiunte al trattato delle Galleggianti* (Additions to the treatise on floating bodies) as joined together. Michele Camerota[138] recalled what had been written about this proximity, remembering that it was Raymond Fredette who hypothesised that «the passage concerning floating bodies was inserted amongst the pages of the *De motu* in order to clarify concepts and correct the theses expounded in those writings». Camarota continues his analysis, recalling that:

> Within an unchanged conceptual horizon the same linguistic solutions adopted in the *De motu antiquiora* also reappear absolutely intact in the text of the "first draft" of the *Discorso*. Thus, the notion of "specific weight" – far from making avail of the convincing definition contained in the printed version – is still hampered by the expressive clumsiness of the writings on motion.
> «*Those bodies or materials which have equal sizes which weigh equally are called equally heavy* » is given in the text of the 1611 text [G.G., Vol. IV p. 36], «*ea inter se aeque gravia dicenda erunt, quae, cum fuerint aequalia in mole, erunt etiam aequalia in gravitate*» is stated in the studies on motion [G.G., Vol. I, p. 251 and pp. 347-348].

Camarota continues:

> But the links between the so-called "first draft" of the *Discorso* and the texts that we are concentrating on are, in truth, even more extensive and profound. All of the reasoning used by Galileo to expound his hydrostatic concepts scrupulously retraces the thesis in the *De motu*, so much so that some passages prove to be faithful translations of similar passages in "earlier studies" on motion.

William R. Shea[139] was the first to notice that both in the *De motu* and in the *Frammenti* that immediately preceded the writing of the *Discorso intorno alle cose che stanno in su l'acqua*, Galileo had not taken into account the finite dimensions of the container, where the level of the water rises according to how much water is displaced by a solid body immersed in it, but that he corrected the mistake in the printed text. The origin of the error is very clear: We just have to compare the two versions of Archimedes' theorems on the floating of bodies, in the *Dialogo*[140] and in the *Trattato*[141].

---

[138] Michele Camerota, *Gli scritti* De motu antiquiora *di Galileo Galilei: il Ms Gal 71. Un'analisi storico-critica*, Cagliari, 1992, pp. 142, 148-149.

[139] William R. Shea, *Galileo's Intellectual Revolution*, 2nd edition, Science History Publications, New York, 1977, pp. 18-22; It. trans.: *La rivoluzione intellettuale di Galileo*, Florence, 1974, pp. 36-40.

[140] G.G., *De motu*, pp. 381-384.

[141] G.G., *De motu*, pp. 254-260.

In the *Dialogo* the figures and the reasoning are very similar to those read by Galileo in Federico Commandino's Latin translation[142]. For convenience I shall use Niccolò Tartaglia's Italian version[143], even though Galileo probably had not read it, to show that the discussion is illustrated by figures that represent sections of the Earth's sphere, with the surface of the water always curved, as the lines that mark the various heights are also curved. Tartaglia wrote:

> We shall suppose a quantity of liquid (let us say water) above the Earth, then with our imagination we shall cut the whole Earth together with that water into two equal parts so that the said cut passes through the centre of the Earth, & we suppose that a part of the surface of that cut be of water, as the surface of the Earth is .a.b. & that the centre of the Earth is point .k. Having done this we shall describe with our imagination a circle above said centre .k. of such size that its circumference shall pass through the surface of the cut of the water, that is to see that the circumference shall pass through e.f.g. & may many lines be drawn from point .k. to said circumference cutting it directly as they are [...]

Figure 2.15 describes exactly what Tartaglia wanted to make clear, which is no detail since such a surface over such a great expanse presupposes that any change in the water level due to the immersion of a solid body cannot be observed.

In their theorems for the immersion of bodies, partial for bodies with a specific weight less than that of water, or total, for the others, Tartaglia and Commandino always stuck to a spherical shape for the surface of the water, almost identical in their illustrations as we can see, where no change in the water level is indicated.

Commandino notes in his introduction[144]: «he [*Archimedes*] likes water not to be level, but to have a spherical shape and that there be a centre in it...» and in proposition II:

> All that which has liquid consistency and [lies] still is a spherical surface and the centre of this sphere coincides with the centre of the Earth.

We can compare fig. 2.16 and 2.17 with the figures in the *De motu*; starting with the very similar ones in the *Dialogo*, fig. 2.18 and fig. 2.19, where the successive levels of the surface of the liquid, before and after a solid body is immersed, are always arcs of a circumference, which recall the drawings by Tartaglia and Commandino, but now they are narrow containers where the introduction of a body raises the water, even if we note a certain disproportion between the immersed volume of the body and the raised volume of the water.

---

142 *Archimedis de iis quae vehuntur in aqua libri duo a Federico Commandino urbinate in pristinum nitorem restituti et commentariis illustrati*, Bologna, 1565.

143 *Ragionamenti de Nicolo Tartaglia sopra la sua travagliata inventione. Nelli quali se dechiara volgarmente quel libro di Archimede Siracusano Intitolato De insidentibus aquae, Con altre speculative pratiche da lui ritrovate sopra le materie, che stano, & chi non stano sopra l'acqua...*, Venice, 1551. I have not been able to consult the earlier publication: *Opera Archimedis Syracusani, per Nicolaum Tartaleum...*, Venice, 1543.

144 *Archimedis de iis quae vehuntur in aqua*, [p. 6 n.n. in the introduction]: In the Commandino edition the figure appears twice on Folios 2v and 4r, with almost all the letters identical to Tartaglia's figure.

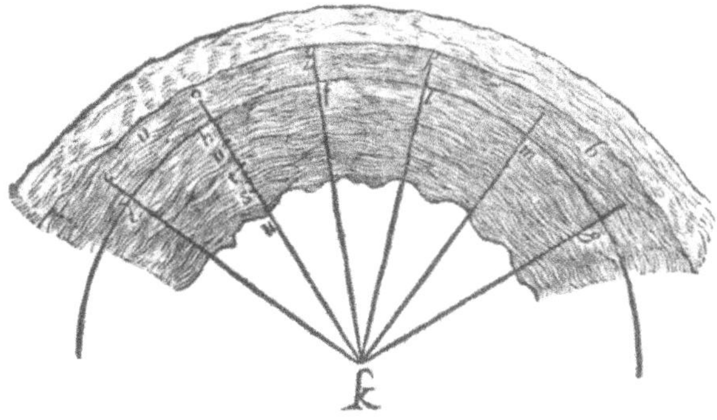

Fig. 2.15 N. Tartaglia, *Ragionamenti … sopra la sua travagliata inventione*, p. 4.

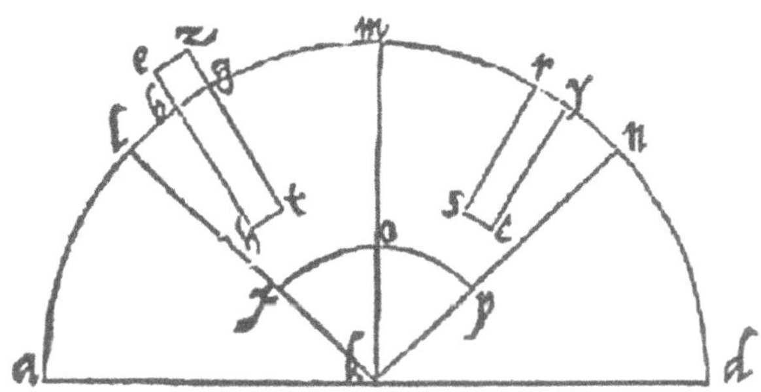

Fig. 2.16 N. Tartaglia, *Ragionamenti … sopra la sua travagliata inventione*, p.13.

The figures change completely in the *Saggio* and in the *Trattato*, because here Galileo introduces drawings that are sections of a cubic container.
In the drawings 2.20a, b the level of the water is initially *ao*. A body lighter than water is immersed. The water rises in the container up to *st*. Galileo indicates by *e* the part of the body above water and by *f* the part under water. It is evident that the space occupied by the body between the extensions of the lines *ao* and *st* was first occupied by air and that the displaced water *aost* should have a volume equal to the part of the body below the extension of the line *ao*. Galileo wrongly identifies the volume *aost* with the volume *f*, making the volume of the displaced water coincide with the volume of the visibly submerged part. If he had also drawn the protraction of the line *ao* he would probably not have fallen into error.
In the drawing in fig. 2.21 *ab* is the initial surface of the water, before the solid body *cd* with a smaller specific weight than that of water is forcibly immersed in the water. Galileo claims that the area *eabf* is equal to the area of *cd*, while in a correct drawing the line *ab* should be much higher up, so as to make the area *eabf* equal to the part of *cd* below the line *ab*.

We can say quite frankly that Galileo made rather a mess of his figures in the *De motu*. It is remarkable that the same figures with the same errors appear in the *Frammenti* which immediately precede the writing of *Le Galleggianti*, a sign that, having left Pisa, Galileo no longer

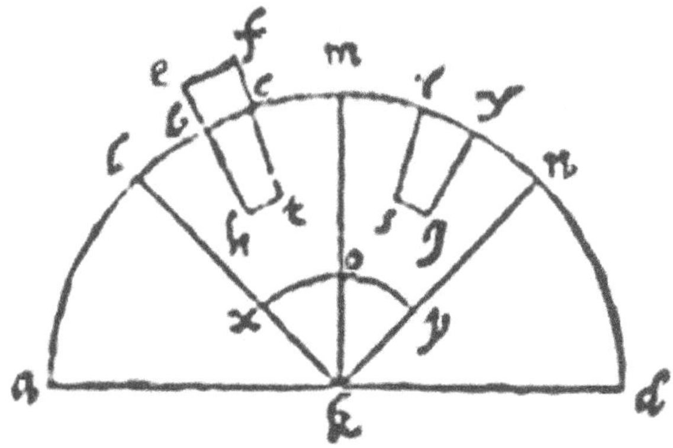

Fig. 2.17 F. Commandino, *Archimedis de iis quae vehuntur in aqua...*, Folios 2r and 4v.

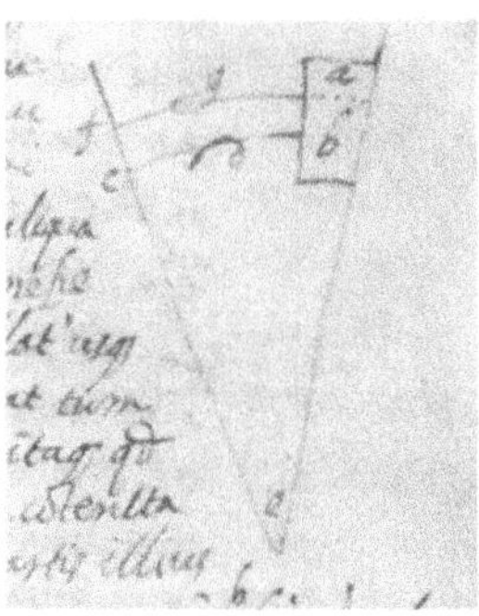

Fig. 2.18 *De motu*, Gal. 71, Folio 27.

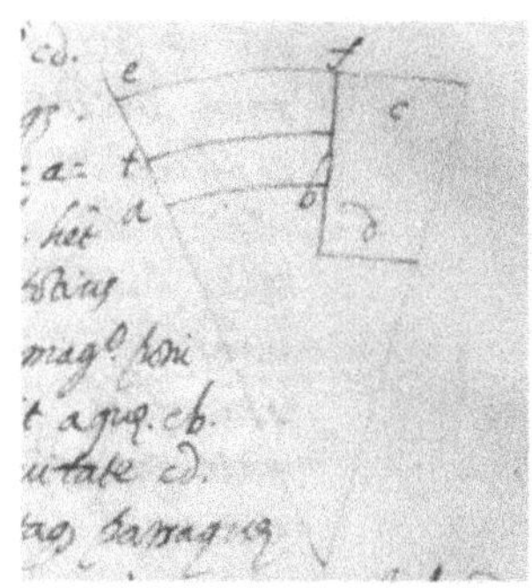

Fig. 2.19 *De motu*, Gal. 71, Folio 31.

concerned himself with them. Conclusion: in his writings of September-October 1611 Galileo picked up his research into motion in water from the point where he had left off in 1590; on the other hand there is no reason why Galileo should have continued cultivating this field of study once he had begun his research into the inclined plane.

Just to be thorough, I tried to see if there was any reference in his letters and I found only one, from February 1609, in which Galileo wrote something about water: it is a letter in which he thanked Antonio de' Medici for helping his brother-in-law Landucci to obtain a favour[145]. Immediately after his thanks he added:

> My brother-in-law also instructs me to write to Your Excellency something new about my studies, since that is his wish, which I am most pleased to receive, and it is a spur to me to speculate more than usual.

[145] G.G., Vol. X, *Epistolario*, pp. 228-230.

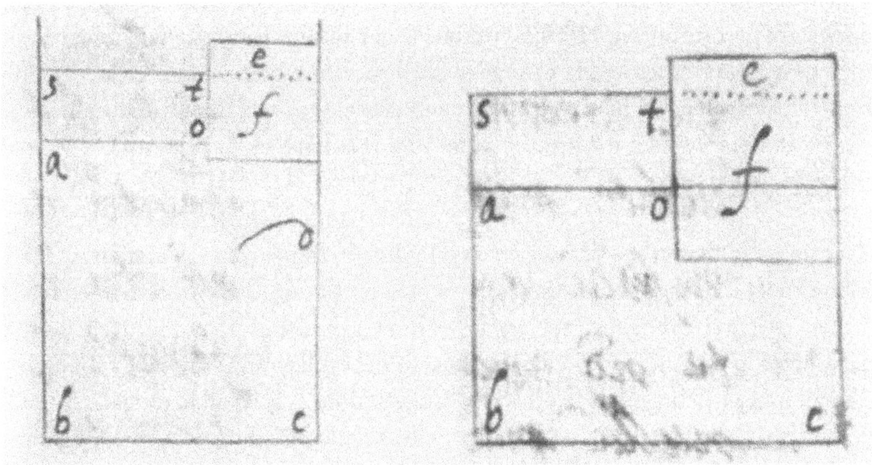

a) b)

Fig. 2.20 a) *De motu*, Gal. 71 (*Trattato*) Folio 129; b) *De motu*, Gal. 71 (*Saggio*) Folio 97.

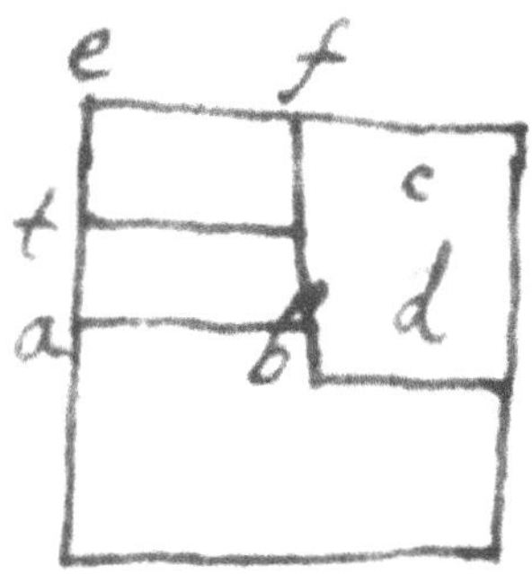

Fig. 2.21 *De motu*, Gal. 71, Folio 149.

The letter is of great importance, because it informs us that Galileo is well advanced in the research which he would only publish thirty years later, after the *Discorsi intorno a due nuove scienze*:

> [...] after my return to Florence I was occupied by some contemplations and several experiments regarding my treatise on mechanics; [...] and yet lately I have found again all the conclusions, with their demonstrations, regarding the forces and resistances of pieces of wood of different lengths, sizes and shapes [...] which knowledge is very necessary to build machines and all sorts of buildings [...] I am now engaged with some questions that remain to me on the motion of projectiles, many of which belong to artillery fire [...]

Right at the end of the letter we find what we were looking for:

In the matter of waters and other fluids, a part still intact, I have also discovered very great properties of nature; but the tightness of time is not enough for me to write them at present, since I have many other letters to send. I shall therefore postpone to greater opportunity telling Your Excellency 3 or 4 conclusions and effects seen and already tested by me, which perhaps outdo in wonder the greatest curiosities that have so far been sought by men. But that is enough for now.

To be convinced that in this passage he was alluding to things other than motion in water we merely have to look in the *Discorsi* for those «*3* or *4 conclusions and effects*» Galileo referred to. One of these effects could be the experiment with the cylinder of water that offers resistance at the separation of its parts[146]; another might concern the explanation why «not with metal pipes, nor with any other machine that raises water by attraction, is it possible to make it rise a hair's breadth more than eighteen *braccia*»[147]; another effect could be the experiment with the wax ball which sinks or rises according to the density of the water «and this experiment is so precise that the addition of just two *grani* of salt (0.1 g), placed in six *libbre* (pounds) (2.037 kg) of water, will make that ball that had only just then sunk to rise up from the bottom»; another with the thermometric experiment spoken of immediately after the experiment with the salt: «heating it or cooling it a little produces the same effect [...] that the ball descends or rises there»[148]; to all of these we can add his reasoning on the sphericity of drops of water[149].

None of these experiments was strictly connected to the cases we are interested in, even if they may all have depended in various ways on his Pisan research carried out in water to study motion.

In his treatise on *Le Galleggianti* the situation was different, because here Galileo did not have the time to develop theories and make tests and checks; he was therefore forced to use discoveries and experiments he had already completed, but when? The most natural answer is: during his Pisan research into uniform motion. There are in fact some notes[150], including those that Galileo wrote almost in a continuous stream, in the early days of the dispute, which reveal a great familiarity with experiments made with weighted wax, which he spoke of in the *De motu*. We quote here some of the most significant ones:

a) Showing with cones that the air contiguous to the upper surface of the solid supports it: because, when placed point down, it floats, since much air stays contiguous with the base; but if it is placed with the point upwards, it sinks[151].

---

146 G.G., Vol. VIII, *Discorsi*, pp. 62-63

147 G.G., Vol. VIII, *Discorsi*, p. 64.

148 G.G., Vol. VIII, *Discorsi*, p. 114.

149 G.G., Vol. VIII, *Discorsi*, p. 115.

150 G.G., Vol. IV, *Diversi fragmenti attenenti al trattato* ..., pp. 22 and 23.

151 G.G., Vol. IV, *Diversi fragmenti attenenti al trattato* ..., p. 20.

b) How can they say that the ball is sustained by its shape, if the maximum circle is below and only a very small surface remains uncovered[152]?

c) Our adversary shall say: here is a ball, and a board of ebony; and the latter shall float and the other sink; therefore the shape is the cause. I answer no; but because of its heaviness. I try. The cause is, that when placed, etc.: but once having reduced the heaviness, without changing their shapes, both, gently placed, stay, and if wetted shall sink to the bottom: so, not the shape, but too much heaviness, is the cause of going or staying[153].

d) A solid equally heavy as water, of cylindrical shape, placed in the water, stays on the upper surface at the level of the water; and pushed down a little, it returns upward, attracted by the air above, indeed it will bear a considerable weight: and that withstanding, when the weight is removed and it is simply wetted, it sinks[154].

Galileo had already noticed the effect due to the surface tension of water and the adhesion between water and solids when he carried out experiments with weighted wax, which he returned to and described in detail in several passages of *Le Galleggianti*, such as this one for example[155]:

Moreover it will be an excellent expedient to take a kind of material most similar in heaviness to water, because such material, in so far as heaviness is concerned is indifferent to sinking and rising; so any small difference that might derive from changes in shape will most quickly be known. Now, to do this, wax is most suitable, since not only does it not undergo any perceptible change from being soaked with water, but it can also be moulded, and the same piece can most easily be made into any shape; and since indeed it is only slightly less heavy than water, by mixing a little lead filings into it it is made most similar in heaviness

---

152 G.G., Vol. IV, *Diversi fragmenti attenenti al trattato* ..., p. 22.

153 G.G., Vol. IV, *Diversi fragmenti attenenti al trattato* ..., p. 22.

154 G.G., Vol. IV, *Diversi fragmenti attenenti al trattato* ..., p. 23. Ebony has a density too different from the density of water: for this reason for an ebony ball no position exists in which the buoyancy, due to the submerged part of the sphere, and the upward force, due to the surface tension, together succeed in not letting it descend. As the sphere is submerged the buoyancy increases but the length of the little ridges, that is to say the circumference of the part of the sphere above the water, diminishes continuously until it becomes zero at the moment when the sphere becomes totally submerged, without it ever arriving at a position of equilibrium with the force of gravity. It is different in the case of the small board: the perimeter is still the same and so the force resulting from the surface tension is always the same. By making the board suitably thinner, the force of weight can be reduced until a thickness is found at which the buoyancy of the submerged part manages to keep the board afloat. Delle Colombe succeeded in finding the suitable thickness and his experiment seemed conclusive. In the agreement however Galileo had rightly reserved for himself the freedom to choose a material as close as possible to the density of water to show that the shape was not the correct explanation. With wax mixed with lead filings Galileo had a substance available with a density very close to that of water with which he could make a sphere and a board of the same weight, so that both, placed slowly in the water, floated, but if they were wetted they sank. In this way he proved his theory, that is that it was the force of adhesion between solid and air, not the shape, that – by creating the little ridges – supported both.

155 G.G., Vol. IV, *Diversi fragmenti attenenti al trattato* ..., p. 88.

> to water. Having prepared such material, and made from it, for example, a ball as large as an orange, or larger, and having made it so heavy that it lies on the bottom, but so lightly that, if a single *grano* of lead is removed, it floats, and adding one it returns to the bottom; then shape that same wax into a very thin and wide strip, and let us return to make the same experiment: it will be seen that, placed on the bottom, with that *grano* of lead it will remain on the bottom; with the *grano*, removed it will rise to the surface; adding it again, it will sink to the bottom. And this same effect will always happen with all sorts of shapes, both regular and irregular [...]; and, to sum up, no difference will be noticed with regard to sinking or not sinking to the bottom, but rather in the speed or slowness, because wider and stretched out shapes will move more slowly, both when sinking to the bottom and when rising, and the other narrower or concentrated shapes more swiftly.

Let us remember that the unit of measurement in Florence is the *libbra* (pound) equivalent to 0.3395 kg; the *libbra* was subdivided into 12 *once* (ounces); the *oncia* into 24 *denari* (deniers); the *denari* into 24 *grani* (grains). So a *grano* was equivalent to 49 milligrams and the sensibility Galileo speaks of here was accurate and obvious when we made our first attempts to reconstruct the experiment on the motion of bodies in water, when we made use of wooden spheres weighted down with lead and brass tacks.

Another effect that Galileo cannot have failed to notice when he made his measurements of density with his small scales is the following[156]:

> Take a pair of scales, with their plates even, in each of which equal weights be placed, so that they are perfectly balanced: it is clear that, placing one of the pans in the water, leaving the other in the air, the one in the air will weigh more and will lift the other, which, being in the water, will be lightened, by means of the heaviness of the water compared to the air. But I do not want that said pan to be plunged in the water, but only that its lower surface touch the water; then start to add weight to the other pan which is hanging in the air: and it shall be seen that as the one is lowered the other will rise, but followed by the water contiguous to it, which, before it separates from the flat surface of the scale, shall be lifted by as much as the side of a knife, and it will withstand the weight of many *grani* and carats added to the other scale; until finally the weight of the water raised and the compression surrounding air will dissolve the continuation of the two surfaces, in which dissolving the other weighted scale will jerk sharply.

In the second of the two density tables that accompany *La Bilancetta* there are items that are certainly flat, such as a gold *ungaro* and a silver *Testoni*, both weighing 576 *grani, i.e.* exactly a Florentine ounce, which corresponds to about 28 g. I do not believe that they are coins but rather small ingots obtained by melting the metal of the coins of that name, and these ingots are certainly flat. It is probable that during the operation of submerging and then withdrawing them from the water Galileo noticed the phenomenon of adhesion: if, for example, after having balanced his scales with the ingot in water, Galileo had moved the counterweight back to the

[156] G.G., Vol. IV, *Diversi fragmenti attenenti al trattato ...*, pp. 39-40.

position that corresponds to its weight in air, he would not have seen the arm tilt until the little ingot was totally emerged because the forces of adhesion would have held it at the surface. This is only one of the possible ways of stumbling across the phenomenon by chance, but it makes us consider the possibility that the discovery dates back to the first use of the *little scale*.

Another example of an argument also to be found in *Le Galleggianti* is in one of the fragments I have already quoted, published in the final pages of the *De motu*[157]:

> It is evident that the difficulty of cleaving the medium is not the cause why wood does not go down in water: for if [in this case] this difficulty were overcome by the form of the mobile, the wood would descend, if, for example, it was given the form of a cone or an arrow; and yet this floats no less than a flat board.

We come across this argument again in the *Discorso* of 1612, together with the experiment with a wax ball and a piece of cork, which here plays the same role that the inflated bladder had in the passage of the *De motu* I have quoted on page 52-53[158]:

> Make a cone or pyramid of cypress, or fir, or wood of similar heaviness (or indeed of pure wax), having considerable height, say a span or more, and put it in water keeping its base down. At once it will be seen that this will penetrate the water, nor will it be one with [*sic*] impeded by the breadth of its base. But it will not go entirely under water, sticking out toward the apex. Already it is evident from this that this solid does not rest from going deeper through impotence to divide the continuity of water, having already divided that with its wide part, which in the adversaries' opinion is the least suitable for dividing water. The pyramid having stopped thus, note what part of it shall be submerged, and then turn it point down. You will see that it does not penetrate the water more than it did before, and if you will mark the place up to which it is immersed, anyone expert in geometry will be able to measure those parts that remain outside the water, which in the one experiment and the other are equal to a hair. Manifestly, from this one may gather that sharp shape, which seemed best suited to fend and penetrate the water, did not fend or penetrate it a bit more than broad and spacious shape.
>
> Anyone who wants an easier experiment may make, of the same material as before, two cylinders, one long and thin and the other short and very wide, putting them in water not sideways but straight up and down. If with diligence you measure the parts of both, you will see that in either of them the submerged part has the same ratio to the part remaining outside the water, and that no greater part is submerged of that long and thin one than of the other, fatter and broader – though the latter is supported on a broad area of water. Therefore difference of shape introduces neither ease nor difficulty in fending and penetrating the continuity of water, and consequently this cannot be the cause of sinking or not sinking to the bottom. Likewise, the nullity of operation of difference of shape is perceived by taking wax and mixing into it many lead filings until it becomes appreciably heavier than water; make

[157] G.G., Vol. I, *De motu*, p. 414.

[158] G.G., *Discorso intorno alle cose che stanno in su l'acqua ...*, Vol. IV, pp. 93-94.

a ball of this and put it at the bottom of water. If you now attach to it just enough cork, or other very light material, to raise it and draw it toward the surface, and afterward mould the same wax into a thin plate or any other shape, the same cork will serve to lift it in exactly the same way.

The ideas are the same as in the *De motu*, although dealt with at greater length.

Some times it is difficult to distinguish what Galileo already knew, because it belonged to the wealth of experience acquired with his experiments while young, from what he worked out at the time of the dispute. In the following passage, Galileo may only have thought of a crucial experiment, which according to him proved conclusively the theory he adopted to explain the way bodies heavier than water float, at the time of the dispute.

Indeed he had to contest the intelligent counter-example presented to him by Ludovico delle Colombe, which used ebony, the only natural material available which is just heavier than water, which normally sinks but which, when it has the shape of a thin board, floats if laid carefully on the surface of the water. The explanation Galileo gave for this phenomenon, although profound and well thought out, is wrong, as was later understood. The experiment I refer to is the following[159]:

> Perhaps some of those gentlemen who dissent from me marvel that I affirm that the contiguous air above has the power to sustain that lamina of copper or silver that keeps itself on water, as if I would in a certain way give to the air some kind of magnetic virtue of sustaining heavy bodies to which it is contiguous. To meet all the difficulties as well as I am able, I have been thinking of demonstrating with some other sensate experience how that little bit of air contiguous and above truly supports those solids that, though by nature fitted to sink to the bottom, do not submerge when placed lightly on water if they have not first been wetted completely: I have found if such a body has sunk to the bottom, then without touching it but merely by sending to it a little air that joins with its top, this is sufficient not merely to sustain, at before, but to lift it and to bring it back up, where (in the same way as before) it stops and rests so long as the assistance of the air joined with it is not lacking to it. For this effect I made a ball of wax, and with bits of lead made this heavy enough so that it slowly descended to the bottom, and I also gave it a very smooth and clean surface. This, placed very gently in water, almost completely submerges with just a bit of the summit exposed, which, so long as it shall be joined with the air, will hold the ball up; but if we remove contiguity with the air by wetting it, it will sink to the bottom and remain there. Now, to make it return to the top and stop close to it by virtue of the same air that before sustained it, push into the water an inverted tumbler, with its mouth down, which will carry with it the contained air, and move this to the ball. Press this glass down until through its transparence it is seen that the air contained in it arrives at the summit of the ball; then slowly draw the tumbler back up and you will see the ball rise, and come to rest again at the surface if you separate the tumbler from the water with great care, so that it does not stir and agitate the water too much.
>
> There exists, therefore, between air and other bodies, a certain affinity that holds them united, so that they are not separated without some little force. The same is likewise seen

[159] G.G., Vol. IV, *Discorso intorno alle cose che stanno in su l'acqua* ..., pp. 101-102.

in water, for it we dip some body into it so that it is completely wetted and then draw it slowly out again, we shall see water follow it and rise up noticeably above the surface before it separates from the body.

The explanation is the reciprocity between air and water, with experiments in which bodies adhere first to one of the two media and then to the other and the trick he resorted to is the outcome of long experience with wax spheres in water, of tenacious research into the causes of the adhesion and of thoughtful observations.

Yet again Galileo had shown his experimental genius, and since in his *Lettera a Tolomeo Nozzolini* (Letter to Tolomeo Nozzolini) he returns to the argument with some more details, I wish to follow him again in this most ingenious experiment[160]:

I do not wish to linger describing better the way in which the wax ball rises from the bottom of the water, due to the air that is sent to it with the inverted glass: that however is not due to the attraction of vacuum, while the glass rises swiftly; instead it is necessary to lift the glass extremely slowly, allowing time so that the water may replace it at its slow rate to forbid the vacuum: but the cause of the ball rising is the air that is contiguous to it. But let Your Lordship note how the experiment proceeds. Make a ball of wax, about as large as a walnut, and make the surface as smooth as possible, which shall be done by pressing it lightly with a clean polished glass; it shall then be counterweighted with a little lead placed inside it, so that when submerged under water, it descends, but with little force, to the bottom: this same ball, placed lightly in the water, will make (its upper surface while it is dry) its small ridges, which, because of the air contained in them, will support it; but if those ridges are broken, it shall descend to the bottom, as heavier than water, and shall stay there: but pushing down on it the inverted glass full of air, as soon as the air arrives at the ball, the water pushed aside by the air gives way, leaving part of the ball uncovered and totally dry, since the wax is very clean and by nature rather greasy; which Your Lordship can see due to the transparency of the glass: so that around that part of the surface, which as I say, remains dry, and surrounded by the air which is in the glass, the little ridges form again; so that, pulling the glass up slowly, the very water that follows it brings the floating ball up again, and sustained not by the attraction of vacuum or any other, but by the air contained within the ridges in the way declared; and using care in separating the tumbler from the water, so that it is not agitated nor has waves, the ball remains afloat as before. This then is the way in which air contributes to the floating of bodies heavier than water.

2.6 *The experiment with the «inverted tumbler»*

The experiment has been described so clearly and in such detail that it can be carried out to the letter and I did so without making any changes. To make the sphere rise I took a normal glass tumbler and a small glass cube, with a base of 7.5 cm × 7.5 cm and a depth of 8.8 cm; for

---

[160] G.G., Vol. IV, p. 304.

the water I had a glass tray 20 cm wide × 30 cm and 7 cm tall. When I repeated the experiment I followed Galileo's recommendation to use a sphere «about as large as a walnut ... with a surface as smooth as possible ... with a little lead placed inside, so that when it is submerged under the water, it descends, but with little force, to the bottom ».

I should warn you that the experiment is a delicate one and does not always succeed. After one sphere which I had to discard[161] I made another sphere with 14 external pellets of 0.1 g each, which I called *L*. It was an immediate success because the sphere rose and always floated. The characteristics of *L* were: *weight* in air 0.024405 kg and in water 0.000230 kg, density 1.009514 kg/dm^3; radius r_M = 0.01793 m.

After checking that the sphere floated in the water and formed its little ridges, I pushed the sphere to the bottom of the tray and I brought the glass cube close to the surface of the water with the open side parallel to it and I submerged it slowly until it touched the bottom with the sphere inside the cube. If you proceed in this way you will always see that «the water pushed asisde by the air gives way, leaving part of the ball uncovered and totally dry» and that only a thin layer of water remains on the bottom[162]. In these immersions the water in the tray rose about 4 mm and arrived ultimately at the height H = 50 mm.

At this point, as the container is slowly raised, you observe that the water inside the cube begins to rise while the sphere still lies resting on the bottom because of its weight, until the part of the sphere that emerges is so reduced that the surface tension of the water becomes capable of bearing its weight and the sphere rises with the water in the cube until it arrives at the surface of the water and then, as Galileo wrote:

> [...] using care in separating the tumbler from the water, so that the water is not agitated nor has waves, the ball remains afloat as before. This then is the way in which air contributes to the floating of bodies heavier than water.

The care to be used consists in avoiding what happens when you proceed according to the most natural method. What normally happens is soon said: when submerging the tumbler you cannot avoid a little air escaping and some large bubbles rise to the surface, this ensures that when the tumbler with the wax sphere inside is raised and it arrives close

---

[161] I made a small sphere, which I call *M*, with characteristics similar to sphere *L*: *weight* in air 0.022835 kg and in water 0.000294 kg, density 1.013044 kg/dm^3; radius r_M = 0.01752 m. Placed carefully in the water, the sphere floated and I saw the little ridges form; but after a little while, when it was now wet, it was very difficult to make it float. With *M* the experiment with the tumbler is unworkable. I made many attempts to bring it up from the bottom to float without succeeding. One explanation is this: *M* had 4 pellets on the outside of 0.1 g each and inside, but not at the centre, a pellet of 3.5 g. When the sphere was on the bottom, the inner lead was not on the vertical from the point of support; when the water rose, the little ridges moved along the surface of the sphere and shrank, without being able to make the sphere assume a position of equilibrium and to detach it from the bottom.

[162] The explanation is simple; when the container reached the bottom, the air inside it received a certain compression: if I indicate the initial height of the air in the cube by h_i and the final height – when the cube is on the bottom – by h_f and the final height of the water in the tray by H, according to Boyle's law, $P_0 h_i = P_F h_f$, with P_0 = 1 atmosphere and $P_F = P_0 + \rho_{Water}\, g(H - h_i + h_f)$. Introducing $K = g\rho_{Water} / P_0 \approx 0.952$ m, we obtain a final relationship $h_f^2 + h_f\,[K(H - h_i) + 1] - h_i = 0$. For H = 0.050 m and h_i = 0.088 m we have h_f = 0.084 m and inside the glass cube the water is only 4 mm high.

to the surface the water inside the tumbler starts to rise above the level of the water in the tray, because the air inside is at a lower pressure than the atmospheric pressure. Finally the difference in level reaches almost a centimetre until the rim of the tumbler detaches itself from the surface and the water inside the tumbler falls, dragging down the sphere which, as the water is mixed, finally remains submerged. Galileo realised this and he described the situation as follows[163]:

> Likewise it is true that the same work is required to push a tumbler or similar vessel down into water when it is filled with air, as to rise it above the surface of water, holding its mouth down, while filled with water, which is constrained to follow the tumbler that contains it and to be raised above the rest of the water into the region of air, just as air is forced to follow the same vessel beneath the water boundary – until, in one case, water rising above of the lip of the vessel precipitates itself within and drives out the air, and in the other case the lip of the tumbler comes out of the water, and entering into the region of air, the water falls out and air comes in from below to fill the hollow of the vessel.

All this can be avoided by tilting the tumbler to increase the surface of the water inside so that there is less difference in height. Care is still needed when arriving at the surface because, due to the effect of the adhesion between the water and the glass of the tumbler, the rim of the tumbler as it moves away from the surface drags after itself a thin layer of water which, because of the difference in pressure between the air inside and the air outside, curves inward until it bursts, creating wavelets which might sink the sphere. To prevent the sphere sinking you just have to move the tumbler slowly so as to make the sphere float on the side where the tumbler is more deeply immersed, and to raise the opposite side slowly.

For Galileo the experiment with the tumbler is crucial because it proves his thesis, *i.e.* that the "little ridges" are due to the greater adherence of the air to the wax and the repulsion shown by the water; therefore it is not an *ad hoc* justification but rather a well thought out argument which is founded on the experiments involving surface tension and adhesion. Floating then is a simple consequence of the formation of the small ridges which is explained by Archimedes' theory[164].

> [...] so the chip of ebony, by its nature heavier than water and therefore going to the bottom if alone placed in water, if placed upon the water with a wafer of air[165] that goes together with the ebony in descending, and if of such size that together they form a composite less heavy than water in that volume which is submerged beneath the water level, this will not go on but will stop; and for no cause other than the universal and common one – which is that bodies less specifically heavy than water do not go to the bottom.

---

[163] G.G., Vol. IV, *Discorso intorno alle cose che stanno in su l'acqua ...*, p. 123

[164] G.G., Vol. IV, *Discorso intorno alle cose che stanno in su l'acqua ...*, pp. 120-121.

[165] This happens when the ebony is not wet.

Was the experiment with the tumbler also carried out at Pisa? Perhaps, and it is striking to think that while carrying it out the explanation may also have occurred to him of a common error, which he chose to insert in the final draft of the *De motu*[166]:

> Now it happens sometimes that certain opinions, however false they may be , continue to exist for a very long time among people; because at first sight they offer some appearance of truth, and because of that no one bothers himself to seek to know if it is worthy of belief. An illustration of such a thing is what is believed about things that are under water, concerning which common opinion asserts that they appear larger than they really are. Now when I was not able to find a cause for such an effect, finally, having recourse to experience, I found that a coin resting in deep water in no way does appear larger, but rather smaller: hence I judge that the one who first has put forth this way of thinking had been led to this opinion during the summer, when plums and other fruits are sometimes put in a glass vessel full of water, whose form recalls the surface of a conoid; they surely would appear far larger than they are to those who view them in such a way that the rays of light pass through the glass. But it is the form of the cup, not the water, which is the cause of such an effect; as we have made clear more extensively in the commentaries to the Almagest of Ptolemy, which (with God's help) will soon be published. Now a sign of this is that, if the eye is placed above the water, so as to be able to observe the plum without the intervention of the glass medium, the plum does not appear larger.

Perhaps it is also for this reason that in the *Trattato* the containers of the water are so square in the drawings that illustrate the principle according to which bodies denser than water cannot float unlike less dense ones.

2.7 *Measuring adhesion with water*

We have reached the end of this *intermezzo*, which was long but necessary because it allowed us to reconstruct Galileo's scientific activity at Pisa with a certain probability, above all his experimental activity which had so far remained rather in the shadow; but before concluding it is appropriate to return to an experiment which has already been seen, which is described in detail in *Le Galleggianti* and is quantified in the weights used, because it was probably carried out in Pisa and revised twenty years later in Florence.

The Pisan period is called to mind by a passage in the *De motu* where Galileo discusses what can make the resistance of the medium increase[167]:

> But if there were some accidental cause, such as, for example, the shape of the mobile, it must not be classified amongst the causes *per se*: and moreover, the shape helps or hinders the mo-

[166] G.G., Vol. I, *De motu*, p. 314.

[167] G.G., Vol. I, *De motu*, p. 265. On p. 404 there is a similar discussion, illustrated by similar pictures.

tion but little, *as we shall show in the proper place*[168]. Also, one must not , as many are in the habit of doing, immediately revert to extremes, by taking, for example, a piece of lead of very large size, and, on the other hand, a tiny blade or a leaf of the same lead, which sometimes will even float on water: for since there is a certain cohesion and (so to speak) a tenacity and a viscosity of the parts of air as well as of water, this cannot be overcome by a very small heaviness.

This passage, in which we have indicated in italics the repeated statements of a later, much deeper, study[169], makes us think that Galileo may have carried out in Pisa some of the experiments that he would only describe completely in 1612[170]:

I fancy myself in a dispute which some of my adversaries about whether shape has any action in increasing or diminishing a weight's resistance to being lifted in air. Undertaking to sustain the affirmative, I declare that a bulk of lead in the shape of a ball will be raised with less force than that some lead made into a very thin, broad plate – as something that must, in a broad shape, fend a vast amount of air, but little of it in that more confined and compact shape. Then, to show how my opinion is true, I first suspended the ball by a thin cord and put in water, trying the cord that holds it to one of the arms of a balance that I hold in the air, while the other arm I proceed to add weight *until that finally lifts the ball out of the water, which requires, say, thirty ounces of weight.* Then I alter the same lead into a flat, thin plate, which I similarly place in water, suspended by three cords so as to hold it parallel to the surface of the water, and in the same way I add weights to the balance pan *until this plate is lifted and taken from the water, showing thus that thirty-six ounces are insufficient to separate it from the water and lift it through the air.* Based on this experiment I affirm that I have fully proved the truth of my position. An adversary now steps forward, and by having me tilt my head down makes me see something I had overlooked. He shows me that in [just] leaving the water, the [lead] plate draws in its train another plate, of water, which, before it divides and separates from the lead plate, rises up above the level of the rest of the water *more than [the thickness of] a knife blade.* He then repeats the experiment with the ball, showing me that only a very small quantity of water adheres to its narrow and compact form. Next he tell me that it is no wonder if, in separating the thin, broad plate from the water, I feel much more resistance than I do in separating the ball, since one must raise a great deal of water along with the plate, which does not happen with the ball. He also call it to my attention that our debate is whether resistance to be raised [in air] is greater in a broad lead plate than in a ball – not whether a lead plate with a great quantity of water [attached] resists more than a ball with a very little water. Thus, he shows me that first to put the plate and the ball in water, in order then to test their resistance in air, is beside our point, because we are arguing over the raising in air of things situated in air, and not over the resistance made in the boundary of air and water by things partly in air and partly in water. Finally, he makes it palpable to me that when the thin plate is in air and

[168] The italics are mine.

[169] This is one of the few subjects listed in the so-called *work plan*, which were not then developed in the *De motu*: «Why the shape of the moveable assists or obstructs motion» (G.G., Vol. I, *De motu*, p. 418).

[170] G.G., Vol. IV, *Discorso intorno alle cose che stanno in su l'acqua …*, pp. 121-122.

free from the weight of water, it is raised by the same force, to a hair, as was the ball. Having seen and understood these things, I can do nothing but admit myself persuaded and thank my friend for his having made me understand what I had previously overlooked. And then, apprised of these phenomena, I reply to my adversaries that our [original] debate was whether an ebony ball and an ebony chip equally go to the bottom in water – not an ebony ball, and an ebony chip that is joined with another chip of air; and, further, that we were speaking of sinking to the bottom, or not, in water, not of what happens at the boundary of air and water to bodies partly in air and partly in water. Neither were we dealing with the greater or less force required to separate this or the other body from the air. And, finally, I tell them that air resists and (so to speak) weighs [up] just as much in water, as water weighs [down] and resists [motion] upward in air, and that it is the same work for us to push under water an inflated bladder as to lift in air that bladder filled with water [...] From this it follows that he no less transgresses the bounds of our debate who produces a chip joined to a quantity of air, to see whether it sinks to the bottom in water, than he who would test resistance to being lifted in air with lead plate joined together with as much water.

Again the italics are mine and I use them to identify the data that will permit me to reconstruct this final experiment. Two points are fixed: the weight of the lead ball in air, which is 30 *once* (0.84875 kg), because the water clinging to a sphere as it emerges is negligible, and the weight of the quantity of water adhering to the lead plate, which is 6 *once* (0.16975 kg).

The volume of the lead sphere is about 75 cm^3 and the diameter of the ball is 5.23 cm, calculated on the basis of its density which is 11.35 kg/dm^3.

In reducing the lead ball into a «thin, flat plane» for which no thickness is indicated, we are helped by the quantity of water lifted, which gives us the volume, which is about 170 cm^3.

Knowing the thickness of the water which is «*more than the side of a knife*», say 0.3 cm just to settle our ideas, we arrive at a surface of about 567 cm^2, which is also the surface of the lead sheet. In order to make the lead ball have this surface we have to beat it until it is reduced to a sheet 23.8 cm^2 and about 1.3 mm thick.

It is a very modern and precise experiment which may have inspired Giusto Bellavitis (1803-1880), professor of descriptive geometry, analytical geometry and algebra at the University of Padua, who gave a very interesting *repeat performance*[171]:

For several months now I have tried to determine experimentally the cohesion of water compared to that of some more or less viscous liquids, with the aim of seeing whether the preponderant molecular attraction of water would be shown.

A brass disc with a diameter of fifty millimetres ($49.^{mm}4$) was suspended from the pan of a scale and rested on the surface of the water: in the other pan a weight equal to the weight of the disc was placed; then other weights were slowly added, until the disc detached itself from the water. After repeating the experiment many times, I estimated that the adhesion of the brass disc and of the water could be considered to be about eight grams ($8.^{g}4$).

[171] GIUSTO BELLAVITIS, *Poche esperienze ed alcune considerazioni sulla coesione dell'acqua*, Atti delle adunanze dell'I.R. Istituto Veneto di Scienze, Lettere ed Arti, 1846-1847, pp. 86-97.

Fig. 2.22 Rectangular brass plate.

> [...] The experiments I made cannot be held to be absolutely accurate, but they are such as to present the cohesion of water rather lesser than greater than the true one. Indeed I did not find it easy to obtain that a brass disc be wetted by the water in its every part [...] When the experiment concerns water much patience is needed in loading very very slowly the pan of the scale, because a small jerk makes the disc detach from the surface.
> [...] The adhesion that I observed in the brass disc on the water is equal to the weight of a column of water which has as its base the disc itself and as its height four millimetres and four tenths ($4.^{mm}4$).

In the two experiments the order of magnitude of the measurements is the same, considering that it is not possible to establish precisely what Galileo meant by a thickness «*more than the side of a knife*» and that the adhesion of the water to lead and to brass may not be the same, but we shall not be satisfied with having found someone who repeated Galileo's observations and now we present an independent reconstruction.

Adhesion experiments with rectangular and circular plates

In the experiment I used two brass plates, one rectangular (fig. 2.22) and one circular (fig. 2.24), and a circular lead plate (fig. 2.25), with more or less equal surfaces.

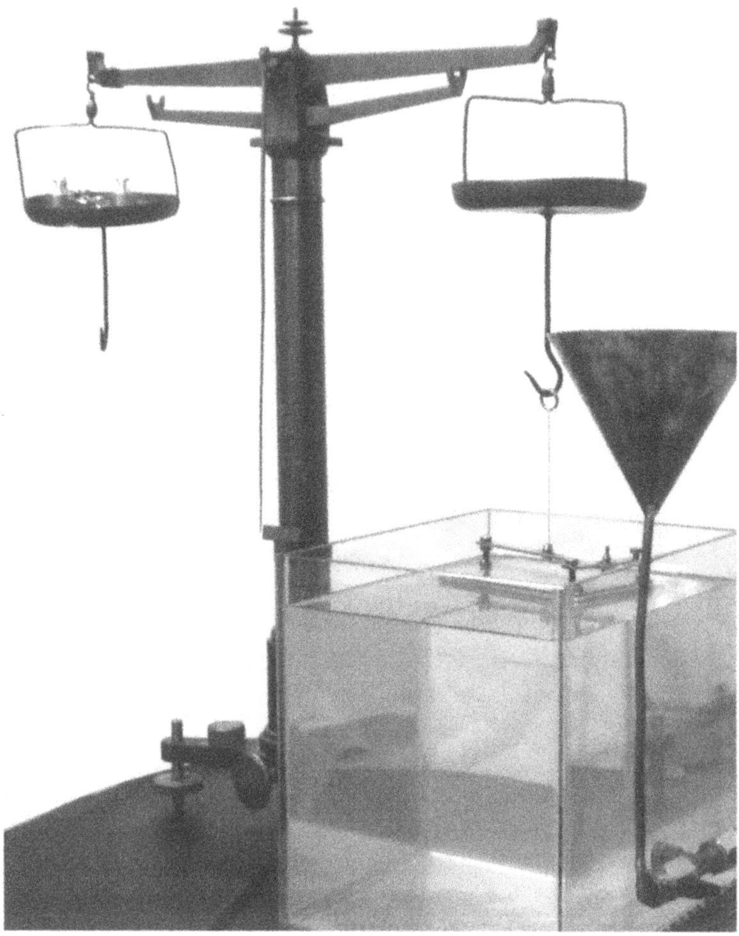

Fig. 2.23 Measurement of the mass of the water suspended from the plate.

The sides of the rectangular brass plate were 0.781 dm and 1.205 dm and the resulting area was 0.941 dm^2.

The diameter of the circular brass disc was 1.094 dm and the resulting area was 0.940 dm^2.

The diameter of the circular lead plate was on average 1.100 dm and the resulting area was 0.95033 dm^2.

Experiment with a rectangular brass plate

In photograph 2.22 two rods can be seen, one can rotate because it is fixed on only one side and its free end is restrained by the other rod; the moveable rod has a small central window in which a bushing connected to the suspension thread can slide. By moving it as required the rectangular plate can be suspended exactly in its centre of gravity so that its lower side stays parallel to the surface of the water.

Fig. 2.24 Circular brass plate.

The experiment presents no particular difficulties and is carried out as follows (fig. 2.23):

a) the plate is suspended from one of the pans of the scale which reaches equilibrium with 251.00 g in the other pan;
b) water is added to the glass tray below so that the level rises until it touches the plate;
c) to improve contact any air bubbles that may form between the plate and the water are removed;
d) further masses are added to the scale until the maximum load is reached beyond which – suddenly – the water detaches from the plate.

The maximum load reached before the brass plate detached itself was 285.00 g.

Having thus measured the mass of the water suspended from the plate, which is 34.00 g, dividing the volume of the water by the surface of the plate we obtain the maximum thickness of the sheet of water attached to the plate: 3.61 mm.

Experiment with the circular brass plate

With this second experiment we wish to verify whether the thickness of the suspended water depends of the shape of the plate, because the circular shape might bear a greater weight since it does not have the discontinuities of the corners.

The brass disc has a ring screwed exactly at its centre and the plate has an overall mass of 207.50 g.

We proceed exactly as in the previous experiment and we arrive at a maximum load, before the disc detaches from the water, equal to 247.50 g.

The mass of the water suspended from the plate is 40.00 g; from which it follows that the maximum thickness of the sheet of water attached to the plate is 4.25 mm: the thickness depends on the shape of the plate.

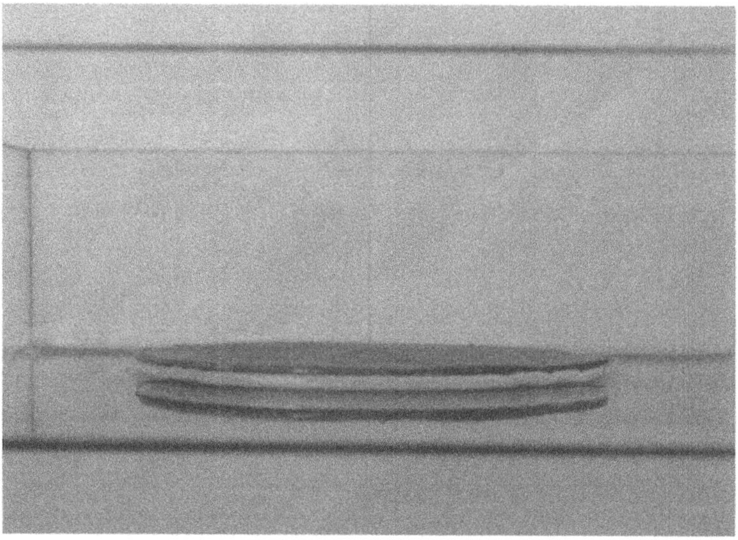

Fig. 2.25 Circular lead plate.

Experiment with the circular lead plate

We wish to check whether the adhesion depends on the substance interacting with the water. The circular disc 1 mm thick is simply suspended from a thread which passes through a small central hole. The mass of the disc in air is 0.11942 g; when it is in contact with the water the scale can be loaded up to 0.15800 kg. The mass of water that adheres to the disc at the moment of separation is 0.03858 kg and its thickness is 4.06 mm (fig. 2.25).

In this experiment both the forces of adhesion between water and metal, which drag the first layer of water, and the forces of cohesion, which keep the molecules of water together, come into play. If we divide the weight of the lifted water by the area of the brass and lead discs, we obtain an estimate of the forces of cohesion in N/m^{-2}, which for the brass disc is about 0.417 N/m^2 and for the lead one about 0.398 N/m^2.

Since I have already abandoned any chronological criterion by introducing *Le Galleggianti*, I shall not hesitate to travel even further ahead in time to *Il Saggiatore* (the Assayer)[172] of 1623 where, in Ch. XXXIX, Galileo is forced by his adversary to discuss yet again the adherence of water to rigid bodies. The Jesuit Orazio Grassi had asked him a question[173]:

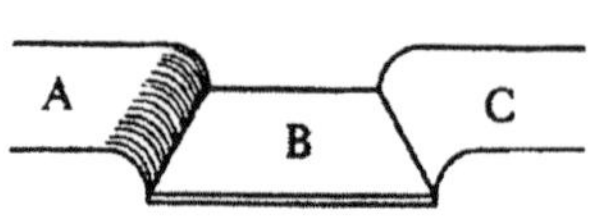

[172] G.G.. Vol. VI, *Il Saggiatore nel quale con bilancia esquisita e giusta si ponderano le cose contenute nella libra astronomica e filosofica di Lotario Sarsi Sigensano...*, pp. 322-324.

[173] G.G.. Vol. VI, *Libra astronomica ac philosophica...*, p. 155.

> I deny that air does not adhere to smooth bodies. A sheet of glass *B*, although it is very smooth, having been placed in water will float no less if it were another, rougher material, and the air adhering to it will by its force restrain the water *AC* from raising itself around the glass lest it flow over and sink the sheet. Why therefore, does not the air depart when pressed by the weight of the water which has been depressed by the glass sheet, but rather clings fast to it and does not yield its place unless driven away by a greater force?

Galileo comments:

> Sarsi continues with this fantasy of his, still pretending that I have said that the air does not adhere to smooth and polished bodies, a thing which is not to be found written either by Sig. Mario or myself. Besides, I do not quite understand what sort of thing he means by this 'adherence'. If he means a coupling which completely resists separation and parting between the surfaces so that they no longer touch, I say that such 'adherence' exists and is very great. The surface of water, for instance, may be detached only by immense force from that of a plate of copper or other material, and in this case does not matter whether the latter surface is polished and smooth or not; a close contact suffices. And this holds bodies united so firmly that perhaps the particles of solid and hard bodies have no other cement than this to attach them together. But this 'adherence' is of no use to Sarsi. Now if he means a conjunction such that the two bodies (I mean that of the solid and of the liquid) cannot move upon each other even by slipping – which would fit in with his requirement – then I say that there is no such 'adherence' not only between a solid and a liquid, but not even between two solids. Thus we see that in two slabs of marble which are quite level and smooth, the first 'adherence' is such that if when [*sic*] lift up one slab the other follows, while the second 'adherence' is so weak that, if the surfaces in contact are not perfectly horizontal but are tilted even a hair's breadth, the lower slab will immediately slip away in the direction of the tilt.
>
> To sum up, the moving of the one surface upon the other will meet no resistance, however great may be the resistance to an attempt to detach and separate them.

Galileo puts forward here the hypothesis that adhesion is the force that holds the parts (atoms or molecules) of solid and hard bodies together and repeats his theory of how the *little ridges* are formed:

> As for the glass plate which stays afloat between the little ridges of water, I say that these ridges not sustain themselves because of the adherence of the air to the plate preventing the water from running over the plate; if this were so, the same thing ought to happen if one placed in the water a similar plate somewhat moistened, for it is incredible that the air would adhere less to a wet surface than to a dry one. Yet we see that when the plate is wet no ridges form, and the water runs swiftly over it. The maintenance of the ridges, therefore, has some other cause than the adherence of air to the surface of the plate. And quite frequently we see large particles of water sustain themselves in convex shape and in relief very much higher than the little ridges which surround the floating plate; for instance, upon the leaves of cabbages.

We certainly cannot expect Galileo to have clear ideas on subjects such as surface tension, forces of cohesion, forces of adhesion, ecc.; but even so, his experiments and analysis are an excellent example of scientific investigation. The heavy emphasis on the phenomenon of «*wettability*», a term still used today to indicate the combination of these effects, once again reveals his great capacity for observation and his extraordinary intuition[174].

> All shapes therefore, of whatever size, shall sink or not, according to whether their tops are wetted or not.

Some will certainly find my reconstruction implausible and say that everything that Galileo wrote in *Le Galleggianti* was discovered by him by some remarkable creative activity in 1611, others will say that all of this is the outcome of a long and continuous work of research begun in Pisa and continued in Padua, but I am convinced that for five or six years, before he went to Padua, Galileo measured the densities of many materials with extreme precision, that he found a reliable way of measuring small fractions of time, probably with a pendulum, that he carried out research on motion in water using minimally weighted wax, that he became aware of the capacity bodies have of floating when their density is barely greater than the density of water and that he finally developed a research method which became the highway he followed for all his future discoveries.

2.8 *Violent motion (non uniform velocity)*

We have seen that Galileo succeeded in giving both a theoretical and experimental consistency to the Aristotelian design of natural motion, studied above all in water where bodies reach a constant velocity more easily. The theory of motion that he had inherited was already fairly developed structurally, compared to Aristotle's original theory, but in the *De motu* Galileo managed to bring it to the greatest point of perfection possible, accepting the existence of vacuum and further examining the different roles played by *gravitas* and *vis* in generating and composing the two Aristotelian kinds of motion – natural motion and violent motion[175]:

a) *gravitas* is the cause of natural motion; it is the intrinsic principle that makes all material bodies move towards the centre of the world, with a velocity that is independent of the dimensions of the body, and which only depends on its density and the density of the medium it moves in and its shape, because both the *gravitas* of the medium[176] and the resistance that the medium opposes to penetration must be subtracted from the *gravitas* of the body;

---

[174] G.G., Vol. IV, *Discorso intorno alle cose che stanno in su l'acqua* ..., p. 120.

[175] G.G., Vol. I, *De motu*, pp. 318-319.

[176] See G.G., Vol. I, *De motu*, p. 295: «Since in every medium the heaviness of heavy bodies [*gravitates gravium*] diminishes by as much as that part of that medium equal to the volume of the solid weighs [*ponderaret*], it is clear that we find the heavinesses of solids whole and not diminished in the only medium in which the heaviness is null: but only vacuum is such ... only in vacuum can we have the true heaviness of heavy bodies».

b) *external force* is the cause of violent motion, both when it acts by contact with the body and later because it leaves in the mobile a residual effect which continuously diminishes with the passage of time and that is traditionally called by the name *impressed force* (*virtus impressa*). The accelerated or decelerated motion is the result of the combined effect of the *gravitas* and the *impressed force*.

We can see when a body is no longer affected by the direct action of an external force and has exhausted the impressed force it initially contained because, in this case, it moves towards the centre of the world (the Earth) with a velocity which is constant and independent of its size. Indeed for Galileo all bodies were composed of a single material made up of particles which provident nature (he also wrote *divinus Opifex* and *Summa Providentia* as well) then distributed in the four elements[177]:

> Indeed, since, as it has pleased more ancient philosophers to assert, there is but one matter of all bodies, and those bodies are heavier that contain a greater number of particles of this matter in a narrower space – as these same philosophers, who were perhaps unjustly refuted by Aristotle in book IV of his *De Caelo*, [308b-309b] asserted – assuredly it was in accordance with reason that bodies that enclosed more matter in a narrower place, should also occupy narrower places, such as are those that come nearer the centre.
> [...] I would not say, however, that the quantity of the matter of water is as great as that of the matter of earth, and that for this reason water, since it is rarer than earth, occupies greater places; but only that, if we take a part of water which weighs the same as a part of earth, and for this reason there is as much aqueous matter as earth [under consideration], assuredly this part of earth will then occupy a smaller place than the water, for which reason, justly, it will have to be placed in a narrower space, that is nearer the centre.

We see therefore that Galileo's atomism has its roots in the studies he carried out while teaching at Pisa. Bodies have different *gravitas* when they enclose in the same volume a different number of elementary particles, contained in the fundamental elements – earth, water, air and fire – present in varying proportions in the substances the bodies are made of.

Galileo did not give a precise quantification of the *gravitas* of a body, he did not indicate a unit of measure for it, he only supposed that it was proportional to the number of particles per unit of volume. Then to be able to define the *gravitas* of a body operatively he resorted to absolute density, understood as the weight per unit of volume; theoretically an absolute measure of the *gravitas* would be obtained if it were possible to measure the uniform velocity that the body reaches in vacuum. This essential and abstract vision would prove fundamental for all his future discoveries.

---

[177] G.G., Vol. I, *De motu*, pp. 252-253. See too on p. 343: «And since the matter of all bodies is all one, certainly those heavy bodies that enclose a greater number of particles of that matter in a narrower space are heavier», and later on p. 345: « and from the countless particles of that more or less rarefied [*matter*] [nature] formed those four bodies that we call elements ... But of those that are formed as bodies from this matter those that, within the same volume, amass a greater number of particles of that matter are called denser; the denser ones then became the heavier ones».

For a body not to move it is necessary for an external force to act on it neutralising[178] the *gravitas* of the body. The external force that keeps the body exactly still, in the simplest case, is directed vertically in the opposite direction from the *gravitas*.

It may be useful to give some examples to illustrate the action of an external force on a body.

Let us consider a sphere lying stationary on the pan of a scale in equilibrium: the pan is applying to the sphere an external force directed upwards; this particular force, when the scale is in equilibrium, is called weight [*pondus*] of the sphere. If the sphere is suspended from a thread and it is stationary, the thread acts on it with a force which is exactly equal to its weight and similarly directed upwards.

According to what Galileo claimed in the *De motu*, weight does not exist in objects but is the result of an interaction when something outside is opposed to the *gravitas* and to the motion that it generates.

Just as today in ordinary speech it is usual to say *weight* even when the word *mass* should be used, so Galileo often used *gravitas* (heaviness) instead of *pondus* (weight), but this does not create too much confusion and it should be noted that heaviness is never expressed with units of weight (pounds, deniers, *grani* etc.). Galileo often felt the need to distinguish *gravitas* from *pondus* and to stress the static and virtual aspect of the latter, which is always associated with the force of reaction[179]:

> a) Now, we are said to be weighed down when a certain weight, which tends downward by its heaviness, rests upon us, and we must resist with our force so that it does not go down any further; it is this resisting that we call being weighed down.
>
> b) The definition of the heavy and the light through motion handed down by tradition is not a good one: for when a heavy or light thing is being moved, it is neither heavy nor light. For that thing is heavy which exerts weight on something; but what exerts weight on something else is resisted by that thing; hence a heavy thing, when it exerts weight, is not moved: as is evident if you have a stone in hand, which then will exert weight when the hand resists its heaviness; but if it is moved downward with the stone, the stone will not then exert weight on the hand. Hence the definition will better be: That thing is heavier which remains under things that are lighter. For if we should say, heavy is what remains downward, and light what remains upward, we would not be defining well, since upward and downward are not distinguished in fact, but only in logic.

In the example I have just given of the sphere hanging from a thread, if I cut the thread the external force stops acting on the sphere but its effect does not disappear immediately. The *gravitas*, which had been neutralised by the external force, does not immediately become active when the external force vanishes but takes a certain time to recover its strength completely: the effect of the external force is said to remain in the sphere for a certain time, and it is this lingering effect which has been given the name *impressed force*.

---

[178] See: G.G., Vol. I, *De motu*, pp. 309-311;

[179] G.G., Vol. I, *De motu*, a) p. 388, b) p. 413.

When the falling motion starts from stationary, from the precise moment when I cut the thread that is holding the sphere, a perfect synchronism occurs between the process of reactivating the *gravitas* and the process of deactivating the *impressed force*, and this process determines the transitional period in which the motion is accelerated[180].

> [...] And there is nothing astonishing in the fact that the stone, as it moves [*upwards*], is light: indeed, it is not possible to attribute any difference between the stone which finds itself with that motion in progression and any other light thing; for we say that something that moves upwards is light, but the stone moves upwards so the stone is light while it moves upwards.
> [...] And there is no reason for us to be astonished that, the stone as long as it is moved, is light: for between a stone in that act of motion and any other light thing, it will not be possible to assign any difference; for since we call light that which is carried upward, and the stone is carried upward, therefore the stone is light as long as it is carried upward.
> [...] Now I would say that that is naturally light which is carried upward naturally; but also that that is light contrary to nature or by accident or by force, which is carried upward contrary to nature, by accident, and by force. But such is the stone impelled by force: and in the stone its own innate and intrinsic heaviness is lost in the same manner as it is also lost when it is placed in media heavier than itself. For a stone which floats on mercury, for example, and does not go down in it, loses all its own heaviness;
> [...] and wood also becomes so light in water, that it cannot be kept down unless by force. And yet neither the stone nor the wood lose their own natural heaviness, but, taken out of those heavier media, they resume their proper heaviness: in the same way a projectile, freed from the force projecting it, displays, by going down, its own real, intrinsic heaviness.

It is only possible to understand what impressed force is if one knows what heaviness is[181]:

> And thus it must be concluded that the mobile, when it is moved by a motion against nature, is moved by a force impressed by a motor: but what that force is is hidden from us.

Natural motion is the motion caused by *gravitas* alone; instead, as long as there is an impressed force within a body that varies over time, then the motion is preternatural. Since the motion observed always occurred in a medium, because it was not possible to carry out experiments in a vacuum, Galileo considered the motion natural even when it did not occur in vacuum, if the body moved downwards according to the vertical and its velocity was constant. This happens, to use modern terminology, when the flow of *outgoing* impressed force is exactly compensated for by the flow of *incoming* impressed force due to the resistance of the medium, so that the effective *gravitas* is constant. This stable situation is always arrived at if the body has enough space available to travel through in its descent, because the medium opposes a growing resistance to the growing velocity of the mobile until equilibrium is established; in this process, obviously, the specific weight and the shape of the body are important and make the differences.

---

[180] G.G., Vol. I, *De motu*, pp. 311-312.

[181] G.G., Vol. I, *De motu*, p. 374.

When a body suspended from a scale is immersed in water it is necessary, in order to maintain equilibrium, to remove from the other pan of the scales a weight equal to the weight of the water that has the volume of the body. This means that the medium acts continuously on the body as a constant force which opposes the *gravitas* and partly neutralises it. When we turn to motion, obviously, we need to add to this resistance the resistance that the medium opposes to the motion, which depends on the velocity, the density of the medium and the shape of the body.

Galileo did not know how to explain what impressed force is and why it conserves the final direction of the external force that generates it, nor even why it is temporary, much less how it depends on the time over which it diminishes, although he believed that it is expended more quickly in substances with lower specific weight like wood, and more slowly in those with greater specific weight such as iron or lead.

His ideas on acceleration are illustrated by an experiment he thought up[182] to explain how it could be possible for the lighter body to precede the heavier one at the beginning of the motion; let us see what it consists of[183]:

> Let there be two mobiles, equal in size; but let one be of wood, the other of lead: and let the heaviness[184] of the lead be **20**, but of the wood **4**; and let them be held up by line *ab*.

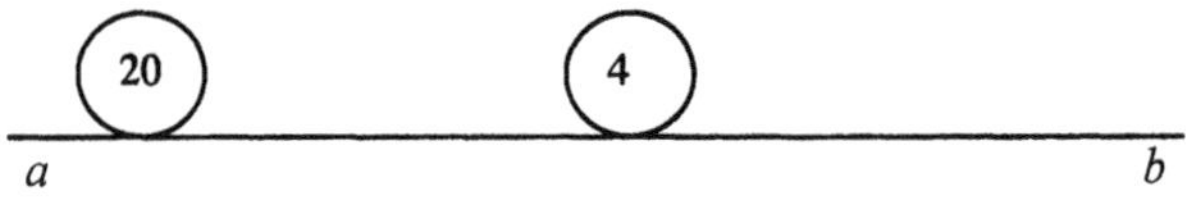

> Firstly then, it is evident that the mobiles themselves press downwards with as much force as the line *ab* pushes upwards[185]. [...] Now when they are abandoned by the line, at their first point of receding they still retain the contrary impressed quality impelling upward, which does not weaken in an instant but progressively; the lead has **20** units of the contrary quality to consume, and the wood **4**. If these qualities weakened equally in each of them, so that, when **1** unit of lead receded, in the wood **1** unit also went away, and, consequently, they had recovered one unit of heaviness, both, indisputably, would be moved with the same speed: but, since in the time during which one unit of the quality has receded from the lead, more

---

182 Galileo claims to have made an experiment dropping two globes of equal volume, but one double the weight of the other, from the top of a tower and to have seen that at the beginning of the motion the lighter one precedes the heavier one and for a certain distance travels faster, even if in the end the roles are reversed. (See G.G., Vol. I, p. 267 in note). The experiment was discussed by T. B. Settle and justified by the difficulty of letting go the heavier weight, which leads to the departure of the lesser weight being earlier than the other. See his article: *Galileo and Early Experimentation*, in *Springs of Scientific Creativity* (R. Aris, H.T. Davis & R.H. Stuewer editors) Minneapolis, 1983, pp. 3-20.

183 G.G., Vol. I, *De motu*, pp. 336-337.

184 The density of lead is ρ_{Pb} = 11.34 g cm^{-3} while the density of wood varies from $\rho_{ord.\ wood}$ = 0.74 g cm^{-3} for ordinary wood to ρ_{Ebony} = 1.26 g cm^{-3} for ebony. Therefore the numbers are given rather at random unless we presume that the wood is weighted by nails or something else.

185 Here we can see an application of the principle of contact action and reaction.

than one has departed from the wood, and, therefore, when the lead has recovered only one unit of heaviness, the wood has acquired more than one, it results from this that the wood is then moved faster; and, again, since when 2 units of the quality had receded from the wood, in the lead less than 2 had gone away, it is because of this that the lead is then moved more slowly. But, because in the end the lead acquires more heaviness than the wood, it follows that the lead is then carried much faster.

We have seen that for Galileo bodies that are equal to each other in shape, but are of different density, which move in a resistant medium, after a phase of accelerated motion reach a constant limit velocity of a value which depends on the specific weights of the two bodies and of the medium. Galileo claimed that in the end the limit velocity reached by lead is greater than that of wood, but he did not say that he had verified this by experiment, he only said that he had verified that at the beginning the wood preceded the lead and on this occasion added a series of significant considerations, as can be seen from the following passages[186]:

> Yet experience shows the contrary: for it is true that wood at the beginning of its motion is carried more speedily than lead; but a little later the motion of lead is so accelerated that it leaves the wood behind, and, if they are released from a high tower, the lead gets ahead of it by a large distance: and I have often put this to the test[187].
> [...] but if heavier ones must consume more force impelling them in the contrary direction, it will surely be necessary that heavier mobiles are moved more slowly, since they undergo a greater resistance. And if, on the other hand, these things are true, it follows that heavier things, after they have consumed so much of the contrary resistance that they are no longer hindered by as much as lighter things are, must go down more speedily: which, again, experience surely shows.
> [...] it must be noted that the contrary quality in a mobile is not weakened because it is assailed by the heaviness of the mobile; for the heaviness cannot accomplish this, since in a mobile filled with the contrary quality it is entirely nullified; but it is by itself that that quality is weakened and leaves the mobile.
> [...] it must be noted that the contrary quality recedes more easily and the more swiftly, the lighter the mobile in which it has been impressed: this can be confirmed by many examples.

I have already referred to the experiment with wooden and lead pendulums in the first paragraph of this chapter, in order to present isochronicity: in this experiment we see that the wooden pendulum stops first, and the only possible explanation is that the impressed force is expended first.

In the last chapter of the *Trattato*, Galileo considered the case of an external force that acts upwards but in an oblique direction, distinguishing two cases:

a) if the motion [upward] occurs on an inclined plane; then the smaller the angle with the

[186] G.G., Vol. I, *De motu*, pp. 334-335.

[187] This is not the only time that Galileo claimed to have done the experiment of a fall from a high tower, even if he never indicated that it was the Leaning Tower of Pisa, as tradition would have it.

horizon the further away the mobile moves «because part of its heaviness is supported by the plane and thus it happens that it can be moved more easily by the driving force»;

b) if the motion [upward] occurs in air, then the mobile is supported and pushed only by the impressed force and the mobile certainly travels further if the line of the motion forms a less acute angle with the horizon.

Galileo justified this distinction with observations on what happens with war machines and bombards because he believed that it is possible to cram in a greater quantity of impressed force when at the moment a projectile is launched the force must overcome a greater resistance.

It took Galileo more than ten years to abandon this explanation of motion which resorts to internal and external causes and to become convinced that it is important to describe the process quantitatively, but without seeking the cause. Galileo tackled all situations: motion in water, where the limit velocity is swiftly reached, motion in air where the limit velocity can hardly be reached, bodies with the same specific weight but different volume and bodies with equal volume but different specific weight and he tried to reduce them all to a single theory; but in the end he did understand that he had to experiment in a medium in which there would be the least influence of the various *accidental factors*: resistance, viscosity, buoyancy, shape and weight and everything else that complicated the theory, and so Galileo would restrict his studies to motion in air.

It is a fact that the young Galileo was fascinated by the theory of impressed force, which opened up a wide field of theoretical and experimental research for him, because when he studied motion he always found himself in the situation of having a mobile full of impressed force, and he dedicated the rest of the *De motu* to the study of *violent* motion. Anyone wishing to discover Galileo's theory on violent motion in his own words will find the passages that I found most interesting in appendix B.

The most favourable situation is when there is the least impressed force; which is why it is preferable for the motion to take place in air rather than water, where the resistance grows with the velocity, and he decided to use the inclined plane on which much of the *gravitas* is cancelled out and the process is slower. The first step he had to take was to measure the impressed force necessary to completely cancel out the heaviness, and so he found the sine law using scales, the most precise instrument available to a scientist at the end of the XVI century.

2.9 *The fundamental theorem of the inclined plane*

What happens when a sphere is placed on an inclined plane? To start with, it should be explained that if *gravitas* is defined as a downward propensity, it is however a quantity that has no direction, unlike external force; therefore when the motion of a body is limited by a constraint then the *gravitas* which has remained free is always tangent to that constraint.

The plane acts exactly as when the sphere is laid on the pan of a scale in equilibrium but now the external force due to the plane, although acting constantly on the sphere, cancels out (constantly) only a part of the *gravitas*, because its direction, perpendicular to the plane, cannot completely counterbalance the *gravitas* in its tendency to descend. To hold the sphere still on the inclined plane another external force is needed and the smallest of all possible forces is the force directed parallel to the plane.

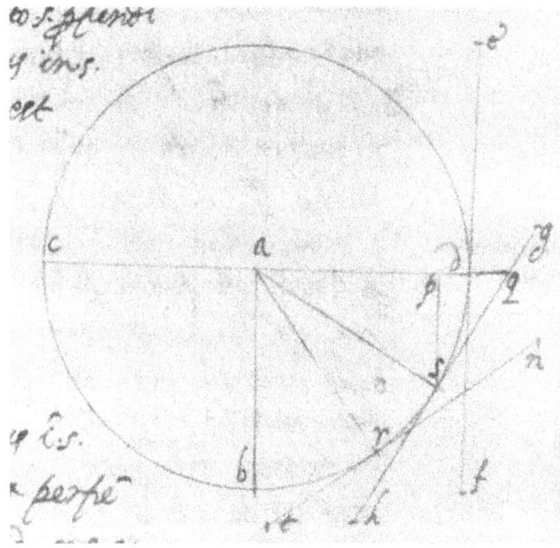

Fig. 2.26 Ms. Gal. 71, Folio 95v.

This additional external force cancels out the remaining part of the *gravitas* which has remained free, and when it is removed, it leaves an *impressed force* in the sphere which immediately begins to decrease: so a process is established in which the fraction of the *gravitas* which is not counterbalanced by the plane becomes progressively active. The fundamental problem of the inclined plane is determining how the fraction of *gravitas* which is not cancelled out by the inclined plane changes with the angle of inclination, and finding the relationship between the velocity with which the sphere descends the plane and the velocity in free fall when the *gravitas* acts at its strongest.

In the «*Chapter*[188] *... in which the proportions of the motions of a same mobile on several inclined planes are discussed*» Galileo demonstrated that the force required to hold still a body placed on an inclined plane is proportional to its weight as the height of the plane is to its length[189]. For this he used the theory of scales. In fig. 2.26, which is the original figure in the manuscript[190], the segment *cad* represents an ideal scale, with extremes *c* and *d* that travel along a circumference when the scale rotates around the centre *a* (therefore he makes an abstraction of its shape and mass). If a weight *W* is placed in *d* an equal weight *W* must be placed in *c* for the scale to be in equilibrium.

Galileo asks us to imagine that only the arm *ad* rotates around the centre *a* assuming in succession the positions *as*, *ar* and *ab*. The weight *W* in *s* is as if it were hanging from the thread *ps*, and so for equilibrium it is now necessary to place in *c* a lesser weight, equal to $W' = (ap/ac)$ W. If the weight that keeps *W* in equilibrium is removed from *c* it is necessary to apply to the

[188] G.G., Vol. I, *De motu*, unnumbered chapter but 14th in order of succession, pp. 296-302.

[189] Galileo never writes that the force is proportional to the sine of the angle of inclination.

[190] In the manuscript there are two very similar figures, the first one (the only one reproduced by Favaro in the first volume of the national edition) lacks the line prolonging the arm of the scales from point *d* to point *q* and this may give rise to some perplexity for the reader.

weight attached to the arm *as* of the scale a force equal to $(ap/ac)W$ in a perpendicular direction to the arm *as*. Galileo now introduces a plane tangent to the circumference in *s*, represented by the straight line *gh* and observes that the force necessary to hold the weight *W* stationary on the inclined plane tangent in *s* is precisely $(ap/ac)W$. He explains thus[191]:

> [...] when the mobile will be at point *s*, its descent at the initial point *s* will be as if on line *gh*; that is why the motion of the mobile on line *gh* will be according to the heaviness the mobile has at point *s*.

The conclusion is[192]:

> [...] the same weight is pulled by force with a smaller force upward along an inclined ascent than along a right one, by as much as the right ascent is smaller than the oblique.

The «fundamental theorem of the inclined plane» is the answer to a question that Galileo asked at the beginning of the chapter[193]:

> For what is asked is why the same heavy mobile, in descending naturally along planes inclined to the plane of the horizon, is moved more easily and more swiftly on those that will maintain angles nearer a right angle with the horizon; and, furthermore, the ratio of such motions made on diverse inclinations is sought.

With the clarification «that it descends in natural motion» Galileo returned to his studies of motion in water in the framework of Aristotelian theory. The question presupposes ideal, completely smooth and perfectly hard planes and a perfectly round body which moves on the planes without any resistance; those things that are called *accidental* are also made abstract; moreover, through reasoning and, perhaps, through experimentation in water[194], Galileo knew that, as in vertical fall, on the inclined plane too the motion is not altered if the weight of the body is changed without changing the material it is made of, at least as long as it moves in the same medium.

The theory of proportions, recalled too in the title of the chapter, is essential in this demonstration as in other demonstrations by Galileo, because it requires relationships between homogeneous quantities and this allows Galileo, as we shall see, to eliminate the weight of the body, a quantity with dynamic consequences that he is unable to deal with. It is said that Galileo's

---

[191] G.G., Vol. I, *De motu*, p. 297: «*quando mobile erit in puncto* s, *in primo puncto* s *suus descensus erit veluti per lineam* gh; *quare mobilis per lineam* gh *motus erit secundum gravitatem quam habet mobile in puncto* s».

[192] G.G., Vol. I, *De motu*, p. 297: «*tanto maiori vi descendere idem grave per rectum descensum quam per inclinatum, quanto maior est inclinatus descensus quam rectus*».

[193] G.G., Vol. I, *De motu*, p. 296: «*Queritur enim cur idem mobile grave, naturaliter descendens per plana ad planum horizontis inclinata, in illis facilius et celerius movetur quae cum horizonte angulos recto propinquiores continebunt; et, insuper, petitur proportio talium motuum in diversis inclinationibus factorum*».

[194] Only if he carried out experiments on an inclined plane without grooves.

acceptance of the theory of proportions was an obstacle to a more advanced formulation of the theory of motion; nothing could be farther from the truth: actually this choice facilitated matters considerably, in fact it was a real necessity.

Galileo wanted to explain why, on an inclined plane, the motion of a body becomes that much faster the closer it is to motion in free fall, *i.e.* when it is least inclined; to do this he proceeded in the demonstration following Aristotle, who treated velocity not as a property of the motion of a body compared to a reference system, as would become usual after Galileo, but as the relationship between the motion of two bodies. Aristotle introduced two definitions to compare the motions of two bodies[195]:

1) a body is swifter than another when it travels the same space in less time;
2) a body is swifter than another when it travels a greater space in the same time.

Just an observation: there is nothing inaccurate in Aristotle's definitions. They are legitimate and also adequate in the context of the theory of proportions and, in particular, the second definition of velocity is the only one that can be considered when it is not known how motion depends on time and how to measure time: the first definition of "swifter", in fact, involves the measurement of time, while in the second it is necessary that the beginning and the conclusion of the two motions be simultaneous, and also the measurement of the distances, but this is all much less problematic than measuring time, especially when dealing with short distances and short intervals of time. The two definitions of velocity, above all the second one, were the only ones used by all the authors who discussed motion until people began, with Galileo, to know how to divide time with great precision, to study motion quantitatively and to speak of instantaneous velocity.

We have seen that Galileo developed his demonstration of the fundamental theory of the inclined plane without ever introducing the measurement of time and so he made use of the second definition of swifter, even if he does not say so explicitly. To answer the question asked at the beginning of the chapter it is necessary to prove that the relationship s/s_i between two spaces s and s_i, travelled in equal times by two bodies, is less than one when the first body descends freely along the vertical and the other descends on an inclined plane of height H and length L.

The fact that Galileo apparently believed that his demonstration was concluded when he found the force necessary to counterbalance the heaviness and support the body on the inclined plane is significant. This force is proportional to the ratio between the height H and length L of the plane, and since already in Galileo's time the ratio between the cathetus and the hypotenuse was called sine and was tabulated[196] from now on I shall write, indifferently, H/L or $\sin \alpha$, where α is the angle of inclination.

---

[195] *The Works of Aristotle*, translated into English under the editorship of W.D. Ross, Chicago, 1952, p. 314 «... it necessarily follows that the quicker of two things traverses a greater magnitude in an equal time, an equal magnitude in less time, in conformity with the definition sometimes given of "the quicker"».

[196] In the *Opus palatinum de triangulis* by Georg Joachim von Lauchen, nicknamed Rheticus (1514-1576), a disciple of Copernicus, published posthumously in 1596, there are the tables of all the trigonometrical functions. Barthélemy Pitiscus (1561-1613), author of the *Trigonometriae sive, de dimensione triangulis, Liber* (1595), published it again in 1613, correcting the many errors in the previous edition on the basis of the original masnuscript, with the title *Thesaurus mathematicus sive Canon sinuum.*

We saw previously that the fraction of the *gravitas* which moves the sphere on the inclined plane is to the total *gravitas* as the component of the force that holds the sphere still is to its weight. With the determination of the *gravitas* «according to the direction» of the plane *gh* the demonstration is complete because it is manifest – he wrote – that «the mobile will move along the line *gh* according to the *gravitas* that it has [*on it*]». The text actually has the expression *manifestum est*, but it is better to examine the point in more depth.

When Galileo wrote «*gravitas in plano secundum lineam gh*» he meant to indicate the *gravitas* which is available or, if you like, free, not neutralised constantly by the reaction of the plane, the residual *gravitas* that moves the body on the plane in the direction *gh* of the maximum descent.

To study motion on the inclined plane it is sufficient to bear two criteria in mind:

a) at the moment when the sphere is released the reduction in the *impressed force* in it, and the corresponding increase in free *gravitas*, is a process that depends only on time (even if it is not known how it depends on time) and not on the angle of inclination, two equal spheres that descend along planes that are inclined at different angles, α_1 e α_2, maintain a constant proportion between their growing free *gravitas* and their growing velocities, given the relationship $\sin \alpha_1/\sin \alpha_2$;
b) the relationship between the spaces travelled does not depend, obviously, on time when the second definition of *swifter* is used.

It follows that the relationship between two velocities, (which is equal to the relationship between the spaces travelled in the same time), depends only on the fraction of *gravitas* of the two bodies that is not cancelled out by the plane. I remind you again that with scales Galileo showed that, if G is the *gravitas* of a body, the quantity of free *gravitas* contained in a body which is held still by an external force on an inclined plane, defined by its height H and its length L, is $(H/L)G$, and therefore it is proportional to $\sin \alpha_i$, if the angle of inclination is α_i.

For the study of motion it is not necessary to know how G is measured, much less what its value is, because in the relationships between velocities of straight line motions with different inclinations compared to the horizon the value of G disappears and only the values of the sine of the angles remain.

As far as the space travelled is concerned, the linear dependence on $G \sin \alpha$ is suggested by two considerations:

1) that the *gravitas* undergoes a proportional reduction at $\sin \alpha$ as a consequence of the support offered by the plane: the demonstration we have just seen ensures that the free *gravitas* is $G \sin \alpha$ along the whole of the plane;
2) that the same effect of breaking the equilibrium and provoking motion can be obtained, both by increasing or diminishing by an arbitrarily small quantity the force that sustains the body in equilibrium on the inclined plane, and by very slightly changing (up or down) the inclination of the plane: the resulting motion is equal.

The dependence of the process on time is, however, unknown and the difficulty of analysing the transitory phase of the accelerated motion compelled Galileo to avoid experiments that involve different times and to restrict himself to a discussion of theorems and properties of motion that occur in equal times.

I believe that we can recognise in Galileo's thought something that, today, we would summarise with the formula: $s(t) = G \sin \alpha \, \Psi(t)$; and we know that the unknown dependence on time, enclosed in the symbol $\Psi(t)$, will be the main object of his research. Within ten years he

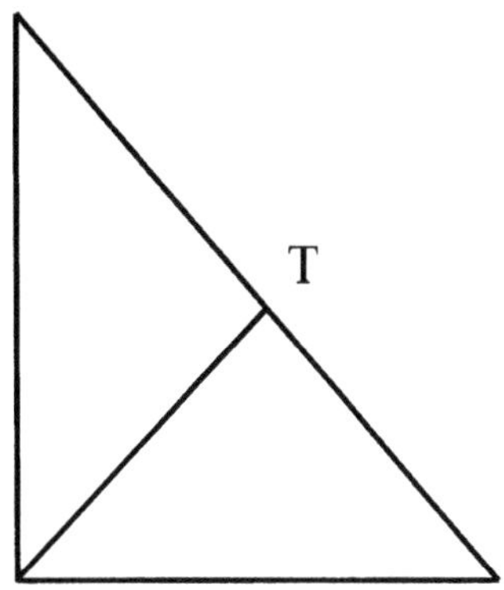

Fig. 2.27

would succeed in discovering the law of motion, determining $\Psi(t)$ as the square of time, and he would even give it a measurement: he would write that *a body, which falls departing from stillness, travels 100 braccia in five seconds.*

With his "fundamental theorem of the inclined plane" Galileo was finally able to determine how much faster the motion along the vertical is, compared to motion on the plane which is inclined by an angle α_i, knowing that its height is H and its length is L_1, like the relationship between the spaces s (along the vertical) and s_i (on the inclined plane) travelled in the same time:

$$v/v_i = s/s_i = G/G \sin \alpha_i = L_1/H$$

Sometimes, skipping the essential intermediate passage, we find it written that, for Galileo, the relationship between the velocities of the two bodies was $v/v_i = L_1/H$ and in this way Galileo is totally brought back to Aristotle, for whom natural motion is essentially a uniform motion, underestimating the role played in the dynamics of the *De motu* by Aristotelian velocity in the description of the initial phase of the motion during which the velocity is not uniform.

Instead the result of the "fundamental theorem" is of extraordinary importance for the history of science for the reason that we shall now illustrate.

Observe that, when $s = H$, the relationship $s/s_i = L_1/H$ can be written $s_i : H = H : L_1$.

This relationship has an instant graphical representation in the triangles ABC and CTB in fig. 2.27. The two triangles have two sides proportional, for the first one the height $CB = H$ and the hypotenuse $CA = L_1$, for the second one the sides $CT = s_i$ and $CB = H$; moreover, they have the contained angle in common: therefore they are similar triangles. The triangle ABC has a right angle in B, so in the other triangle the angle in T is a right angle.

From here follows the rule to find the distance $s_i = CT$ along the inclined plane CA travelled in the same time as the fall along $s = CB$. The distance travelled is obtained by drawing from point B, where s ends, the perpendicular to the inclined plane CA. The breadth that Aristotle gave to the comparison between the velocities of two mobiles, introducing a definition that does not depend on time, the Aristotelian concept of *gravitas* as a universal propensity towards the centre, and the mechanism of *impressed force*, all together, led to the discovery of this rule that we can read in the *Dialogo* and in the *Discorsi*.

Galileo in fact, while still in Pisa, as early as awesome three years 1589-1592, arrived at this and other extraordinary results that he would only make known some forty or more years later . Here is how he described the rule of average velocities between *vertical fall and descent along the inclined plane* in the *Dialogo sopra i due massimi sistemi*[197]:

> In the time that one body fall all the distance *CB*, the other descends along *CA* only to the point *T*, upon which falls the perpendicular drawn from the point *B*. [...] From this you see how it is true that the motion along *CB* is swifter than that along the incline *CA*, (taking *C* for the beginning of the motions compared); for the line *CB* is longer that *CT*.

Salviati – it is him speaking – had said by way of introduction: «expect science another time, namely when you see the things demonstrated by our Academic on local motions». In the Leiden edition of the *Discorsi* however the demonstration is not there. It returns in the addition that Galileo, who had now become blind, dictated to Vincenzo Viviani at the end of 1639; Viviani immediately transcribed it into dialogue form and inserted it[198] in the first edition of the *Opere di Galileo Galilei* (Bologna, 1655).

2.10 *Some problems regarding motion on the inclined plane*

We are arriving at the end of chapter 14 of the *De motu*: before concluding Galileo presented some problems; in reality the first one serves to complete the demonstration of the fundamental theorem establishing with what velocity two inclined planes which have the same height and different length are traversed.

At Padua, some years later, when Galileo would arrive at the concept of instantaneous velocity and would discover the way to measure it, he would ask himself a question which is the most significant one since it does not depend on the Aristotelian definition of velocity: *what is the final velocity* when the height is the same? And the answer would be: *all bodies reach the same final velocity*. It is one of the fundamental principles for his whole theory of motion, made known much later in the *Dialogo*[199]. This is a principle that he would carry with him for almost fifty years and that only in the last years of his life, when already blind, he would succeed in transforming into a theorem deducible from more general principles.

---

[197] G.G., Vol. VII, *Dialogo*, p. 50.

[198] G.G., Vol. VIII, *Discorsi*. The original text dictated by Galileo is on p. 445 while the dialogue version, in which Viviani intervened, is on p. 218.

[199] G.G., Vol. VII, p. 47.

Here I give the complete text of the problem and its demonstration[200]:

From the things that have been demonstrated, it will be easy to obtain the solution of certain problems such as the following: First: given two inclined planes, whose right descent is the same, to find the ratio of the swiftnesses of the same mobile on them.

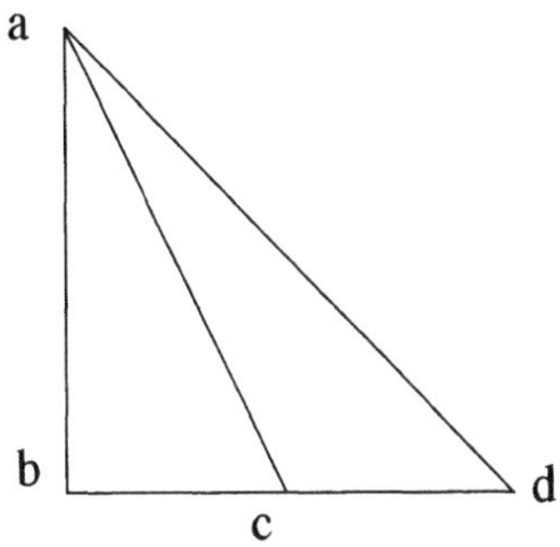

For let the right descent be *ab*, and the plane of the horizon *bd*, and let *ac*, *ad* be the oblique descents: it is now asked, what ratio the swiftness on *ca* has to the swiftness on *ad*. And, since the slowness on *ad*, is to the slowness on *ab* as the line *da* is to the line *ab*, as was shown above ; and just as line *ab* is to line *ac*, so the slowness on *ab* is to the slowness on *ac*; it will follow, *ex aequali*, that just as the slowness on *ad* is to the slowness on *ac*, so line *da* is to line *ac*: hence as the swiftness on *ac* is to the swiftness on *ad*, so line *da* is to line *ac*. It is therefore certain that, the swiftnesses of the same mobile on different inclines are to each other inversely as the lengths of the oblique descents, provided that these hold equal right descents.

Here too, if it is read superficially, we can get the impression that the young Galileo was showing egregious indifference to the reality of accelerated motion and that he failed to escape from the Peripatetic constraints of constant velocity proportional to the force, but once again we have to remember that he only wanted to determine the spaces travelled in the same time over the two planes. We apply the construction indicated in fig. 2.27 to the two inclined planes and we arrive at fig. 2.28 after having performed the following steps:

1) *AB*, *AE*, *AF* are the spaces travelled in the same time along the vertical and along the inclined planes, points *E* and *F* having been identified by the perpendiculars to the two planes;
2) from the figure we immediately see that when *BE* is perpendicular to *AD* and *BF* is perpendicular to *AC*, then *A*, *B*, *E* and *F* are found on a single circumference;
3) from the figure we also see that $AE/AF = AC/AD$. The paths so determined, and therefore the velocities, are in inverse ratio to the path between the lengths of the two planes, as the problem requires.

A more formal way of arriving at the same result follows the Galileian hypothesis of breaking down into products:

[200] G.G., Vol. I, *De motu*, p. 301.

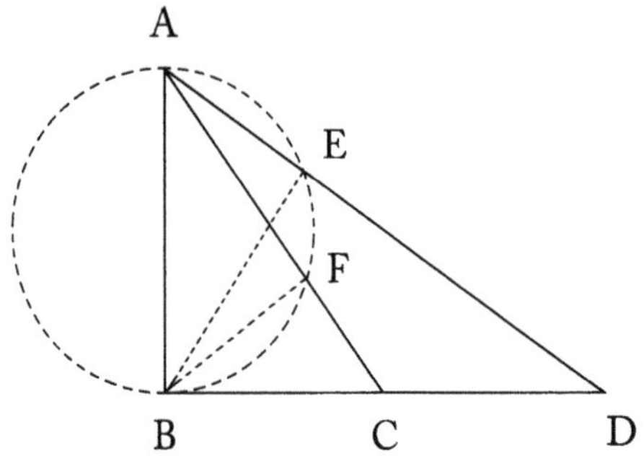

Pag. 2.28

$s_1/s_2 = \sin\alpha_1/\sin\alpha_2$.

If the inclined planes have the same height H the relationship becomes

$s_1/s_2 = L_2/L_1 > 1$.

On the plane which forms the greater angle α_1 with the horizon the Aristotelian velocity is greater and this can be seen immediately in fig. 2.28 where $AF > AE$.

Figure 2.28 is, basically, the geometrical representation of the *theorem of chords*, to prove which it is not necessary to know the law of motion, *i.e.*, how motion depends on time.

In the *Discorsi* Galileo would give no less than three demonstrations of this theorem[201], a unique case in all his writings, a sign of how important it was, and the first person he showed it to was Guidobaldo del Monte in 1602 in the letter that will be studied with greater detail in the 5th chapter. In the *Discorsi* he states the following:

THEOREM VI, PROPOSITION VI

If, from the highest or lowest point of a vertical circle, any inclined plane whatever are drawn to its circumference, the times of descent through these will be equal.

The second problem is presented thus[202]:

> [...], we can find inclined planes on which the same mobile observes a given ratio in its swiftnesses. For let the given ratio be that which line *e* has to *f*; and let *da* to *ac* in the previous figure be made as *e* to *f*: what was asked will then be resolved. Also other similar problems can be resolved: as, being given two mobiles of different genus, equal in size, to set up a plane inclined in such a way that the mobile which in vertical motion was moved faster than the other goes down on this plane at the same speed as

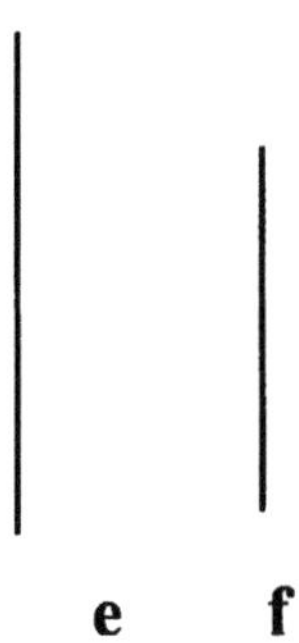

[201] G.G., Vol. VIII, *Discorsi*, pp. 221-223.

[202] G.G, Vol. I, *De motu*, p. 301-302.

that of the other in its vertical motion. But, since these things and others similar can easily be found by those who have understood what was said before, we deliberately do not mention these and similar things.

The second problem can also be easily solved with the theorem of chords: we simply draw a semi-circumference with a diameter greater than the greater velocity, indicated here by **e**, and then trace from the top of the semi circumference two chords with the lengths **e** and **f** of the two velocities. The chords are travelled in the same time and the velocities are therefore proportional to the spaces so determined, over the inclined planes (which have the same height, equal to the diameter of the circumference). The velocity is understood yet again in the Aristotelian sense "of the swiftest". Note that Galileo solved the problem of how to treat the two velocities individually by showing their values as lengths of segments, thus confirming that they are the spaces travelled in the same time over the two inclined planes[203].

It is clear that when he says «we deliberately do not mention these and similar things» Galileo wanted to tell us that he had found other applications of the theorem of the inclined plane (probably the theorem of chords).

The last exercise, proposed but not demonstrated, is very interesting, because he considers the behaviour of two spheres of different material, for example iron and wood, which have different velocities, because at the beginning of the motion the wooden one moves more swiftly. Let *OB* be the vertical path travelled by the wooden sphere and *OA* the path travelled in the same time by the iron sphere. Take a circumference with centre *O'*, with $OO' = O'B = OB/2$ and another circumference with centre *O* and radius *OA* (fig. 2.29). Let *C* be one of the two points at which the two circumferences intersect. The wooden sphere travels in the same time the distance *OC* on the inclined plane on which it lies and the vertical distance *OB* due to the theorem of chords; in its turn *OB* is travelled in the time taken by the iron sphere to travel *OA*. The wooden sphere on the inclined plane and the iron sphere along the vertical travel the same space in the same time and therefore they have the same velocity.

The demonstration of the theory of chords, which Galileo did not treat explicitly in the *De motu*, is jotted down between the pages of Ms. Gal. 72 on a small sheet of paper which dates back to his first years in Padua[204]; it is folio 151r, which seems to me to be one of the oldest of those that deal with the theorem of chords. The text alongside the figure is as follows:

[203] In the *Discorsi* (G.G., Vol. VIII, p. 286) he will say: «... it is necessary to assign some measure for speeds to be commonly understood and accepted by all, that is, one that will be the same for everyone. As explained previously, the Author deemed suitable for such a purpose the speed of a naturally falling heavy body, of which the growing speeds keep the same tenor everywhere in the world. Thus, for example, the speed acquired by a one-pound [*d'una libbra*] lead ball starting from rest and falling from a height of one pikestaff [*picca*] is always and everywhere the same, and for that reason it is very well suited to stand for [*esplicar*] the impetus deriving from natural descent». Note how Galileo takes into account the resistance of air (choosing the spherical shape as standard), the material and the weight of the falling body, while he does not fix the height, which, like the metre preserved at Sèvres, must be a "pikestaff", thus overcoming the myriads of units of measure in use, varying from town to town. He then talks of impetus, because his definition also gives a measurement of the quantities of motion acquired by the body.

[204] Ms. Gal. 72, f. 151r. The note dates from early in his Paduan period. G.G.N.M.: «Little star encircled with crown. Drake's identification: Watermark type 3. Drake's description: Mountains below cartwheel 30 mm; overall height 53 mm».

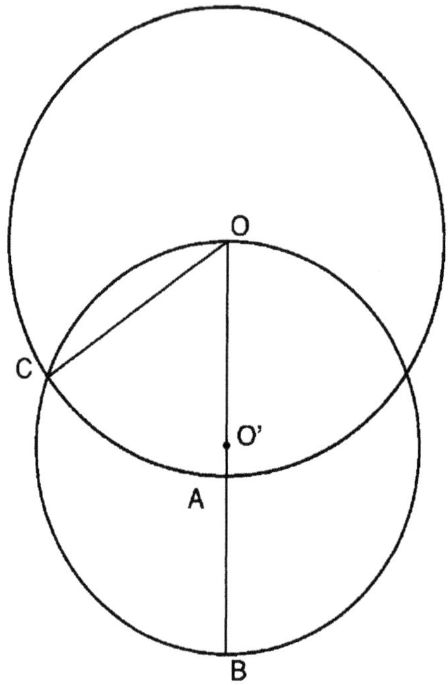

Pag. 2.29

Let *gd* be the vertical line on the horizon, while let *df* instead the inclined line: I say that the motion from *g* to *d* and from *f* to *d* will take place in the same time.
Indeed the momentum on *fd* is equal to that on the tangent in *e*, which is parallel to that same *fd*; so, the momentum over *fd* is to the total momentum as *ca* [*is*] to *ab*, that is to say [*as*] to *ae*. Just as *ca* [*is*] to *ae*, so *id* to *da*, and the double *fd* to the double *dg*; thus the momentum over *fd* is to the total momentum, we mean along *gd*, like *fd* to *gd*: therefore the motion through *fd* and through *gd* will take place in the same time (fig. 2.30).

To understand rather more easily this concise demonstration, which is little more than a few notes, I add that the radius *ae* of the circumference with diameter *gd* intercepts the chord *df* in the midpoint *i* because *e* is the point of tangency on the circumference of a line parallel to *df*. The rectangular triangles *aec* and *dai* are similar because the angle in *e* of the first one is equal to the angle in *a* of the second. So *ca* is to its hypotenuse *ae* as *id* is to its hypotenuse *ad*. The momenta on the diagonal *gd* and on the chord *df* are as their lengths and so the paths travelled grow in proportion to the heaviness and the times are equal.

The momentum[205] Galileo referred to indicates the intensity of the *gravitas* along the plane

[205] In the following chapter we shall see what Galileo meant by momentum in *Le Mecaniche*: «And so momentum is that impetus to go downwards, composed of heaviness, position and other things by which this propensity may be caused». Galileo would later write in the *Discorsi* remembering this old treatise of his (G.G., Vol. VIII, p. 216): «Given the inclined plane *AF*, for example, and taking as its elevation above the horizontal the line *FC*,

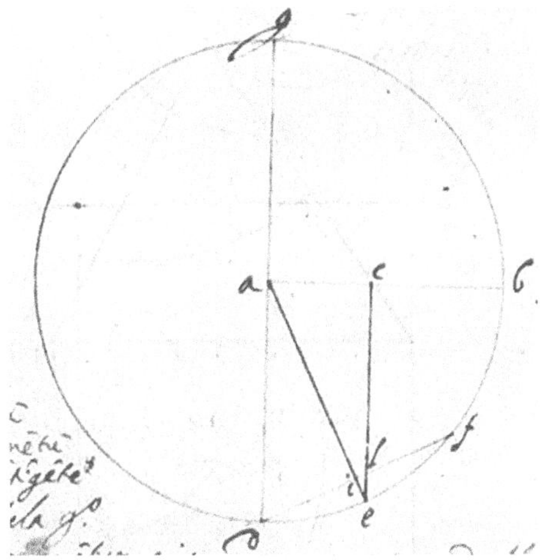

Fig. 2.30 Ms. Gal. 72, Folio 151r.

(*momentum super df*) which remains constant and is proportional to the total *gravitas* (*total momentum*) along the vertical: we saw in the *De motu* that their relationship is the sine of the angle of inclination.

Since they are motions that occur in the same time, the ratio between the velocities is equal to the ratio between the paths travelled, and this is obtained without having to specify how the velocity depends on time, since it is now clear to him that the process of the reduction in the impressed force is a process that does not depend on the angle of inclination:

$$V_{GD}/V_{FD} = GD/FD.$$

Here the velocity is obviously the second of the Aristotelian velocities.
For the use that Galileo made of the first definition of velocity see appendix C.

2.11 *The first ever formulation of the force of inertia*

In the same chapter in which he demonstrated the law of the inclined plane, Galileo also presented what can be called the first ever formulation of the *Principle of inertia*.

It was a necessary observation, with the aim of eliminating an erroneous conviction due to

---

along which the impetus of a heavy body and its momentum in descent is maximum, we seek the ratio that this momentum has to the momentum of the same moveable along the incline *FA*, which ratio, I say, is inverse to that of the said lengths. This is the lemma to be put before the theorem that I hope then to be able to demonstrate. It is manifest that the impetus of descent of a heavy body is as great as the minimum resistance or force that suffices to fix it and hold it [at rest].

the mathematician Pappus, as Galileo would explicitly state in his *Le Mecaniche*[206], even if authoritatively endorsed by Guidobaldo del Monte[207].

> The present speculation was also attempted by Pappus of Alexandria in the 8th book of his *Mathematics Collections*; but, to my mind, he did not reach his purpose, and he was blinded in the assumption he makes where he supposes the weight must be moved in the horizontal plane by a given force: which proves false, any detectable force not being required (having removed accidental impediments, which the theoretician does not consider) to move the given weight in the horizon so that one seeks in vain with which force it is to be moved on the elevated plane.

So here is how he defined the principle, starting from motion on the inclined plane[208]:

> But it must be understood of this demonstration [*of the law of the inclined plane*] that there exists no accidental resistance (roughness either of the mobile or of the inclined plane, or also of the shape of the mobile); but it must be presupposed that the plane is somehow incorporeal, or at least very carefully smoothed and hard, so that, while the mobile exerts weight on the plane, it may not cause the plane to bend, and somehow come to rest on it, as in a trap. It is also necessary that the mobile be perfectly smooth, and of a shape which does not resist motion, like a perfectly spherical shape would be, and, of the hardest material, or else fluid like water. If all these things are thus disposed, any mobile on a plane parallel to the horizon will be moved by a minimal force, indeed by a force smaller than any given force. And this, since it seems quite difficult to believe, will be demonstrated by the following demonstration.
> And so let there be a circle, whose centre is *a*, and a balance *bc* that can move about its centre *a*, and which is parallel to the horizon; and let the perpendicular *ad* be drawn from the centre *a*, directed towards the centre of the world; and let us imagine that some weight is suspended from point *d* (fig. 2.31).
> It is then manifest that the weight at *d*, as it is moved in the direction of *c*, goes up necessarily. I say, then, that any force applied on point *b* can move the weight at *d*, and that it necessarily moves it. For consider a weight, however small, suspended from point *b*, and as the weight at *d* is to the weight at *b*, let line *ba* be to another line, to which it is assumed that line *ae* is equal. Now if d is suspended from point *e*, then it will weigh equally with the weight in *b*; neither one will be moved by the other, nor will the balance incline [see my notes below]. But the weight at *d* suspended from *a* is lighter than if it is suspended from *e*, since it is weighed not only nearer the centre, but suspended from the centre itself: it is necessary that the weight at *d*, suspended from *a*, is moved by the weight at *b*, and that the balance inclines on the side of *b* and that *d* goes up[209].

---

206 G.G., Vol. II, *Le Mecaniche*, p. 181.

207 *Guidiubaldi e marchionibus Montis Mechanicorum Liber*, Pesaro, 1577, on p. 124v; *Le Mechaniche dell'illustriss. Sig. Guido Ubaldo de' Marchesi Del Monte; tradotte in volgare dal Sig. Pigafetta*, Venice, 1581, f. 121-121v.

208 G.G., Vol. I, *De motu*, pp. 298-299.

209 Once again the perpendicular *ad* is imagined as a rigid arm without weight. Nevertheless Galileo's argument does not describe exactly what we should expect: indeed, applying a small weight in *b*, it descends and the weight in *d*

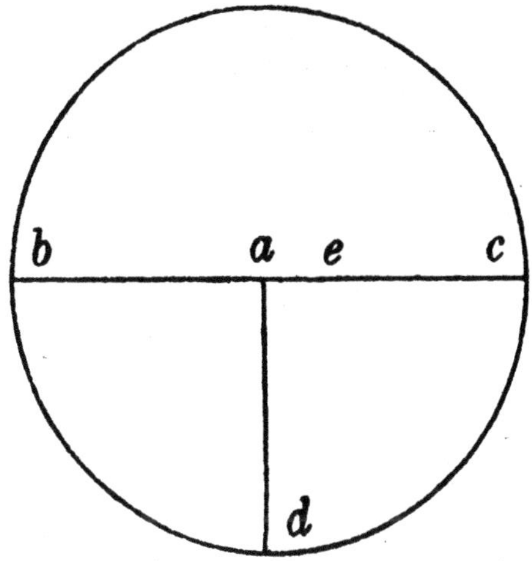

Fig. 2.31

> Therefore, if by any force any weight at *d* not only is moved, but even is raised, what wonder is it, that the same weight *d* should be moved, on a non ascending plane, by the same force or even a smaller one, than the force at *b*? Furthermore: a mobile, having no extrinsic resistance, will go down naturally on a plane inclined no matter how little below the horizon, with no extrinsic force applied; as is evident in the case of water: and the same mobile does not go up on a plane erected no matter how little above the horizon except violently: it therefore remains that on the plane of the horizon itself it is moved neither naturally nor violently. Now if it is not moved violently, hence it will be able to be moved with the minimum of all possible forces. We can also demonstrate this differently: namely, that any mobile, subject to no extrinsic resistance, can be moved on a plane which is directed neither upward nor downward by a force smaller than any proposed force whatever [...]

Galileo could maintain that on a horizontal plane an *arbitrarily small* force generates the motion because there is no external resistance to overcome, as happens with upward motion and because all the *gravitas* is already constantly nullified by the force of reaction of the supporting surface. This is a process in which no further impressed force is introduced and so, in the ideal case in which there is no friction or other accidentals to slow down the motion, the sphere, once in motion, continues in the state of uniform motion.

Galileo avoided discussing the dynamic aspects that inevitably spring to mind: why is it that the force applied does not introduce an impressed force and what does the resistance that opposes the mobile depend on. Here he simply identifies in the weight of the sphere the most

rises and goes beyond the point of equilibrium and an oscillatory regime is installed, and this is true even in the impressed force scheme. In practice, if the weight in *b* is big enough, the oscillations are rapidly suppressed because of the inevitable friction and, if it is small, there is no motion.

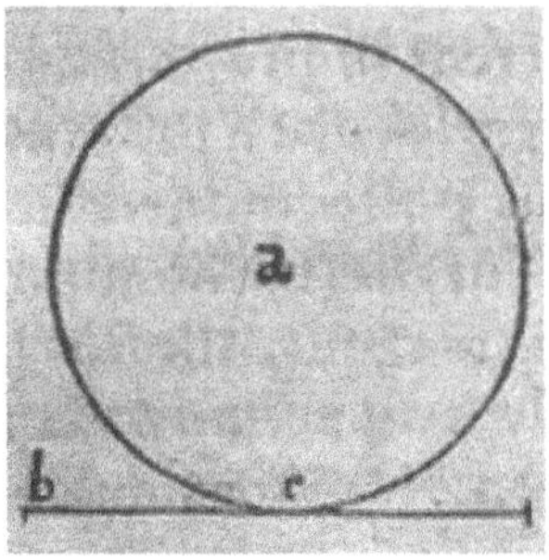

Fig. 2.32 G. Cardano, Basel, 1570, p. 41.

relevant cause that increases the obstacles in the way of the motion but he does not omit consideration of a further difficulty linked to the spherical shape of the Earth[210]:

> [...] And the things we have demonstrated, as we have said above, must be understood concerning mobiles free from all extrinsic resistance: but since it is perhaps impossible to find such mobiles in the realm of matter, let no one be astonished, in putting these things to the test, if the experiment is disappointing, and a large sphere, even if it is on a horizontal plane, cannot be moved by a minimal force. For to the causes already mentioned, there is added this: namely, that a plane cannot be really parallel to the horizon. For the surface of the Earth is spherical, to which a plane cannot be parallel: that is why, since a plane touches a sphere in only one point, if we recede from such a point, it is necessary to go up: that is why the sphere, with reason, will not be able to be removed from such a point by any minimal force.

Girolamo Cardano, perhaps, was once again Galileo's inspiration[211], because in his *Opus Novum*[212] he wrote:

> Fortieth proposition: *any spherical body which touches a plane in a point is put into motion by any force that can open up a breach in the medium.*
> Let ***a*** be a perfectly spherical body tangent to plane ***b*** at point ***c*** (this indeed is necessary as was shown by Euclid in the sixteenth Proposition of the third [*book*] of the Elements) (fig. 2.32). I maintain that it will be put into motion by a force that is capable of dividing the air.

[210] G.G., Vol. I, *De motu*, pp. 300-301.

[211] RAFFAELE GIACOMELLI in *Galileo Galilei giovane e il suo «De motu»* (Pisa, 1949) pointed out that Nicola Cusano in *De ludo Globi* had previously written about the conservation of motion of a sphere that touches the plane in a single point.

[212] GIROLAMO CARDANO, *Opus novum de proportionibus numerorum, motuum, ponderum aliarumque rerum misurandarum, non solum geometrico more stabilitum, sed etiam variis experimentis & observationibus rerum in natura, solerti demonstratione illustratum, ad multiplices usus accomodatum, & in V libros digestum*; Basel, 1570, liber V, pp. 41-42. G.G., Vol. I, *De motu*, pp. 298-299.

Indeed since it does not rise nor descend, but it moves almost in a circle around the centre of the world, it carries no weight. Not even by the dimensions of the contact, which is a single point, so only the impediment of air remains. From this it is clear that the plane must be of most hard material, that will not yield in any way, otherwise [*the sphere*] touches in more than one point. It is difficult for it to happen that the sphere touches the plane in one point, as in elementary things, either because the plane will not be exactly straight, or [it will] not be so hard that it really does not yield, or not placed in equilibrium, or the sphere will not be exactly round.

2.12 *The first ever formulation of the principle of action and reaction*

Galileo introduced a form of principle of action and reaction in which the equality between contrary forces is conserved in some situations different from static situations such as, for example, in scales in equilibrium, because equality exists during motion. He alludes to it in a chapter called[213]:

Chapter [...] In which all the things that have been demonstrated above are considered from a physical point of view, and natural mobiles are reduced to the weights of a balance.

The discussion begins thus:

[...] Thus let us consider a piece of wood which goes up in water and floats on water: now it is manifest that the piece of wood is carried upward with as much force, as is necessary to submerge it by force under water. Hence if we find how great a force is necessary to hold the wood under water, we will have what is sought.

Wood floats in static equilibrium because its overall weight is equal to the weight of the water pushed aside by the immersed part of the wood (when the immersion of the wood does not change the height of the water, as occurs for example with the sea). To submerge the wood completely in water it is necessary to apply a force equal to the weight of the further mass of water that would be displaced. His reasoning continues in this direction[214]:

[...] but if the wood were not lighter than water, that is, if it were as heavy as an amount of water equal to its own size, then surely it would be submerged, and would not be raised above the water: therefore, a force that is as great as the heaviness by which the heaviness of the wood is surpassed by the heaviness of the said amount of water, suffices to submerge the wood.

---

213 G.G., Vol. I, *De motu*, p. 274.

214 G.G., Vol. I, *De motu*, p. 274.

Naturally the force that acts during the immersion determines the velocity and the acceleration with which the operation is carried out and it is always greater than the force necessary to hold the wood still in the position reached at any one time. The latter force however is practically equal to the minimum force necessary to move the wood minimally. Galileo harked back to this discussion when he considered the inclined plane[215]:

> In order then that we may be able to attain this, what we noted above must first be taken into consideration: namely, that it is manifest that what is heavy is carried downward with as much force, as would be necessary for pulling it upward by force; that is, it is carried downward with as much force as that with which it resists going up[216].

This principle authorises the shift from static measurements with scales to dynamic ones. We can be certain of the equality between action and reaction when, for example, a sphere on the inclined plane is connected to a freely gravitating weight by means of a thread and a pulley. As we shall see in the next chapter, Galileo showed in *Le Mechaniche* that if the relationship between the weight of the sphere on the plane and the other weight is equal to the relationship between the height and length of the plane then there is equilibrium, and if one of the bodies is pushed then the motion that is established is uniform, and this happens because the centre of gravity of the system with two bodies moves along a horizontal line.

---

[215] G.G., Vol. I, *De motu*, p. 297.

[216] After 35 years Galileo used the same words in the *Discorsi intorno a due nuove scienze*; see G.G., Vol. VIII, p. 216: «Here it is manifest that the impetus in descent is as much as is the resistance, or minimal force that is enough to forbid it and stop it».

3. *Le Mecaniche* (1592-1600)

At Padua Galileo had a salary that today we would consider middling to low; in order to meet the demands of his relatives and the commitments he had undertaken for his sisters' dowries he was forced to resort to private teaching, welcoming into his home students from various Italian regions and, above all, foreigners of high rank to whom he offered special courses (fortifications, the use of the compass-calculator that he had perfected, *etc.*) and amongst these courses we must certainly include the theory of simple machines, a subject that had then become fashionable as a result of the first Latin translations of the *Problemi meccanici* (Mechanical problems) attributed to Aristotle[217].

Indeed in 1547 we find, the edition commented by Alessandro Piccolomini: *in Mechanicas quaestiones Aristotelis paraphasis*; thirty years later Guidobaldo del Monte published his *Mechanicorum liber* (Pesaro, 1577) which Filippo Pigafetta soon translated into Italian (Venice, 1581); Simon Stevin in his turn published in Flemish the *De Beghinselen der Weegconst* (Leiden, 1586) in an edition illustrated with magnificent engravings; later Henry de Monantheuil published the Greek text and the commented Latin translation of Aristotle's *Mechanica* (Paris, 1599).

In the years 1597-98 Galileo also gave a course on Mechanical Questions at the university of Padua, but ever since 1593 the first notes began to circulate of a private course which, in a few years time, would become a valuable treatise, *Le Mecaniche*, which, perhaps because of his unresolved economic difficulties, he did not publish despite the interest and novelty of his lessons[218]. Nearly thirty years later one of these copies reached Marin Mersenne who translated it and published it in Paris in 1634, while the first edition of the Italian original in Padua only appeared in 1649. We shall give two passages of this work which seem relevant for motion, starting from some definitions[219]:

---

[217] *Aristotelis Mechanica Vittoris Fausti industria in pristinum habitum restituta ac latinitate donata*, Paris, 1517. The Greek original of the *Quaestiones mechanicarum* had appeared in the *editio princeps* of Aristotle's *Opere* (Venice, 1497) edited by Niccolò Leoniceno, who later produced a Latin translation with the title *Aristotelis Quaestione mechanicae*, which was published in the *Opuscula nuper in lucem edita*, Venice, 1525 and then in *Operum Aristotelis tomus tertius*, Basle, 1542; Niccolò Leoniceno, who was born at Lonigo, Vicenza in 1428 and died in Ferrara in 1524, was a professor at Padua and then Ferrara, and he described syphilis for the first time in *De epidemia quam Itali morbum gallicum vocant*, Venice, 1497.

[218] Francesco Maurolico's *Problemata Mechanica* were published in 1613, thirty-eight years after his death. The edition of Bernardino Bardi's book, *In mechanica Aristotelis problemata exercitationes*, was also posthumous, published in Mainz in 1621 four years after the author died.

[219] G.G., Vol II, *Le Mecaniche*, pp. 159-160.

We call *heaviness*, then, that tendency to move naturally downward which, in solid bodies, is found to be caused by the greater or lesser abundance of matter (*materia*) of which they are constituted.

Moment is the tendency to move downward caused not so much by the heaviness of the movable body as by the arrangement which different bodies have among themselves. It is through such *moment* that a less heavy body will often be seen to counterbalance some other of greater heaviness, as in the steelyard a little counterweight is seen to raise a very heavy weight, not by excess of heaviness, but rather by its distance from the suspension of the steelyard. This, combined with the heaviness of the lesser weight, increases its *moment* and impetus to go downward, with which it may exceed the *moment* of the other, heavier weight. The *moment* is that impetus to go downward composed of heaviness, position and anything else by which this tendency may be caused.

Centre of gravity is defined to be that point in every heavy body around which parts of equal moment are arranged. Thus, imagining such a body to be suspended and supported from the said point, the parts to the right will balance those to the left, the parts to the fore those to the rear, and those above will balance those below, so that the heavy body thus suspended will not tilt in any direction, but, placed in any location and position, provided that is suspended from the said centre, it will remain stable. And this is that point which would go to unite itself with the general centre of all heavy things – that is, with the centre of the Earth – if could descend in some free medium.

Whence let us draw this supposition: Any heavy body will move downward in such a way that its centre of gravity will never depart from the straight line produced from this centre (placed at the first point of the motion) to the general centre of heavy things. This is a very reasonable assumption; for since this single centre must go to join the common centre, if not impeded it will necessarily go to meet this by the shortest line, which is the unique straight line.

Reading the treatise, which has had several editions, we perceive that Galileo's thought had advanced considerably since the time of the *De motu*; we find words with new meanings such as: moment, impetus or momentum, centre of gravity, force of percussion, journey of force; new ideas such as: «the velocity of the mobile with the power to increase momentum in the mobile». But above all there is the formulation of the motion of a constrained system of bodies, defined by the motion of the centre of gravity along the vertical. And all reference to impressed force has disappeared.

The principle of inertia is also more clearly argued[220]:

[...] hence it is perfectly clear that *on an exactly balanced surface the ball would remain indifferent and questioning between motion and rest*[221], so that any the least force would be suffi-

[220] G.G., Vol.II, *Le Mecaniche*, p. 180.

[221] The italics are mine. Here Galileo emphasises the state of rest rather than that in uniform motion and he states that a minimum force is required to alter it when the resultant of all the forces in play is zero; (in the *De Motu* he said that «a force that is less than any given force» was sufficient). Later we shall see, again in *Le Mecaniche*, that Galileo discussed the motion of two bodies *E* and *F*, tied together by a rope. Body *E* moved on an inclined plane

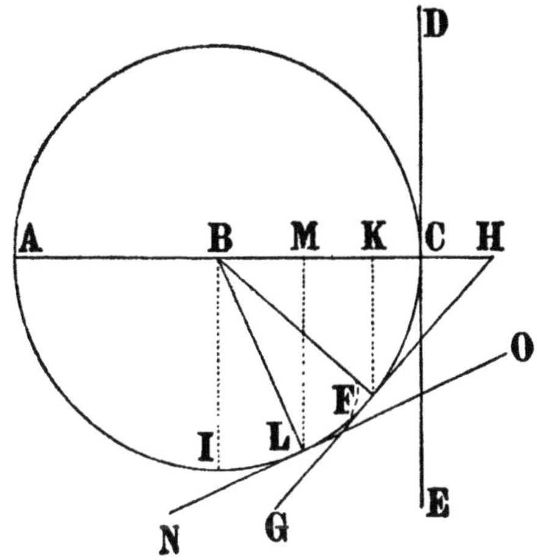

Fig. 3.1

cient to move it, just as on the other hand any little resistance, such as that merely of the air that surrounds it, would be capable of holding it still. From this we may take the following conclusion as an indubitable axiom: That heavy bodies, all external and adventitious impediments being removed, can be moved in the plane of the horizon by any minimum force.

Of all the mechanical instruments discussed in *Le Mecaniche*, the *Screw*, described as an inclined plane wrapped around a cylinder[222], puts forward highly innovative content.

The presentation of the law of the inclined plane is accompanied by a figure similar to the one in the *De motu*, which I reproduce (fig. 3.1) because the letters used are different and,

which had a pulley at its higher end while body *F* was hung vertically beyond the pulley. Galileo observed that the heaviness of *F* worked against the heaviness of *E* and showed that the actions compensate each other only if the heaviness of *E* is to the heaviness of *F* as the height of the plane is to its length. When that happens the system is at rest or moves with constant velocity «because heavy bodies do not resist transversal motions, except in so far as they move away from the centre of the Earth». Note that in the experiment on the inclined plane with a pulley Galileo – before anyone else – introduced the following principle: two bodies linked together move with inertial motion if and only if the centre of gravity of the pair does not move away from the centre of the Earth. The experiment is easy to perform if one resorts to the expedient of compensating for the friction by adding on a weight to body *F* which is descending. The motion occurs in a reference system which is to all intents inertial since in the experiment the movements of the Earth are negligible (it does not last long) and the non-homogeneity of the gravitational field along the inclined plane can obviously be ignored. A few years later Galileo would discuss the equivalence of inertial systems in uniform relative motion (the experiment on the fall of a body from the top of the mast of a ship in motion or stationary) with the Jesuit Andreas Eudaemon-Ioannes at Padua but he tackled the subject more thoroughly in 1624 in his letter to Francesco Ingoli (see chapter 14).

[222] To use Galileo's words: «having taken the same triangle, he turned it and wrapped it around the cylinder *ABCD*; in such a way that ... it generated on that cylinder the helical line drawn by the line *AEFGH*, which vulgarly we call the thread of a screw». Here he closely followed Guidobaldo del Monte, from whom he also took the quotation «speculation that was attempted again by Pappus of Alexandria», not to accept it, as his noble patron had done, but to rebut it decisively.

without having them in front of us, the reasoning would be difficult to follow[223]. I omit the first part in which the scales with a folding arm are presented because it proceeds in the way we have already seen, but I find it interesting however to set out the conclusion[224]:

> But to consider this heavy body as descending and sustained now less and now more by the radii *BF* and *BL*, and as constrained to travel along the circumference *CFL*, is not different from imagining the same circumference *CFLI* to be a surface of the same curvature placed under the same movable body, so that this body, being supported upon it, would be constrained to descend along it.
> For in either case the movable body traces out the same path, and it does not matter whether it is suspended from the centre *B* and sustained by the radius of the circle, or whether this support is removed, and it is supported by and travels upon the circumference *CFLI*.

The first step therefore is to substitute the folding arm of the scales which can assume any inclination, exemplified by the segments *BC*, *BF*, *BL* and *BI*, with an underlying cylindrical surface, with a circular section which is *CFLI*, because the force necessary to sustain the weight *P* in each of those positions of the arm is the same as the force that is necessary to sustain the weight *P* on the underlying surface at points *C*, *F*, *L*, *I*. In chapter 5 we shall see that the argument of a cylindrical surface, used by Galileo here, may have given Guidobaldo del Monte the idea of an experiment to carry out in a large cylindrical box, to test the truth of Galileo's hypotheses.

The second passage consists of substituting the underlying cylindrical surface with a plane tangent to it and passing through the position of the weight. In the triangle *FKH* which accompanies the conclusion of the demonstration in *Le Mecaniche*, the letter *H* is the intersection of the protraction of the horizontal arm *BC* with the inclined plane *FH*[225]:

> So that, passing to the present separate[226] diagram, (fig. 3.2) the *moment* downward of the movable body on the inclined plane *FH* has the same proportion to the total *moment* with which it presses down in the perpendicular *FK* as this line *KF* has to *FH*.
> This being the case, it is clear that the force that sustains the weight on the perpendicular *FK* must be equal to the weight, so that to sustain it on the inclined plane *FH* there will suffice

---

[223] G.G., Vol. II, *Le Mecaniche*, p. 181. In his letter of 17 June, 1615 G. B. Baliani sent Galileo «Vieta's proposition, of the proportion required to pull a weight up variously inclined planes». The text reproposes Galileo's demonstration from *Le Mechaniche* and contains the same drawing with the same letters. Galileo replied acknowledging the text as his own but the correspondence on this matter has been lost. They corresponded about the authorship of the treatise again in 1639, Baliani on 1 July and 19 August; Galileo on 1 August and on 1 September. In his August letter Galileo wrote: «And here I wish to say to you again that I have no memory of those writings that you say were sent to you already as Viette's thoughts, which I have claimed as mine; and yet I would like to refresh my memory of them, with your favour, and in particular of the writing on percussion». In the September letter Galileo acknowledges himself to be the author of *Le Mecaniche*, when he declares: «The writing on percussion is certainly mine, done more than 40 years ago, but then I greatly expanded it, and explained much more widely».

[224] G.G., Vol. II, *Le Mecaniche*, p. 183.

[225] G.G., Vol. II, *Le Mecaniche*, pp. 185-186.

[226] In the original it is *più distinta*, meaning clearer [Note of the Author.]

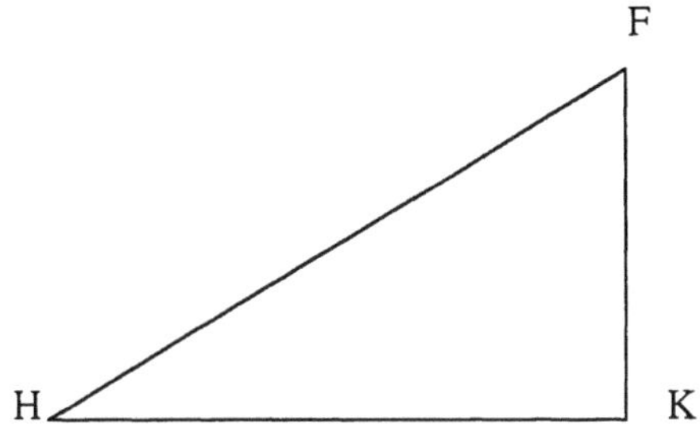

Fig. 3.2

one as much less than that as this perpendicular *FK* is less than the line *FH*. And since, as has been mentioned at other times, the force to move the weight need only insensibly exceed that which sustains it, we derive this general conclusion: That upon the inclined plane the force has the same proportion to the weight as the perpendicular dropped to the horizontal from the end of the plane has to the length of the plane.

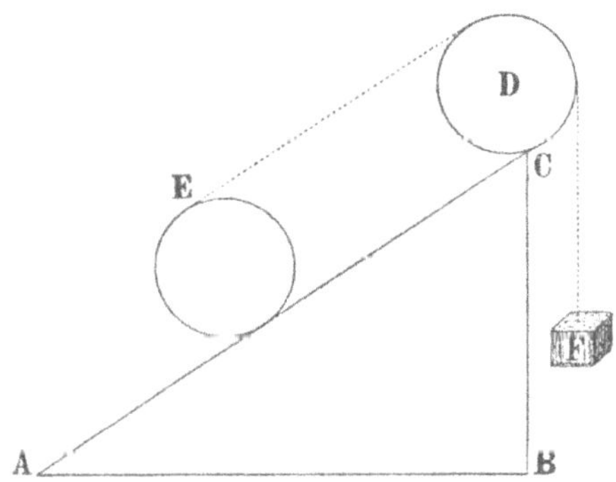

Fig. 3.3

In examining the screw another very interesting experimental installation, obtained by adding a pulley to the tip of the inclined plane[227], is described for the first time (fig. 3.3):

For let suppose in the triangle *ABC* the line *AB* to be horizontal, *AC* to be the inclined plane whose height is measured by the perpendicular *CB*, and a movable body to be placed on the plane *AC*, and linked by the cord *EDF* to a force or weight placed at *F*.
Then if its proportion to the heaviness of the weight *E* is the same of that of the line *BC* to *AC*, from what has been proven, the weight *F* will descend, drawing the movable body *E* along the inclined plane without the weight *F* measuring a greater space in descending than the movable body *E* measures along the line *AC*. But here it should be noticed that although

[227] G.G., Vol. II, *Le Mecaniche*, pp. 185-186.

the movable body *E* will have passed over all the line *AC* in the same time that the other heavy body *F* will have fallen through an equal interval, nevertheless the heavy body *E* will not have been removed from the common centre of heavy things more than the distance along the perpendicular *CB*, while the heavy body *F* descending perpendicularly will have dropped by a space equal to the whole line *AC*. And since heavy bodies do not have any resistance to transverse motion except in proportion to their removal from the centre of the Earth, then the movable body *E* not being raised more than the distance *CB* in the whole motion *AC*, while *F* has dropped perpendicularly as much as the whole length of *AC*, we may rightly say that the travel of the force *F* has the same ratio to the travel of force *E* as the line *AC* has to the line *CB*, or as the weight *E* has to the weight *F*. Therefore it is very important to consider along what lines the motions are made, and especially of inanimate heavy bodies, whose *moments* have their whole power and their entire resistance in the line perpendicular to the horizon; and in the lines, transversely rising or falling, they have only that power, impetus, or resistance which is greater or lesser according as the inclination approach more or less to the perpendicular elevation.

The inclined plane equipped with a pulley (fig. 3.4-3.6) would be used again in his later writings: in the demonstration that he asked to be added to the third day of the *Discorsi* (to complete the demonstration of the theorem of the equal final velocities) and for a final time at the end of the larger fragment on the force of percussion.

Torricelli would use the idea of uniting two bodies with a cord, making them move on two planes which are differently inclined but of the same height[228], and in the point in which they join, at the top, a pulley is placed in which the cord linking the two bodies runs. The heavy bodies thus linked have a single motion, as if they were a single body, so that «as is done with scales, with a pulley or with any other mechanical instrument: such a heavy body will never move, unless its centre of gravity descends» and this constitutes the fundamental principle of his *De motu gravium naturaliter descendentium*[229]. When the masses of the bodies are inversely proportional to the length of the planes, we have equilibrium and moving them together, their centre of gravity always moves on a horizontal line.

To Torricelli this principle seemed more evident than the fundamental theorem of the inclined plane, always used by Galilei in his demonstrations, and he substitutes it. However, before Torricelli and well before Christiaan Huygens[230], Galileo was the author of the Principle of the Centre of Gravity, as it is sometimes called, because it is evident from what he wrote here: «heavy bodies do not pose resistance to transversal movements, except in so far as they move in them away from the centre of the Earth» that he was applying this rule to the centre of gravity

[228] This artifice had been used for the first time by Giordano Nemorario in order to apply the axiom of the «*gravitas secundum situm*» to the inclined plane. The proof had been published in the *Iordani opusculum de ponderositate*, Venice, 1565, pp.7-7v, which had been revised in manuscript form by Niccolò Tartaglia who had completed it with the drawings.

[229] *Opere scelte di Evangelista Torricelli*, UTET, Turin, 1975, pp. 158-160. The Latin original is in *Opera Geometrica*, Florence, 1644, pp. 99-100.

[230] Christiaan Huygens, *Oeuvres Complètes*, Vol. XIX, The Hague,1937, p. 56.

Fig. 3.4 Protractor.

Fig. 3.5 Pulley and counterweights.

Fig. 3.6 Inclined plane with a pulley.

of the system of bodies which move *transversally* and which, therefore, do not move with natural motion individually, and all of this is examined more explicitly in a fragment of dialogue, written by Galileo before he went blind, in answer to a serious difficulty presented to Salviati by Sagredo[231]:

> SAGREDO: let scales with unequal arms, *AC* the longer, *CB* the shorter, be sustained at point *C*: seek the reason why it happens that, when two equal weights *A*, *B*, are placed at the extremes, the scales do not stay at rest and in equilibrium but incline to the side of the longer arm, transferring as in *EF*. The reason that is commonly given is that the velocity of weight *A*, in descending, would be greater than the velocity of weight *B*, since the distance *CA* is greater than *CB*; thus the mobile *A*, equal to *B* in weight, surpasses it in the momentum of the velocity, and so prevails over it, and descends raising the other (fig. 3.7). There is doubt about the value of this reasoning, which does not seem to be conclusive: because it is certainly true that the momentum of a heavy body grows, linked with velocity, over the momentum of an equally heavy weight which is at rest; but it is rather hard to be able to learn that, if both are placed at rest, that is to say where there is no motion, nor one velocity greater than another, that the fact of being greater, which is not there but is still to come, can produce a present effect, and I truly find some notable difficulty.

[231] G.G., Vol. VIII, *Frammenti attenenti ai Discorsi*, pp.438-439. (Note by A. Favaro «in Viviani's hand, who, at the top of the fragment, warns: «Of this I have the original». The whole fragment is cancelled across with a line».)

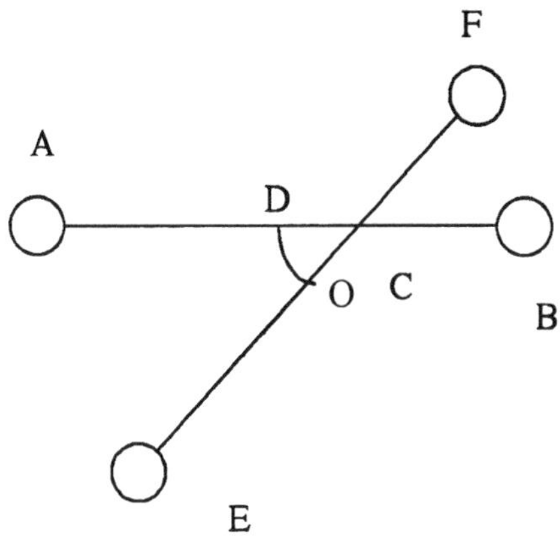

Fig. 3.7

SALVIATI: V. S. has good reason to doubt; and I still not being well satisfied by this discourse, sought to calm myself by another very simple and quick way, without supposing anything more than the first and very common notion, that is to say that heavy things go down in all ways that are allowed to them. When in the scales *AB* you place two equal weights, if you leave it to move freely, it will move down to the centre of heavy things, keeping always the centre of its gravity (which is the middle point *D*) on the straight line which goes from it to the universal centre; but if you oppose a hindrance to this motion under the centre *D* then the motion will stop, with the scales staying with its weights in equilibrium; but if the hindrance is placed outside centre *D*, as it would be in *C*, that hindrance will not stop the scales, but will divert the centre *D* from the perpendicular along which it was travelling, and will make it descend along an arc *DO*. In other words the scale with the two weights is a single body and a single weight, with its centre of gravity at point *D*, and this single heavy body will descend as much as it can, and the descent is regulated by its own centre of gravity: when you suppose its support, the centre *D* descends in *O*, and so that which descends is the whole aggregate and compounded body of the pair of scales and its weights. The answer then, precisely to the question why the scales tilt etc., is because, like the one that is a single mass, it descends and moves as close as it can to the common centre of all heavy bodies.

The discussion of the inclined plane with the pulley leads to the generalisation of the principle of inertia, which predicts that bodies maintain their state of rest or of uniform motion in a straight line whenever the forces on them cancel each other out.

Le Mecaniche conclude with an annexe on the Force of Percussion [232] already partly reproduced in the first chapter; here we give its *incipit*:

[232] G.G., Vol. II, *Le Mecaniche*, p. 188.

To investigate what is the cause of the force of percussion is most necessary for many reasons. First, because in this there appears to be something much more marvellous than that which is perceived in any other mechanical instrument; for when a nail is struck to fix it in some very hard wood, or a stick that must penetrate into very firm ground, each is driven forward by the force of the percussion alone; without which, if we were to place the hammer on either, it would not move, nor would it do so even if a much heavier weight than the hammer were so placed. This effect is truly marvellous, and is the more worthy of speculation in my opinion because, so far as I know, none of those who have philosophised about it before us has hit the mark, which we have to take as a certain and sure sign of the obscurity and difficulty of such speculation.

4. 1592-1610: «The best eighteen years of my life»*

I discussed the *De motu* at length in the second chapter not merely to set out clearly the beginnings of the intellectual journey of a scientist who was a great innovator, but also because his research method was certainly born then and above all because careful reading of that text shows that Galileo left Pisa with new ideas on local motion: the isochronicity of the pendulum, the fundamental law of the inclined plane, the principle of inertia and the theorem of chords are very useful tools in order to free the *science of motion* from the burden of Aristotelian ideas.

No significant documents have survived from his first few years at Padua; however, if we reflect on the suggestions and inspiration that may have come to him from his Pisan discoveries, in view of how much he proved to know later on, it is not impossible to arrive at a reliable reconstruction of Galileo's experimental and theoretical activity in his first ten years at Padua. Later there are letters dated 1602 to Guidobaldo del Monte and dated 1604 to Paolo Sarpi which fix a certain date for other discoveries: in the first letter there is the analysis of the isochronicity of the oscillations of a pendulum and the presentation of the theorem of chords, in the second the law of naturally accelerated motion. Later the documents become more numerous and allow us to follow Galileo's work with greater certainty.

The first work that Galileo published bears the title *Le operazioni del compasso geometrico et militare* (The operations of the geometric and military compass) and it was printed in 1606 "in the house of the author" in only 60 copies; one can wonder why Galileo did not try to publish the *De motu* when he was still at Pisa, putting together the best of his various writings, since he was looking for a better paid post. Probably he did not have the money to do it, especially after the death in 1591 of his father who left the burden of a large family to his eldest son; also, making known his criticisms of Aristotle is a risk that a young man at the beginning of his university career could not afford[233]: Aristotelian thought was dominant in the circles that controlled cultural policy and that decided whom to appoint to university chairs; it is obvious that in the selection of professors scholars who conformed and were loyal to the contents of the subjects traditionally taught in the faculties of Arts were preferred. What would someone

* G.G., Vol. XVIII, p. 109, Galileo to Fortunio Liceti in Padua, from Arcetri on 23 June, 1640.

[233] G.G., Vol. I, *De motu*, p. 412: «*Erant multi qui, postquam mea scripta legerint, non ad contemplandum utrum vera sint, quae dixerim, mentem convertent, sed solum ad disquirendum quomodo, vel iure, vel iniura, rationes meas labefactare possent*». (There will be many who, after they have read my writings, will turn their mind, not to consider whether the things I have said are true, but only to seek in what way, whether rightly or wrongly, they could undermine my opinions.)

who had read, for example, this lively description of his potential colleagues have thought of this candidate for a professorship[234]?

> Now here it does not escape me that there is a great number of more recent philosophers [*philosophantium*] who profess to know things which they know more by relying on the authority of others than by demonstration: these persons, if they heard such things, would immediately undertake to reply, and they would be satisfied to throw in a couple of words, even if they had nothing to do with the subject; for a little later they would add, such an opinion has been more than sufficiently and fully refuted before; and it is with similar turgid terms that they persuade themselves and their listeners, who are even more ignorant than they, of their opinions. For to these people, if they were to hear my arguments, and retorted that my reasoning is not conclusive, because I speak now of upward motion and now of downward, which is contrary to Aristotle's intention, or brought forward similar remarks without any soundness, to these people, I say, it would seem that my opinion has been more than sufficiently refuted [...]

The innovative part, isolated from its Aristotelian context, would already by itself have been enough to give rise to a small book but here I think that Galileo was again governed by prudence: having gone to Padua he found himself in a circle of young progressive aristocrats and enthusiastic students who encouraged him to continue with his theoretical and experimental research and he had glimpsed its great innovative possibilities; by now he no longer needed to publish and, on the contrary, wanted to benefit from the lead he had already built up in order to construct a solid doctrine and in this he would be so fussy that he would only publish the book on motion forty-five years later.

This modern and updated vision, which is the highlight of the *De motu*, would be printed indirectly because it would be widely used in his two greatest works in which Giovan Francesco Sagredo would often expound the ideas of the young Galileo in contributions deftly gauged to prepare the ground for Filippo Salviati in his role as spokesman for the older Galileo, the experienced member of the Accademia dei Lincei[235] (Lincei Academy).

At Pisa Galileo acquired the habit of making experiments to verify his theories: in the *Bilancetta,* which we have already mentioned, he described his original hydrostatic scales with the instructions how to use them and he drew up a list of the densities of various materials which bears witness to the great precision of his measurements; in the *De motu* bodies dropped from a tall tower are repeatedly referred to; there are also practical observations on various peculiarities such as, for example, the wooden sphere which, falling together with an iron sphere, initially precedes it or the explanation why, contrary to common opinion, a coin in deep water appears smaller, with a curious reference to the magnifying effect of a tumbler full of water because of the cone-shaped surface of the glass, and then there are references to the motion of bodies that move up or down in water (wood, wax, inflated bladders ...), to objects with very different density (lead, iron, oakum ...) being thrown, to the oscillations of pendulums, to spheres that spin for a long time on their own axis, to the properties of adhesion and cohesion of water, etc.

---

[234] G.G., Vol. I, *De motu*, p. 398.

[235] It was the first Academy of Scientists in Italy. [Note of the Author.]

According to his method of proceeding, involving both experiments and theory, the most important theoretical results concerning the inclined plane, although firmly based on the theory of scales, had to pass through experimentation for verification and this must have been Galileo's first occupation at Padua.

The comparison between the space travelled in the same time by a sphere on the inclined plane and by another in free fall is an exercise which is easy to resolve theoretically but difficult to verify with an experiment because the vertical fall occurs in a very short time. This is one of the points where Galileo had to put his theory to the test and all he needed was a plane and two spheres[236]. The plane he used the first few times was certainly not the one described in the *Discorsi* which was an expensive instrument: whoever built it had to plane perfectly the narrow side of a ruler about 12 *braccia* long [*6.6 m*] and carve into it a channel about a finger's width wide and, finally, to glue strips of smoothed vellum to protect the corners of the channel, taking care to overlay the pieces in succession after having thinned the edges, as bookbinders do, so as to let the ball move without hindrance. This second plane was the work of some good craftsman, a difficult job, both in the cutting of the groove which finally had to be absolutely straight, and in the choice of the wood which had to be well seasoned, so as to avoid it warping sideways. Probably this plane was only built later, between 1602 and 1604 or even later, the outcome of many previous experiments, carried out on a normal plank without grooves, a few *braccia* long and sufficiently wide.

His research into motion encouraged him, therefore, to put into practice the theory of the inclined plane and above all to verify the theorem of chords: he had to check that the ratio between the space travelled on the inclined plane by one ball and the vertical distance (in free fall) travelled by the other ball in the same time is equal to the ratio between the height[237] and length of the plane.

At first sight it all seemed simple: he dropped a sphere along the plane and at the same time dropped another sphere, vertically; across the plane he placed an obstacle, which he moved backwards or forwards until the impact of the sphere against the obstacle did not coincide with the impact of the other sphere with the floor so that the two sounds were perfectly simultaneous. He measured the paths and then repeated the experiment several times, changing the inclination of the plane, until he was certain that the result corresponded to the theorem, independently of the angle of inclination[238].

Anyone who has repeated the experiment knows that the results are not at all clear and it is not difficult to understand what Galileo may have found. Let us see him at work: first, to have a long path on the plane, he increased the angle of inclination until it seemed to him that the sphere continued to roll down without any problems; let us say, for the sake of simplicity, that

[236] In a note dated 5 July, 1599, the date on which his accounts with the mechanic Marcantonio Mazzoleni begin, I found written: «to the smelter, for two balls Lire 4», but it is rather probable that he had arranged for other spheres to be cast on previous occasions.

[237] By the height of the inclined plane we understand the vertical distance between its extremes, so that when it is drawn with an oblique segment, its height is the distance between the two straight lines parallel to the horizon which contain it exactly.

[238] The reconstruction of this experiment with all the difficulties that have to be overcome will be shown in chapter 13.

the angle is 30°. Then, he raised the plank as high as he could, in such a way however as not to complicate excessively the manual operations he had to carry out, and at the same time to be able to drop the sphere vertically from a fairly great height, for example 4 *braccia*.

Even so, the time of the fall is very short, about 0.67 seconds: in this time Galileo expected the sphere on the plane to travel a space of 2 *braccia*; instead, at best, if the experiment was carried out very well, he found that the sphere descended along the plane rather less, around 1.4 *braccia*, because of the rolling that reduces the space by a factor $K = 5/7$ (and even less if the plane has a groove to guide the sphere).

We shall soon see that this is the crucial experiment in all of Galileo's research, and he would continue to find the result inexplicable, from when he became aware of it to the end of his days. Initially the uncertainty would not have worried him because of the inevitable imprecision of the experiment: indeed, the departure of the two spheres is never exactly simultaneous and the place to put the obstacle remains uncertain, because the sounds of the two impacts are not clear and are different one from the other. Usually the times of the two paths will be different from one another by at least a tenth of a second and so the results oscillate at random with values between 1.1 and 1.9 *braccia*, or more. The experiment must have seemed very inconclusive to him, because it was so imprecise.

Galileo could, however, verify the theorem with two planes with different inclinations but which are at the same height, because an immediate consequence of the theorem of chords is that the ratio between the spaces travelled in the same time on the two planes is inverse to the ratio between their lengths. In the new experiment the paths could be longer and it is not necessary for the planes to be very inclined, with the advantage that the motions will be much slower and the errors will have less effect.

This is all very well, but there is a difficulty: a second inclined plane is required.

Thinking how to avoid the complication of letting two exactly equal spheres descend along two planes Galileo must have wondered if it was possible to carry out two experiments in succession on a single plane: the first time letting a sphere descend for a certain arbitrary space s_1, on an inclined plane with height H, length L_1 and angle of inclination α_1 given by $\sin \alpha_1 = H/L_1$; then making the sphere descend along the same inclined plane, still of height H, but with length L_2 and angle of inclination α_2, given by $\sin \alpha_2 = H/L_2$.

The experiment consists in determining the space s_2 which is travelled in the same time as s_1, but to do this obviously he needed an instrument to measure time. But we know that Galileo discovered the isochronicity of the pendulum when he was still at Pisa and that perhaps he had already used it to measure time in his experiments on motion in water; if he had not done so then, could this have been the opportunity to do so[239]?

With this new experiment he could obtain very satisfactory results, because now the factor $K \geq 5/7$, which is present in the two motions, elide in the relationship s_1/s_2.

It is not difficult to imagine the method that he followed[240]. Let us put ourselves in his place:

---

[239] There can be no doubt that in the early years of the XVII century the pendulum became for Galileo an instrument to measure time. This is witnessed to by the letter to Paolo Sarpi in 1604 which we shall consider later.

[240] These are imaginary descriptions but there are not many changes that can be made: the reader can try and think them up himself.

let us choose a fairly long plank [241]; first let us rest one end of the plank on a trestle and let us arrange another trestle, lower than the first, underneath the plane, more or less halfway: the point of departure of the experiments will always be exactly over the higher trestle and let H_1 be its height from the ground; the length L_1 is the length between the two trestles and let H_2 be the height of the point on the plane exactly over the second trestle; the angle of inclination α_1 is obtained by $\sin \alpha_1 = (H_1 - H_2)/ L_1$.

Let us choose on L_1 an arbitrary distance s_1 and let us delimit the path with a very heavy obstacle. After this, let us roll down a sphere and let us record the time taken to travel s_1. To do this, let us lengthen or shorten the string of the pendulum so that s_1 is completed, for example, exactly in a number *n* of (simple or complete) oscillations. Then, let us increase the inclination by moving the lower trestle forward: the part of the inclined plane between the two trestles is lengthened, and we indicate it by L_2; the new angle of inclination α_2 is obtained from $\sin \alpha_2 = (H_1 - H_2)/ L_2$. Let us allow the sphere to descend and let us move the obstacle until the path travelled s_2 happens exactly in the same number n of oscillations. The result that we find is $s_1/s_2 = L_2/ L_1$ and the theorem is verified.

It is quite possible that after he had carried out this simple and precise experiment, which proved that his theoretical results were correct, it occurred to Galileo to measure the times t_1 and t_2 necessary for the sphere to travel completely those two paths L_1 and L_2 between the two trestles and to make the comparison between L_1/L_2, and t_1/t_2.

If he did think of it before having started the experiment then he would have already made a considerable mental jump forward because he decided to study relationships that are a hybrid between the two Aristotelian velocities: they are not measurements of spaces travelled in the same time and they are not measurements of times spent travelling the same space; they are measurements of something with a significance and usefulness that were still not known, and making these measurements he still did not know what they would lead to: he was led by his extraordinary physical sense, the same intuition that, after he had built his telescope, would move him to turn it skywards; and he was spurred on by another precious gift: intellectual curiosity.

The experiment which I imagine he could have done proceeds exactly like the previous one; only to measure the time we have to make an observation. A pendulum divides time into exactly equal parts, but this is both an advantage and a limitation, because the instrument is not required in order to know exactly the intermediate time between two oscillations. If Galileo again adjusted the length of the pendulum so that L_1 is travelled exactly in a whole number of oscillations n_1, it would have been necessary to ensure that the subsequent path travelled L_2 was completed exactly in a whole number of oscillations n_2, certainly different from the first: the motion had to begin with the beginning of an oscillation and had to end exactly when the last oscillation had been completed.

Galileo had to change the length of L_2, by moving H_2, until he could obtain, in the descent between H_1 and H_2, a whole number of oscillations of the same pendulum with which he had measured the time before the first descent[242], and in this way he could make ratios with whole numbers and deal with certain times.

---

241 One with a length of 6 *braccia* (3.3 metres) would do, longer would be even better.

242 If Galileo already knew the relationship between the length and period of the pendulum, for the second measure-

Galileo repeated the experiment with other paths L_3, L_4, $\dots L_n$: with each one he discovered that the times were proportional to the lengths of the path[243]. If we indicate by n_1 and n_r the number of oscillations of the pendulum necessary to travel respectively L_1 and L_r, we obtain

$$L_1/L_r = n_1/n_r \,.$$

From research carried out at the time of the *De motu* Galileo knew that the space travelled L depends only on H/L and on an arbitrary function of time, which we have indicated by $\Psi(t)$, using the symbolic language we are more used to; so we write the relationship L_1/L_r in the following form:

$$L_1 / L_2 = (H/L_1)\,\Psi(t_1) \,/\, (H/L_2)\,\Psi(t_2) = L_2\Psi(t_1)/\, L_1\Psi(t_2)$$

and so

$$L_1^2/L_r^2 = \Psi(t_1)/\,\Psi(t_r) = (n_1/n_r)^2.$$

I have preferred to use symbolic expressions, for brevity and for the convenience of today's readers, less accustomed to long descriptions than XVI century readers, and also more intolerant of them, but I could have avoided using $\Psi(t)$ by writing instead: «the value assumed at time t of the unknown quantity on which the space travelled depends».

Let us consider that the time t_1 and the value $\Psi(t_1)$ are always the same as the distances L_r vary, let us introduce a constant $C = \Psi(t_1)/n_1^2$ rewriting the relationship $\Psi(t_r) = \Psi(t_1)\; n_r^2/n_1^2$ as $\Psi(t_r) = C\,n_r^2$

So I arrive at the following result: $\Psi(t)$ is a growing function of t which verifies the relationship $\Psi(t) = C\,t^2$ at constant intervals of time $t = nT$.

Galileo was well aware that L_1 can be changed at will and so also the period T of the pendulum, lengthening and shortening the thread, and so for an arbitrary time t he could adapt the pendulum in order to have

$$t = n\,T\,.$$

---

ment of time, instead of seeking the exact position of the second trestle so that the path L_2 is travelled in a whole number of oscillations of that pendulum, he could move the second trestle forward randomly and simply lengthened the thread in order still to have a whole number of oscillations to travel L_2. The ratio between the two times is obtained by calculating the square root of the ratio between the two lengths given by the pendulum. So he had the possibility of repeating the experiment an arbitrary number of times. Knowing which of the two methods he followed is of no importance for the result, even if it is much more important to understand the use he made of the pendulum as a clock.

243 Unlike the first experiment, in which one of the bodies falls vertically, when the travel times on two inclined planes are measured and then compared the common factor K, due to the rolling and the grooves, is not a disturbance. For this very reason Galileo developed his whole theory according to two very separate situations: a) motion on the inclined plane; b) motion of projectiles. When he put the two types of motion together he always found insurmountable difficulties, until he discovered the mechanism that permits slowed down vertical motion. We shall see later the case of a sphere that rolls along the groove in the plane: compared to the time for the perpendicular the time when inclined is increased by a factor $K^{1/2} = [1-(c/d)^2]^{1/2}\,[7/5-(c/d)^2]^{-1/2}$, where c is the width of the groove, d is the diameter of the sphere. So friction becomes important for small angles of inclination. For factor K see appendix D.

So, from the arbitrariness of the length of the pendulum and the paths, it follows that $\Psi(t)$ is proportional to t^2 and thus

s = constant $(H/L)\ t^2$.

Did Galileo find the equation of motion this way? It is possible this was the way to arrive at the law of uniformly accelerated motion.

If we read in the *Discorsi* the four axioms that follow the definition of uniform motion, we can see that here the concept of velocity has remained the same Aristotelian concept; for example, axiom IV says:

> The velocity with which a greater space is travelled in the same time is greater than the velocity with which a lesser space is travelled.

This unchanging definition of "swifter" is due to the fact that here uniform motion is being talked of. Only when he passed from equable motion to uniformly accelerated motion was Galileo forced to consider a *new velocity*, which varies with continuity as the motion proceeds, a velocity made up of *degrees* just as a line is made up of points. There is a certain date where the whole mental process is concluded; we find it in his letter dated 16 October 1604 to Sarpi where he states[244]:

> Thinking again about matters of motion in which, to demonstrate the events I had observed, I lacked a totally unquestionable principle that I could put forward as an axiom, I resorted to a proposition which is very natural and evident; and having supposed this, I then show the rest, that is to say the spaces passed by natural motion are in proportion double the times, and in consequence the spaces passed in equal times are like the uneven numbers *ab unitate*, and the other things. And this is the principle: that the natural mobile grows in velocity with that proportion that it moves away from the beginning of its motion.

The letter to Sarpi shows that in 1604 he had not yet understood that the variable to consider is time. For a long time his experiments in air would have been similar to those he carried out at Pisa in water and he would have tried to arrive at uniform motion, reducing the inclination of the plane. As at Pisa he will have started to mark the path travelled over the plane in 1, 2, ..., *n* oscillations and, even holding the plane almost horizontal, he will have realised that the marks moved apart and that the distance between them grew like uneven numbers. The letter to Sarpi strongly suggests that the approach with which Galileo may have arrived at the law of motion is linked to his experiments in Pisa.

In the precise moment when Galileo grasped that the theory of impressed force could not lead to quantitative laws, only then did he understand that accelerated motion is the real natural motion, and only then did he begin to reflect on the results he had available. This is my reconstruction of Galileo's experimental activity in Padua up to 1604.

A certain step in this development is revealed to us by the letter that he wrote to Guidobaldo del Monte in 1602.

---

244 G.G., Vol. X, p. 115.

5. 1602: The theorem of chords and the isochronicity of pendulums. The letter to Guidobaldo del Monte

A letter[245] from Galileo to Guidobaldo del Monte written at the end of 1602, which luckily survives, bears witness to some results arrived at in his first ten years in Padua, above all in his research into the isochronicity of oscillations and his study of motion on the inclined plane, for which Galileo had by now given up seeking the causes, making do with describing it exactly. Let us read very carefully the contents which refer to a previous letter sent to him by Guidobaldo which has been lost.

> May Your Most Illustrious Lordship forgive my untimeliness, if I persist in trying to persuade you of the truth of the proposition of motions in equal times in the same quarter of a circle; because, since to me it always[246] seemed marvellous, now it seems even more so, while it is considered impossible by Your Excellency: so I would deem it a great mistake and failure on my part, if I were to allow it to be repudiated by your speculation, as something that is false, since it does not deserve this comment, much less to be banished from the intellect of Your Excellency, who more than any other can soonest bring it back from the exile of our minds. And since the experiment, with which I mainly clarified this truth to myself, is as certain as it was confusedly explained in my other letter[247], I shall repeat it more clearly. So I take two thin threads, equally long two or three *braccia* each, and let them be *AB*, *EF*, (fig. 5.1) and I attach them to two nails *A*, *E*, and at the other ends *B*, *F* I tie two equal lead balls (although it would make no difference if they were not equal[248]), then I move each of these threads away from its perpendicular, but one a great way, as it would be for the arc *CB*, and the other very little, as it would be according to the arc *IF*. I then let them go freely at the same moment in time, and one begins to describe large arcs, similar to *BCD*, and the other describes small ones, similar to *FIG*, and yet the mobile *B* does not take more time to pass through the whole arc *BCD* than the other mobile *F* does to pass through the arc *FIG*. Of this I make myself certain as follows:
> The mobile *B* passes through the great arc *BCD*, and returns through the same *DCB*, and then returns towards *D*, and 500 and 1000 times it goes reiterating its reciprocations; the

---

[245] G.G., Vol. X, pp. 97-100.

[246] Here "always" suggests that the discovery of the theorem of chords is very old.

[247] One of the many letters that have been lost.

[248] Galileo knew well that the frequency is independent of the mass.

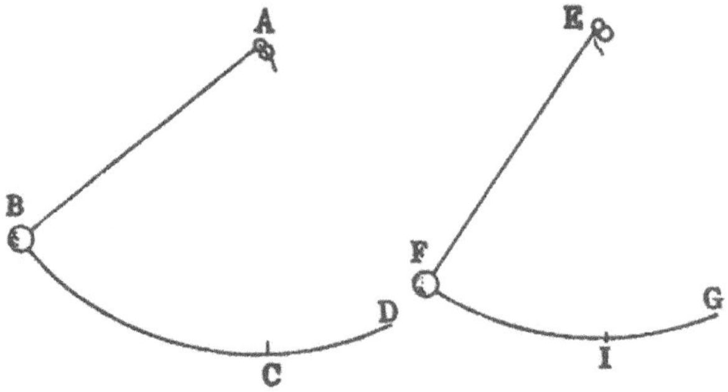

Fig. 5.1

other one likewise goes from *F* to *G*, and hence returns to *F*, and likewise it will make many reciprocations; and in the time that I count, for example, the first hundred great reciprocations *BCD, DCB* etc., another observer counts another hundred very small reciprocations through *FIG,* and he does not count a single one more: a most evident sign that each and everyone of these great *BCD*'s consumes as much time as each of the minute *FIG*'s. Now if the whole of *BCD* is passed through in the same time as *FIG,* then their halves, which are the falls through the unequal arcs of the same quarter, shall be done in equal times. But without my having to count more, Your Excellency will see that the mobile *F* will not make its very small reciprocations more frequently than the mobile *B* will make its large ones, but always they shall go together.

I shall stop here for a first comment. We have seen in the *De motu* that Galileo wrote about the amplitudes of pendulums of different weights and materials but of the same length. After moving them equally from the vertical he let them go together and after a certain number of oscillations he observed that their amplitudes were different: the heavier one conserved a greater amplitude than the other; once moved away equally, the capacity to acquire more *vis impressa* gives the heavier pendulum the possibility of staying in motion longer. So isochronicity was a chance discovery.

In the pages we are reading now there is no trace of the Pisan experiment, but it is probable that Galileo had already described the *De motu* experiment to Guidobaldo in a letter that has been lost or during some encounter at his villa at Montebaroccio.

Now, instead, he was communicating to Guidobaldo a significant variation in the experiment: the pendulums, both of lead, are moved away from the perpendicular, one more and one less; the experiment is set up precisely in order to prove the constancy of the frequency as the initial amplitude varies.

The experiment was repeated with great care by James MacLachlan[249] and the results indicated by Galileo were essentially confirmed, and the explanation is simple: after a few tens of oscillations, the amplitudes become reduced enough to ensure isochronicity from then on[250]. Let us return to the letter:

> The experiment, that you told me you did in a large box, may be rather uncertain, both because perhaps its surface may not be very clean, and maybe because it is not perfectly circular, and again since one cannot in a single passage observe so well the moment itself at the onset of the motion: But if Your Illustrious Lordship still wishes to take this hollowed out surface, let the ball *B* go freely from a great distance, as it would be from point *B*, which will pass through *D*, and at first it will make its reciprocations with great intervals, and at the end small, but not for this reason more frequent than the former.

What did this experiment, which Guidobaldo had done in a single passage, consist of? Galileo – a few lines before – in illustrating the motion of the pendulum, described a similar path, using the same letters : «*The mobile B passes through the great arc BCD...*»; and now wrote: «let the ball *B* go freely from a great distance, as it would be from point *B*, which will pass through *D* ...». The properties of the pendulum are introduced to convince Guidobaldo that *«the proposition of motions in equal times in the same quarter of the circle»* is true: indeed, if the large and small oscillations occur in the same time, so will their halves.

Guidobaldo seems to believe it is false and the box experiment may be an attempt of his to prove it. How? I can put forward a hypothesis which, although not very probable, serves to call attention to this point which has remained obscure. I suppose that Guidobaldo wanted to test Galileo's proposition as follows: if it is true, then two equal spheres let drop in the box simultaneously from different heights have to reach the lowest point at the same time, for example hitting in unison an obstacle placed across it at the bottom. For Guidobaldo the result was unsatisfactory, but amongst other objections Galileo wrote that « the experiment, that you told me you did in a large box, may be rather uncertain, ... since one cannot in a single passage observe so well the moment itself at the onset of the motion». Did Galileo mean that it is difficult to release the two spheres at the same time? Or was he suggesting that when they are released, one may involuntarily impart a velocity to one of the spheres? The obscurity of the text forces me to admit that Guidobaldo's experiment is indecipherable for now.

---

[249] JAMES MACLACHLAN, *Galileo's Experiments with Pendulum: Real and Imaginary*, Annals of Science, Vol. 33, 1976, pp. 173-185. MacLachlan states in the summary: «His report of observations of two lead balls on equal long strings is shown by reconstruction to have been a real experiment».

[250] ADRIANO CARUGO, on p. 699 of his comment on the *Discorsi* (Turin, 1958), already observed: «Galileo used pendulums of a discrete length, such that it would be difficult to notice perfect isochronicity in them, even for such an acute experimenter as he was. To make more obvious the difficulty of being able, experimentally, to spot the erroneousness of the supposed isochronicity, it is useful to observe, as an example, that if, of two pendulums of equal length, one makes a circular oscillation of 30 degrees of amplitude, and the other makes one of only 3 degrees, according to Poisson's formula it is found that the delay of the first with respect to the second can be estimated as one oscillation in 250 approximately».

I must raise another point: Galileo and Guidobaldo were discussing two similar experiments at a distance. They are two cases of the oscillatory motion of a sphere constrained to travel along an arc: in one experiment it is restrained by a thread, in the other by the curved wall of a box. It seems rather strange that the results that the two scholars speak of can be left to their subjective judgements. Only a pendulum of a length adjusted to the duration of the reciprocations in the box, oscillating synchronously with the rolling sphere, can prove the constancy of the phenomenon over time.

The fact that the two subjects are mentioned so close together in the letter makes us think that Galileo used a pendulum to prove the isochronicity of the reciprocations in the box.

I do not know if it occurred to Galileo and Guidobaldo to compare the period of the sphere oscillating in a box of radius R, with the period of a pendulum of length $L = R$ which therefore follows the same trajectory[251]. The periods are not equal: in the box the sphere, because it rolls, proceeds more slowly[252] and the ratio between the period of the pendulum T_p and the period of the sphere T_s rolling in the box is $T_p / T_s = (5/7)^{1/2} \approx 0.85$. The great interest of these circular motions is that, unlike what happens with the inclined plane, the time of descent does not grow in proportion to the length travelled but is almost constant.

The experiment with the box is also interesting for the relationship of common research between the young Galileo and the old Guidobaldo because here we see Galileo carrying out experiments and explaining them to the elderly mathematician, to whom the results, and the consequences that Galileo managed to draw from them, seem unreasonable. We must remember that when we speak about the experiment on parabolic motion that they carried out together. I return to my transcription:

> As for the unreasonable opinion that, taking a quarter 100 miles long, two equal mobiles may pass through, one the whole length and the other only a palm's width, in equal times, I say it is true that it is marvellous; but if we consider that a plane may slope down just as little as does the surface of an extremely slowly flowing river, that a mobile will not have travelled in it naturally more than a palm's width in the time that another on a very inclined plane (or instead together with having received a very great impetus even on a gentle slope) will have travelled a hundred miles: nor is this proposition by itself peradventure more improbable than that which states that the triangles between the same parallel lines and with equal bases are always equal, it being possible to make one very short and the other a thousand miles long, I think I have proved this conclusion, no less unimaginable than the other.
>
> Let the diameter *BA* of the circle *BDA* be vertical to the horizon, and from *A* to the circumference let lines be drawn *utcumque AF, AE, AD, AC* (see fig. 5.2 and 5.3): I show[253] equal mobiles fall in equal times both along the perpendicular *BA* along the inclined planes accord-

[251] When I first wrote these lines I had not yet discovered that Mersenne too had had this idea and carried out the experiment: I missed it because Mersenne mentions the experiment in an unexpected place, that is to say in the introduction to the *Harmonie Universelle*, written after completing the text of his book, one of many considerations mainly related to music and musical instruments. See later in chapter 20 (section 20.3)

[252] The period of the oscillations in the crate is: $T = 2\pi\ [\ (7/5)\ R/g]^{1/2}$.

[253] Galileo only enunciated the theorem, postponing the demonstration to another time.

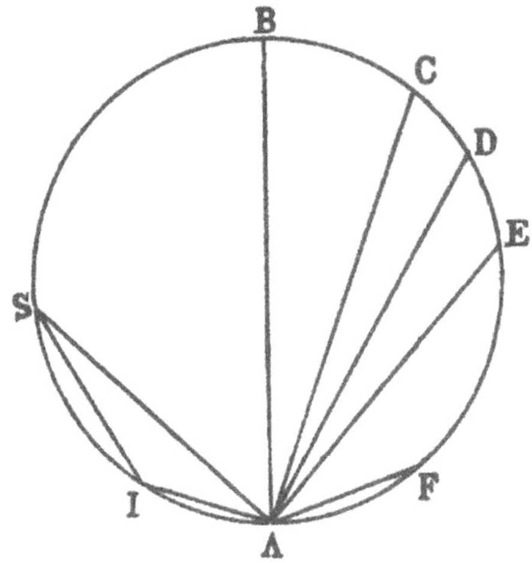

Fig. 5.2

ing to the lines *CA, DA, EA, FA*; so that, leaving at the same moment from points *B, C, D, E, F*, they will arrive at the same instant of time at the end *A*, and let the line *FA* be as small as one wishes it to be[254].

And perhaps this will appear even more unlikely, although I have proved it too, that since the line *SA* is not greater than the chord of a quarter, and the lines *SI, IA utcumque*, that same mobile makes the journey *SIA* sooner, departing from *S*, than just the journey *IA*, departing from *I*.

Thus far I have demonstrated without overstepping mechanical terms; but I cannot manage to prove how the arcs *SIA* and *IA* passed in equal times: which is what I am seeking[255].

Do me the kindness of returning Master Francesco's hand kiss to him[256], and tell him that when I will have a moment's leisure I shall write to him of an experiment, which already came to me in my imagination, to measure the momentum of percussion[257]: as to his question, I consider excellent that which Your Illustrious Lordship says, and that when we begin to deal with matter, by its accidents the propositions considered in the abstract by the geometrician begin to be altered; so since one cannot assign certain knowledge of them, thus perturbed, so the mathematician is absolved from their speculation.

---

[254] See. G.G. Vol. VIII, *Discorsi*, p. 221, *Frammenti attenenti ai Discorsi*, p. 393.

[255] G.G., Vol. VIII, *Frammenti attenenti ai Discorsi*, pp. 419-422.

[256] Galileo addressed a certain Francesco, who was in Guidobaldo's villa at Montebaroccio: he could only be Guidobaldo del Monte's eldest son. Guidobaldo had ten children by Felice della Rovere, the illegitimate daughter of Guidobaldo II Duke of Urbino: Francesco Maria, Costanza, Orazio, Niccolò, Alessandro, Giulio, Carlo, Antonio, Uguccione and Giovanni. I exclude the possibility that he could be the « Francesco my servant» referred to by Guidobaldo in his letter of 3 September 1593, because Galileo calls him "Master Francesco" and returned his hand kiss.

[257] See. G.G., Vol. II, *Le Meccaniche*, p. 190.

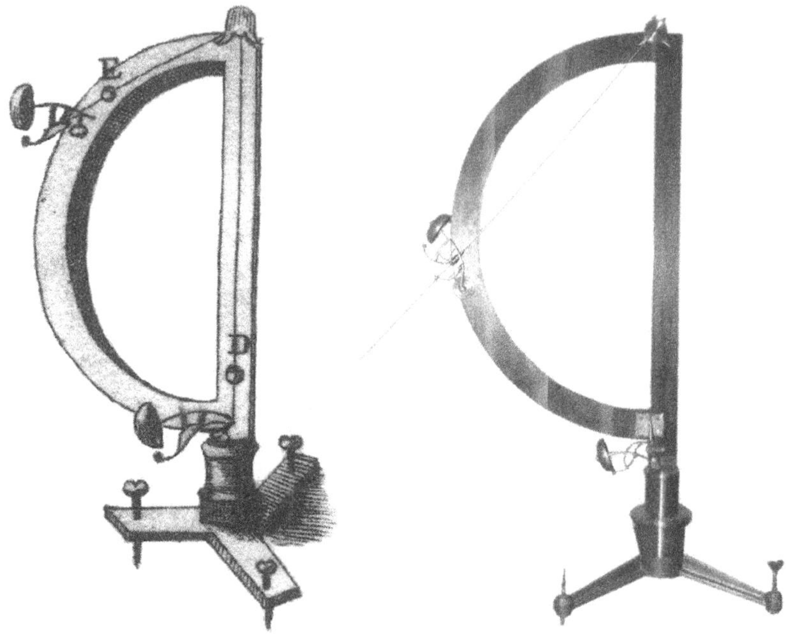

Fig. 5.3 On the left the experimental apparatus set up to prove the theorem of chords by Carlo Alfonso Guadagni, who was the first professor of experimental physics at the University of Pisa, and on the right the working reconstruction to be found in the *Laboratorio di Galileo Galilei.*

I have been too long and tedious with Your Illustrious Lordship: be so kind as to forgive me, and love me as your most devoted servant. And I kiss your hands with all reverence.
From Padua, 29 November 1602
Your Most Illustrious Lordship's Most Obliged Servant
Galileo Galilei

Concluding his letter, Galileo politely concedes to Guidobaldo the prerogatives of precision a mathematician enjoys and to himself the practical limits of an experimenter, thus justifying the doubts his older friend had had. The undertaking he made to Francesco strikes me as very interesting «I shall write to him of an experiment, which already came to me in my imagination, to measure the momentum of percussion». We talked about it at length at the beginning of the first chapter. That was in the year 1602!

The theorem of chords, the attempt to use it to prove the isochronicity of oscillations, reappeared 35 years later in another letter, addressed to Lorenzo Realio[258], in the negotiations with

[258] G.G., Vol. XVII, pp. 96-105. See too, for a similar discussion, G.G., Vol. VII, *Dialogo*, pp. 475-477, where he discussed the two subjects at length, and G.G., Vol. VIII, *Discorsi*, pp. 139-140, where the relationship between the period and length of the pendulum is also given.

the States General of Holland about the determination of longitude at sea, almost in the same terms but with in addition the description of his instrument to measure time with the pendulum which beats the seconds[259]:

> If in a circle, vertical at the horizon, the perpendicular is drawn upward from the intersection point, and in consequence shall be the diameter of the circle, and from the point of contact, that is to say from the sublime term of the diameter, as many chords as we wish are drawn, over which we understand mobiles to descend as on inclined planes, the times of their passages over such chords and over the diameter itself will all be equal; so that if, *e.g.*, from the lowest contact to the circumference the subtended chords of 1, 4, 10, 30, 50, 100, 160 gr. are drawn, the mobile over such inclinations and lengths will descend for all in equal times and also in the whole of the perpendicular diameter. And this too happens in the parts of the circumferences of the two lower quadrants, in which, as if they were grooves[260] in which a heavy globe descends, in such time it shall pass over the circumference of the whole quadrant as if it started to move 60, 40, 20, 10, 4, 2 or a single degree away from the lowest point of contact. In truth a most marvellous accident, of which anyone may become sure by suspending a small globe of lead, or other heavy matter, by a thread tied above, and then moving it away from the perpendicular state until it is one quarter high; then let it go freely, it will be seen to go back and forth, making very many reciprocations, at first large, and then continuously diminishing, until it is reduced to not moving more than a single degree this way or the other from the perpendicular state; and always travelling along the same circumference, it shall be seen that the vibrations, large, medium, small and very small, are always made in equal times. And wishing to make a clearer experiment, let two such small globes be suspended from two threads of equal lengths, and moved one aside from the perpendicular, and away from it by a great arc of 80 degrees or more and the other only two or three degrees, and let them be left free, let one count the vibrations of one of the pendulums, and another the vibrations of the other pendulum, and they shall find themselves most closely together counting a hundred, for example, of the great ones, when indeed the other will have counted a hundred of the very small ones.
>
> From this most true and steady principle I derive the structure of my device to number time, using not a weight hanging from a thread but a pendulum of solid and heavy matter, as would be brass or copper. This pendulum I make in the shape of a sector of a circle of twelve of fifteen degrees, with a semidiameter of two or three palms' width; and the larger it shall be, so with less tedium can one observe it. I make this sector thicker in the semidiameter in the middle, thinning it progressively towards the outer edges, where I make it end in a rather sharp line, to avoid as far as possible the impediment of the air, which alone hinders it.

[259] To regulate time Galileo indicated this method to Realio: «before it stops it will go hither and thither reciprocally a great number of vibrations; which to be able to go continuing according to need, it would be well if he who attends gives it a lively impulse in time, reducing it to the ample vibrations: and having counted, for once, with patience the vibrations made in a natural day, measured with the revolution of a fixed star, one will have the number of vibrations in an hour, in a minute or smaller part».

[260] In the description Galileo, referring to the channels, may have been thinking of the experiment with the crate.

Fig. 5.4 The pulsilogium reconstructed based on a figure by Santorio (but not to the correct scale because in the original drawing the scale is divided uniformly).

[...] We can then, having made this experiment with a pendulum of any length we choose, increase it or diminish it, so that every vibration has the time of a second, since the lengths of such pendulums maintain between them duplicated proportion of the proportion of the times.

The theorem of chords and the isochronicity of oscillations are always presented together, because ever since the letter to Guidobaldo, as we saw in the conclusion, Galileo hoped to be able to relate isochronicity, supposed to be a property of arcs, to motion on an inclined plane, substituting for the arc a series of polygonals made by inserting an ever growing number of chords, ... but he never succeeded.

It seems inevitable to me that Galileo, having pendulums with lengths he can vary, would also observe how the length of the oscillation changes: it is the principle by which the *pulsilogium* (fig. 5.4) works, the apparatus mentioned by Santorio in 1602, which measures the frequency of a patient's pulse by varying the length of the cord of a pendulum[261].

---

[261] Santorio Santorio described the use of the pulsilogium and drew it for the first time in *Commentaria in prima fen primi libri Canonis Avicennae*, Venice, 1626, but he quoted it by name in *Methodus Vitandorum errorum omnium qui in arte Medica contiguunt*, Venice, 1602. Santorio knew Galileo and had also treated him. *Honi soit qui mal y pense*!

6. Before 1604: The law for falling bodies. Experimental results

The letter to Guidobaldo in 1602 offers us an overview of the knowledge that he had acquired on local motion and a fact that is unmissable is that here there is no trace of the law of motion. Only two years later, in a letter to Brother Paolo Sarpi, Galileo proclaimed: «the spaces passed through by natural motion are in double proportion to the times».

Before discussing the merits of this second text I must, however, jump forward twenty years to show that Galileo, even if he taught astronomy according to Ptolemy at the University of Padua, nevertheless knew the profound link that exists between local motion and cosmic motion. We know this from an observation that Mario Guiducci made to Galileo, referring to a conversation he had had with Father Orazio Grassi[262]. Guiducci, who was in Rome, wrote to him on 13 September 1624[263]:

> Our reasoning was all about a proposition of yours, my dear Sir, which he said had been told to him by a Father Andrew[264], a Greek, a most principled person in his religion, who said he had heard it from you in Padua: *i.e.* that a body let fall perpendicularly from the masthead of a ship, fell close alongside and to the foot of the mast, whether the ship moved or was still [...]

The experiment of a fall from the top of a ship's mast, which was absolutely not decisive for the problem of the motion of the Earth, will be amply discussed together with the new formulation of the principle of inertia in Galileo's answer to the text that Francesco Ingoli had addressed to him in 1615 (*De situ et quiete terrae contra Copernici systema disputatio* – Discussion about the site and immobility of the Earth contrary to the Copernican System), an answer that was not sent because of the restrictions imposed on him by Cardinal Bellarmino[265], destined for

---

262 Author of the *Libra astronomica ac philosophica* (1619), in which he had criticised the *Discorso delle comete* (1619) by Galileo and Guiducci; Galileo in his turn had raised the tone of the argument with *Il Saggiatore* (1623).

263 G.G., Vol. XIII, pp. 205-206.

264 This was the Jesuit Andrea Eudaemon-Ioannes, born in Crete, who had taught theology at Padua. The episode dates back to before the so-called *war of the interdict* 1606-1607, when all Jesuits had to leave Padua.

265 «The decree which suspended the *De revolutionibus* by Copernicus and the book *Didaci a Stunica ... In Job commentaria*, published at Toledo in 1584: «*donec corrigantur*» is dated 5 March 1616; but already on 25 February the warning to Galileo had been decided (effected the following day): «*Illustrissimus Dominus cardinalis Millinus notificavit reverendis Patribus Dominis Assessori et Commissario Sancti Officii, quod relata censura Patrum Theologorum ad propositiones Galilei mathematici, quod sol sit centrum mundi et immobilis motu locali et terra moveatur etiam*

publication in 1624 and then prudently set aside. Here I would like to point out that he may perhaps already have thought of the connection between local motion and the motion of the Earth discussed with the Jesuit at Padua when he wrote to Kepler in 1597[266]:

> But since this is the opportune moment not to deplore the miseries of our century, but for me to congratulate you for the confirmation of the truth of most beautiful discoveries, so I shall only add this and I shall promise: that your book[267] will be read by me with a well disposed spirit, because I am sure that I shall find beautiful things in it. I shall do so even more willingly because many years past I came to agree with the opinion of Copernicus and from that point of view the causes of many natural results, that are without doubt inexplicable according to common opinion, have also been found by me. I have defended with much reasoning and I have fought against the contrary arguments [...]

Putting forward arguments in favour and fighting those contrary ones[268], especially discussing *the experiment of the mast of a ship*, is exactly what he would do in his letter to Ingoli.

Let us return to the chronological sequence; it is October 1604 and Brother Paolo Sarpi sent Galileo a question and a problem[269]:

> While sending you the enclosed, it occurred to me to propose to you a subject to be resolved, and a problem that keeps me in doubt. We have already concluded that no heavy body can be drawn to the same point upwards unless with a force, and consequently with a velocity. We have established (so you, my dear Sir, lately claimed and invented) that through the same states it will come back down as those it went up through. It was I know

---

motu diurno, Sanctissimus ordinavit illustrissimo Domino cardinali Bellarmino, ut vocet coram se dictum Galileum eumque moneat ad deserendas dictam opinionem; et si recusaverit parere, Pater Commissarius, coram notario et testibus, faciat illi praeceptum ut omnino abstineat huiusmodi doctrinam et opinionem docere aut defendere, seu de ea tractare; si vero non acquieverit, carceretur». (The Most Illustrious Lord Cardinal Millino has notified the reverend Fathers Lords Assessors and the Commissioner of the Holy Office that, due to the censuring by the Theological Fathers of the opinions of the mathematician Galileo, that the Sun is at the centre of the world without moving by local motion and that the Earth also moves by daily motion, the Most Holy [Father] ordered the Most Illustrious Lord Cardinal Bellarmino to call the aforesaid Galileo before him and to caution him to abandon this opinion; and if he refused to obey, the Father Commissioner, before a notary and witnesses, was to command him to abstain totally from teaching and maintaining such an opinion and doctrine or to examine it; if instead he did not consent he was to be imprisoned.)

266 G.G., Vol. X, pp. 67-68.

267 Kepler had sent him his *Prodromus dissertationum cosmographicarum, continens mysterium cosmographicum de admirabili proportione orbium coelestium, deque causis coelorum numeri, magnitudinis, motuumque periodicorum genuinis et propriis, demonstratum per quinque regularia corpora geometrica,* published the year before.

268 Galileo spoke publicly very early on of the importance of the priciple of inertia in cosmology as we can see from what Benedetto Castelli wrote to him on 1 April 1607: «Then from your doctrine, Sir, that to start motion all that is needed is the mover but to continue it it is enough to have no obstacle, it makes me laugh when they exalt this doctrine as that which makes me come into the awareness of the existence of God; so that if motion were truly eternal, I could become an atheist and say we have no need of God, a foul blasphemy» (G.G., Vol. X, pp. 170-171).

269 G.G., Vol. X, p. 114, letter dated 9 October 1604. Sarpi is in Venice and Galileo at Padua.

> not what objection of the bullet of the harquebus: the fire here muddies the force of the instance. But let us say: a strong arm, firing an arrow with a Turkish bow, passes totally through a plank; and if the arrow descends from the height to which the arm with the bow can draw, it shall be very little passed. I believe that the instance is perhaps slight, but I do not know what else to say.

The problem that kept him «in doubt» occupies the rest of the letter and is, as Sarpi admitted, formulated in Peripatetic terms: supposing that a same force pushes materials of different specific weight (gold and silver), he asked if they would receive equal impressed force, if they reach the same distance and if they have the same velocity. It almost seems as if he had read the *De motu*.

Galileo, answering, informed Brother Paolo Sarpi by letter of the first mathematical law in the history of mechanics in a few simple words[270]:

> Thinking over the question of motion in which, to prove the events I had observed, I lacked a totally indubitable principle that could be put forward as an axiom and I resorted to a proposition which has much that is natural and obvious; and having supposed this, I then prove the rest, *i.e.* that spaces passed through by the natural motion are in double proportion of the times, and in consequence the spaces passed through in equal times are like odd numbers *ab unitate* and the other things.

I have already transcribed part of the letter but it is so important that I do not mind repeating it. The spaces travelled are measured in successive units of time as happens when a pendulum is used, and they depend on it quadratically; the velocities are measured in relation to the space travelled and depend on it linearly. In Ms. Gal 72 there is a folio[271], contemporary to the letter, that deals with the same subject matter in much more detail; let us read it:

> I suppose (and perhaps I shall be able to prove) that the heavy body falling naturally increases its velocity continuously as the distance from the limit whence it left increases:, *e.g.*, if the body leaves from point *a* and falls along the line *ab* I suppose that the degree of velocity in point *d* is as much greater than the degree of velocity at *c*, as the distance *da* is greater than *ca*, and so the degree of velocity at *e* to the degree of velocity at *d* as *ea* to *da*, and so at every point of the line *ab* we find degrees of velocity proportional to the distances of those same points from the limit (fig. 6.1). It seems to me that this principle is very natural and that it corresponds to all the experiments that we see in the instruments and machines that operate by percussion, where the percussor has an effect that much greater the greater the height it falls from: and having supposed this principle I shall prove the rest.

---

270 G.G., Vol. X, p. 115, letter dated 16 October 1604.

271 From G.G.N.M Folios 128r and 128v. Drake's identification: Watermark type C9. Drake's description: House 32 × 18 mm. Date of earliest letter with this watermark is October 1604. I have given the text in the edition offered by G.G.N.M.

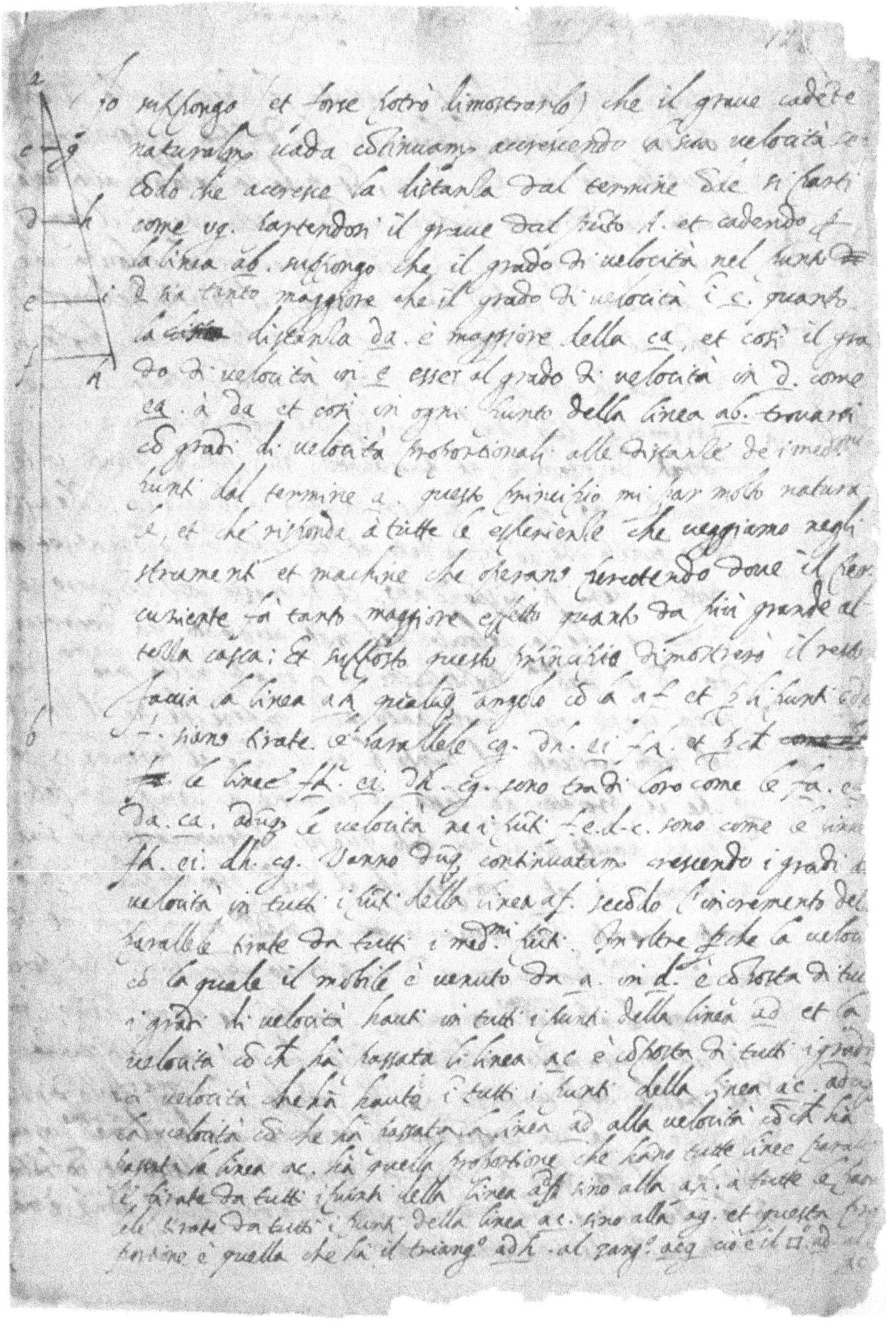

Fig. 6.1 Ms. Gal. 72, Folio 128r.

> not what objection of the bullet of the harquebus: the fire here muddies the force of the instance. But let us say: a strong arm, firing an arrow with a Turkish bow, passes totally through a plank; and if the arrow descends from the height to which the arm with the bow can draw, it shall be very little passed. I believe that the instance is perhaps slight, but I do not know what else to say.

The problem that kept him «in doubt» occupies the rest of the letter and is, as Sarpi admitted, formulated in Peripatetic terms: supposing that a same force pushes materials of different specific weight (gold and silver), he asked if they would receive equal impressed force, if they reach the same distance and if they have the same velocity. It almost seems as if he had read the *De motu*.

Galileo, answering, informed Brother Paolo Sarpi by letter of the first mathematical law in the history of mechanics in a few simple words[270]:

> Thinking over the question of motion in which, to prove the events I had observed, I lacked a totally indubitable principle that could be put forward as an axiom and I resorted to a proposition which has much that is natural and obvious; and having supposed this, I then prove the rest, *i.e.* that spaces passed through by the natural motion are in double proportion of the times, and in consequence the spaces passed through in equal times are like odd numbers *ab unitate* and the other things.

I have already transcribed part of the letter but it is so important that I do not mind repeating it. The spaces travelled are measured in successive units of time as happens when a pendulum is used, and they depend on it quadratically; the velocities are measured in relation to the space travelled and depend on it linearly. In Ms. Gal 72 there is a folio[271], contemporary to the letter, that deals with the same subject matter in much more detail; let us read it:

> I suppose (and perhaps I shall be able to prove) that the heavy body falling naturally increases its velocity continuously as the distance from the limit whence it left increases:, *e.g.*, if the body leaves from point *a* and falls along the line *ab* I suppose that the degree of velocity in point *d* is as much greater than the degree of velocity at *c*, as the distance *da* is greater than *ca*, and so the degree of velocity at *e* to the degree of velocity at *d* as *ea* to *da*, and so at every point of the line *ab* we find degrees of velocity proportional to the distances of those same points from the limit (fig. 6.1). It seems to me that this principle is very natural and that it corresponds to all the experiments that we see in the instruments and machines that operate by percussion, where the percussor has an effect that much greater the greater the height it falls from: and having supposed this principle I shall prove the rest.

---

[270] G.G., Vol. X, p. 115, letter dated 16 October 1604.

[271] From G.G.N.M Folios 128r and 128v. Drake's identification: Watermark type C9. Drake's description: House 32 × 18 mm. Date of earliest letter with this watermark is October 1604. I have given the text in the edition offered by G.G.N.M.

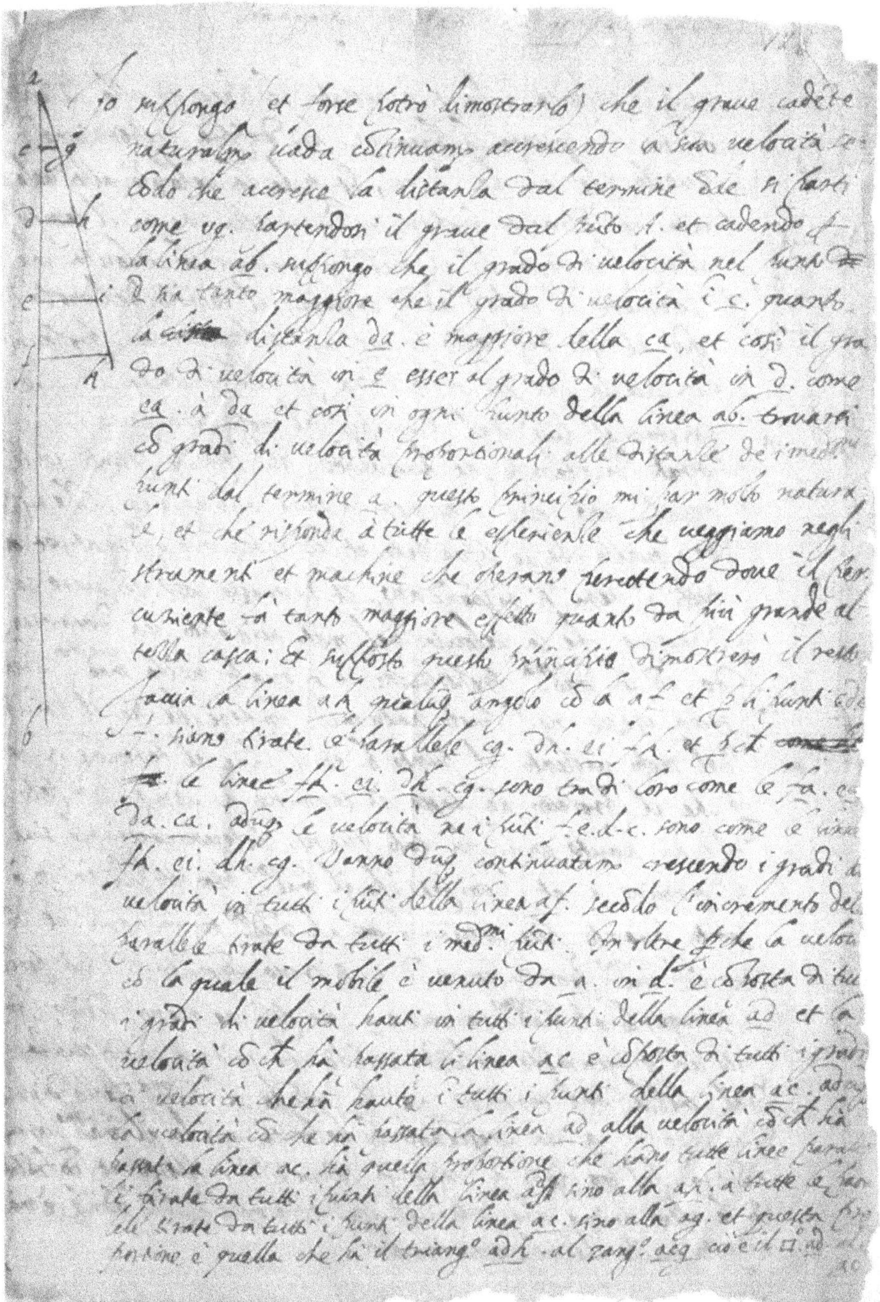

Io suppongo (et forse potrò dimostrarlo) che il grave cadente
naturalm.te vada continuam.te accrescendo la sua velocità se-
condo che accresce la distanza dal termine onde si partì
come v.g. partendosi il grave dal punto a. et cadendo p.
la linea ab. suppongo che il grado di velocità nel punto
d sia tanto maggiore che il grado di velocità in c. quanto
la distanza da. è maggiore della ca, et così il gra-
do di velocità in e esser al grado di velocità in d. come
ea. à da et così in ogni punto della linea ab. trovarsi
co gradi di velocità proporzionali alle distanze de i med.mi
punti dal termine a. questo principio mi par molto natura-
le, et che risponda à tutte le esperienze che veggiamo negli
strumenti et machine che operano percotendo dove il per-
cuziente fà tanto maggiore effetto quanto da più grande al-
tezza casca: Et supposto questo principio dimostrerò il resto.
Faccia la linea ak qualunque angolo co la af et per li punti c d
e f siano tirate le parallele cg. dh. ei. fk. et perchè
le linee fk. ei. dh. cg. sono tra di loro come le fa. ea.
da. ca. adunque le velocità nei punti f.e.d.c. sono come le linee
fk. ei. dh. cg. vanno dunque continuatim crescendo i gradi di
velocità in tutti i punti della linea af. secondo l'incremento delle
parallele tirate da tutti i med.mi punti. In oltre perchè la velocità
co la quale il mobile è venuto da a. in d. è composta di tutti
i gradi di velocità hauti in tutti i punti della linea ad et la
velocità co che ha passata la linea ac è composta di tutti i gradi
di velocità che ha hauto in tutti i punti della linea ac. adunque
la velocità co che ha passata la linea ad alla velocità co che ha
passata la linea ac. ha quella proportione che hanno tutte linee paral-
lele tirate da tutti i punti della linea ad sino alla ah. a tutte le par-
allele tirate da tutti i punti della linea ac. sino alla ag. et questa pro-
portione è quella che ha il triang.o adh. al triang.o acg cioè il □ ad al □ ac

Fig. 6.1 Ms. Gal. 72, Folio 128r.

> [...] The distances then from the beginning of the motion are like the squares of the times and, dividing, the spaces travelled through in equal times are like the odd numbers *ab unitate*: which corresponds to what I have always said and observed by experiment; and so all the truths match.

The note shows that Galileo has made considerable progress, even if something of the previous century still lingers in his thinking; for example, to justify the claimed proportion between space and velocity he uses the argument of the greater effect that a *percussor* has when falling from a greater height. A great innovation, as well as of course as the law of motion, is the introduction into his reasoning on instantaneous velocity (the *degree* of velocity). The letter continues with an unfortunate and impossible attempt to reconcile the quadratic dependence of space on time with the velocity that grows proportionally to the space travelled.

The conclusion of the theoretical part is particularly interesting because he claims to have known for a considerable time (as revealed by that «*I have always said*») that the space travelled increases with the square of time but even to have «*observed by experiment*»[272].

Finally Galileo answers the question that Sarpi had asked, confirming the symmetry between upward motion (still described by the Aristotelian term of violent motion) and downward motion (natural motion).

> And if these things are true, I show that the velocity of violent motion decreases with the same proportion with which, in the same straight line, natural motion grows. So let the beginning of the violent motion be point *b*, and the end be limit *a*. And in order that the projectile does not pass limit *a*, so the impetus that it had in *b* was such as could push it as far as limit *a*; and the impetus that the same projectile has in *f* is as much as can push it to the same limit *a*; and being the same projectile in *e*, *d*, *c*, it is found joined with driving forces able to push it to the same limit *a*, neither more nor less: so the impetus rightly wanes as the distance of the mobile from limit *a* decreases. But like the same distance from limit *a* the velocity grows when the same heavy body falls from point *a*, as was supposed above and compared to our other first observations and demonstrations: then that which we wanted to prove is shown.

[272] From G.G.N.M, Folio 128v.

7. Folio 107v: The experimental confirmation of the law of motion

One of the papers in Ms. Gal. 72 with the watermark from his Paduan period[273] is Folio 107v and fig. 7.1 shows the part that concerns motion. Many scholars[274] have proposed various interpretations of it, convinced that it shows the results of an experiment on an inclined plane in which a sphere is allowed to descend with zero initial velocity.

Anyone examining the document and reflecting on the calculations, all similar to one another, which succeed each other from top to bottom in a kind of progression, may wonder if between one operation and another Galileo is measuring something. The calculations are linked together by the table in which the results of the operations are gathered together: it seems almost as if the table had been composed while Galileo was doing the calculations, which followed step by step as he measured the distances on the inclined plane.

If it were not for the table the calculations would be rather mysterious. So let us look at the table, made up of three columns: in the first column (which is written very close to the edge of the paper and is rather uneven and may perhaps have been added at the end) we find the series of the squares of the integer numbers from 1 to 8; in the second there is the series of the integer numbers 1, 2, ..., 8 and in the third column there are the results of the calculations. Remembering that Ms. Gal. 72, with very few exceptions, only contains notes that concern motion it is natural to recognise in the second column on the left the units of time (number of oscillations

---

[273] G.G.N.M.: «Crossbow, form 1. Drake's identification: Watermark type 6a. Drake's description: Thin crossbow 36 × 35 mm».

[274] Bibliography according to G.G.N.M.: DAMEROW P. *et al.*, *Exploring the Limits of Preclassical Mechanics*, New York, 1992, pp. 150, 163; DRAKE S., *Galileo at Work: His Scientific Biography*, Chicago-London, 1978, pp. 86-91, 96-98, 101, 112, 131; DRAKE S., *Galileo: Pioneer Scientist*, Toronto, 1990, pp. 9-14, 30-31, 95-98; NAYLOR R.H., *Galileo's Theory of Projectile Motion*, Isis, Vol. 71, 1980, pp. 550-570; DRAKE S., *Galileo's Constant*, Nuncius, Vol. 2, 1987, pp. 43, 46, plate 6, 51-52; NAYLOR R.H, *Galileo's Theory of Motion: Processes of Conceptual Change in the Period 1604-1610*, Annals of Science, Vol. 34, 1977, pp. 371-377, 380-381; DRAKE S., Physis, Vol. 16, 1974, *Galileo's Work on Free Fall in 1604*, p. 312; NAYLOR R.H., *Galileo: the Search for the Parabolic Trajectory*, Annals of Science, Vol. 33, 1976, p. 156, footnote; NAYLOR R.H., *The Role of Experiment in Galileo's Early Work on the Law of Fall*, Annals of Science, Vol. 37, 1980, pp. 372-373, 376-377; DRAKE S., *Galileo Gleanings XVIII: Galileo's 1604 Fragment on Falling Bodies*, British Journal for the History of Science, Vol. 4, 1969, p. 350; DRAKE S., *Galileo's Notes on Motion Arranged in Probable Order of Composition and Presented in Reduced Facsimile*, Florence, 1979, Istituto e Museo di Storia della Scienza, p. LII; WALLACE W.A., *Galileo and his Sources: the Heritage of the Collegio Romano in Galileo's Science*, Princeton, 1984, p. 267.

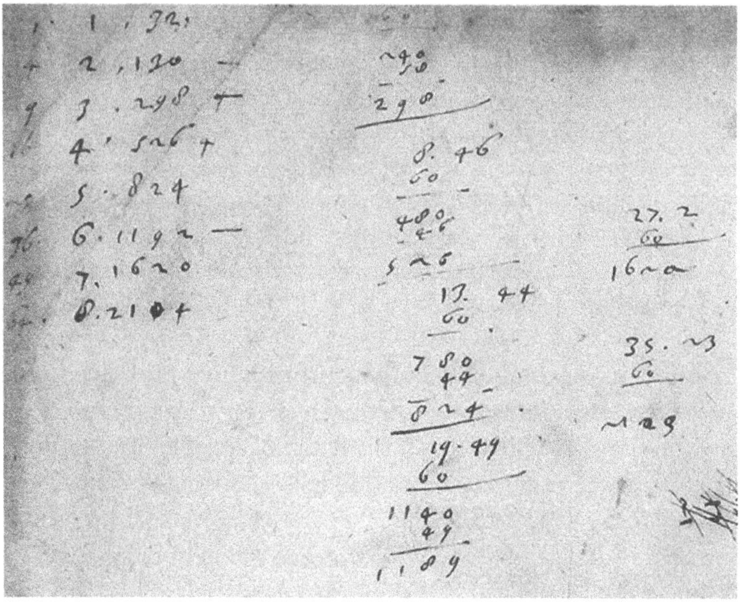

Fig. 7.1 Ms. Gal. 72, Folio 107v.

of the pendulum ranging from 1 to 8), in the first column the squares of the times and in the third the spaces travelled[275].

The calculations that appear on the right in fig. 7.1, with which the *table* on the left was constructed, are perfectly comprehensible if we imagine the method followed to measure the spaces travelled in 1, 2, …8 oscillations. The measuring instrument is, perhaps, a pole two or three *braccia* long, along which the Florentine quarters of *braccia* are marked. The first quarter of a *braccio* on the pole is further subdivided into *soldi* and into *piccioli*[276].

---

[275] I cannot accept the hypothesis that the table constructed by Galileo gives the measurements, taken at equal distances, on a suspended chain, to see if it assumes the appearance of a parabola. The proposal was put forward by JÜRGEN RENN, PETER DAMEROW, SIMONE RIEGER, and MICHELE CAMEROTA, in *Hunting the white elephant: when and how did Galileo discover the laws of fall* (Max Plank Institute for the History of Science, Berlin, 1998), preprint n° 97. The authors, considering a maximum depth of 2123 points, calculated the distance between the points of suspension, arriving at 24 000, exactly one hundred *braccia*, that is to say about 55 meters, which is the height of the Leaning Tower of Pisa.

[276] In his experiments on the inclined plane did Galileo use the *braccio a terra* or the *braccio da panno*? Over time the *braccio a terra* was always less commonly used but Galileo indicated it precisely in the *Dialogo* (G.G., Vol. VII, pp. 250-251) when he calculated the time necessary for a heavy body to travel the «distance from the lunar concave to the centre of the Earth, which is 196 000 miles, making the distance of the concave 56 semidiameters of the Earth, as the modern author does, and the semidiameter of the Earth 3500 miles of 3000 *braccia* each, as are our Italian miles»; and a few lines later he explained how he arrived at this time: «having (as I have said) observed with diligent experiment how such a mobile passes, falling, the height of 100 *braccia* in 5 seconds, we shall say: If 100 *braccia* are passed in 5 seconds, 588 000 000 *braccia* (for such are 56 semidiameters of the Earth) in how many seconds will be passed?». M. Mersenne in his *Harmonie Universelle*, wrote on p. 87 that the *braccio* that

Fig. 7.2 Leonardo Ximenes: *I sei primi elementi della geometria piana…* (The first six elements of plane geometry…), Venice, 1752.

Figure 7.2 is taken from an engraving from 1752, dry printed to avoid the distortions that occur on damp paper during printing, so as to give the exact measurement of the Florentine quarter of a *braccio*, of the Parisian half foot and of the ancient Roman half foot (the size of the engraving has not been retained): in the representation of the quarter of a *braccio* only the first *soldo* is subdivided into 12 *piccioli*.

We cannot exclude the possibility that Galileo used a rolled up tape on which the distances were marked in quarters of *braccia* and in *soldi*, like those still used today by topographers, architects and all those who have to deal with large dimensions, and that he measured space of less than a quarter of a *braccio* with a ruler subdivided into 60 *piccioli*.

Figure 7.3, which is taken from *LE FORTIFICAZIONI DI BUONAIUTO LORINI … IN VENETIA MDCIX*, (an expanded re-edition of the book already published in 1597), seems part of a tape where only the *soldi* are marked but not the *piccioli*.

If we agree on this initial hypothesis, the rest becomes clear: Galileo, perhaps helped by an assistant[277], let the ball descend along the inclined plane exactly when the pendulum passed

Galileo used measured 20 inches «*de pied de Roy dont on use à Paris … puis que nous donnons 5000 pieds à un mille d'Italie que contient 3000 brasses*» (of the King's foot that we use in Paris ...since we consider that 5000 feet form an Italian mile that contains 3000 *braccia*). Remembering that the King's foot is divided into 12 inches and that in 1635 the foot measured 0.3266 metres we have a measurement for the *braccio* equal to 0.544 metres. Immediately afterwards however, on p. 88, he added that while he was writing he had been given the measurement of the Florentine *braccio* «*la quelle a justement 21 poulce & demi de Roy*» (which is exactly 21 and a half king's inches) which today corresponds to 0.585 metres. For me what he adds is interesting: «*ce quart de brasse demeure divisé en 60 parties, & consequemment la brasse se divise en 240 parties*» (this quarter of a *braccio* is divided into 60 parts and consequently the *braccio* is divided into 240 parts), because these *parties* are the *piccioli*. Leonardo Ximenes, in his book *I sei primi elementi…*, Venice, 1752, on p. 18 wrote: «Two *braccia* were in use amongst our ancestors; which some authors clumsily confuse. The first they call *braccio a terra*, which they used to measure land and geographical matters. The second they called *braccio da panno*, precisely because it is used in the trading and calculating of cloth. Now in our days this second *braccio* has become so common, even when measuring land, that the former is almost in disuse. So this *braccio da panno* is divided into 20 *soldi*, and each *soldo* into 12 *piccioli*».

277 There was no shortage of them: since 1599 he had had the skilful mechanic Marcantonio Mazzoleni available, and from 1606 the faithful Alessandro Piersanti, but he could also fall back on some of the students in his house or his friends. I also had help: Maurizio Meliani and Stefano Gennai took the measurements with me while Alberto Di Lieto did the statistical calculations in this paragraph for me.

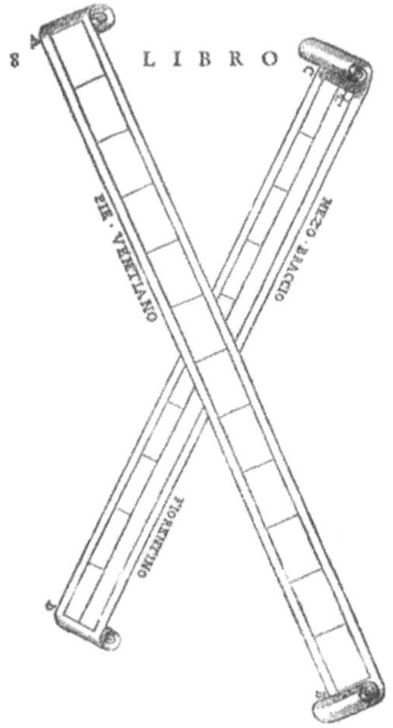

Fig. 7.3 The Florentine half *braccio* and the Venetian foot.

through the vertical and each time he marked on the plane the space passed after a certain number of oscillations, without interrupting to measure the distance. Probably he repeated the experiment several times for the same number of oscillations until he was certain that the motion had lasted exactly as long as the oscillations. Then he measured with the ruler or tape all the distances travelled: for each one he wrote on the sheet of paper the number of quarters of a *braccio,* with next to them the number of *piccioli* (always less than 60) necessary to complete the distance; he turned the whole distance into *piccioli*, multiplying by 60 the number of quarters of *braccia*, and added to the result the *piccioli* he had already found.

For the first two oscillations of the pendulum there are no calculations because the distance is less than a quarter of a *braccio*. For some distances his calculations give results different from those that he then inserted in the table: for 2 oscillations an isolated 128 appears but in the table there is 130; for 6 oscillations he calculated 1189 *piccioli* compared to the 1192 given in the table, for 7 oscillations 1622 *piccioli* compared to the 1620 in the table and finally for 8 oscillations Galileo measured[278] 2123 but then wrote only 2104.

What follows is an analysis of Folio 107v, a document of fundamental importance for the history of Galileo's ideas.

[278] For four measurements, those for 3-4-5-6 oscillations, Galileo wrote the number of quarters of *braccia* and next to them the *piccioli* that complete the measurement, then he multiplied the first number by 60 and underneath the result he wrote the missing *piccioli* and the total. When he came to 7 and 8 oscillations he avoided doing the addition and wrote the remaining *piccioli* directly, 2 and 23, superimposing them on the zeros of the results; in particular for the last measurement he wrote $35 \times 60 = 2100$, and above the two zeros wrote 23, so that the result seems to be 2129 but it is only a combined effect of the zero with the superimposed three.

7.1 *Analysis of the document*

If the plane and the groove that guided the sphere had been without defects, if Galileo had carried out the experiment to perfection, if his measurements had been absolutely precise, dividing the space travelled S by the square of time t we should find a practically constant value, as foreseen by the law of motion in its mathematically ideal formulation, $S = pt^2$; in particular we should obtain for the space travelled after n oscillations of the pendulum: $S_n = n^2 S_1$.

In the table the following information is collected: in the first column the number of oscillations 1, 2, ...8 is written progressively; in the second column are the spaces $S_n^G (n = 1, 2, \ldots 8)$, measured by Galileo[279]; in the third column are the ratios S_n^G/n^2, all consistent with one another. Taking the average of the third column we get $S_M \approx 32.81$ points. A more sophisticated statistical elaboration produces an almost identical result: $p \approx 32.95$, $dp \approx 0.06$, so the percentage error is $dp/p \sim 0.2$ %.

Alberto Di Lieto, who made this analysis, assures me that the result is stable and does not depend on how the errors on individual pieces of data are considered. This is remarkably precise, so much so that some scholars had doubts, but we shall see that it is not difficult to arrive at a precision of the same order in experiments carried out today according to Galileo's method, and I have no doubts about the truthfulness of Galileo's data, even while taking the following observations duly into account.

In the reconstruction of the experiment it is evident that the measurement of the space travelled in a single second is very uncertain because of the difficulty of making the beginning of the motion coincide with the pendulum passing over the vertical, so it is possible that the number of 32 *piccioli* indicated in the table may not be the result of measurement and that Galileo may have arrived at it by dividing by 4 the space that he wrote down next to it, 128 *piccioli*, travelled in two oscillations, then taken to 130 in the table.

Even measuring the space travelled in 8 seconds is difficult, because of the great velocity reached by the ball. The substitution of 2123 by 2104 could be explained thus: Galileo must have noticed the great discrepancy of 75 points compared to what is obtained by multiplying the first space of 32 points by $8^2 = 64$; for this reason he preferred to use the space travelled in 4 oscillations, from which he extrapolated the space of the 8 oscillations, $526 \times 4 = 2104$, because he believed that the central value was more reliable. But this is only a hypothesis.

The relationship $S_n^T = 32.81\ n^2$ allows us to reconstruct the series of values that ideally verify the law of motion exactly (fourth column) and to estimate the gap between the results of Galileo's experiments Galileo and the values reconstructed theoretically (fifth column). The difference is always extremely small.

We now intend to prove that in Folio 107v the essential data are written down of one of the many experiments carried out around 1604, on the basis of which Galileo claimed in good faith for 30 years that a body falls from a height of 100 *braccia* in 5 seconds, then to correct the time assigned, which he reduces to 4 *pulse beats*, only after 1632, probably after the experiments on motion done with his new machine to study percussion.

---

[279] Note that when the result of the calculation done by Galileo does not coincide with the number he then wrote in the table both numbers have been inserted and the first number is the value chosen by Galileo for his table.

n	S_n^G	S_n^G / n^2	$S_n^T = 32.81n^2$	$S_n^G - S_n^T$	$(S_n^G - S_n^T)/S_n^G$
1	32	32/1 = 32	S_1 = 32.8	– 0.8	– 2.4%
2	130 / 128	130/4 = 32.5	S_2 = 131.2	– 1.2	– 1.0%
3	298	298/9 = 33.1	S_3 = 295.3	+ 2.7	+ 0.9%
4	526	526/16 = 32.9	S_4 = 525.0	+ 1.0	+ 0.2%
5	824	824/25 = 32.9	S_5 = 820.3	+ 3.7	+ 0.5%
6	1192 / 1189	1192/36 = 33.0	S_6 = 1181.2	+ 10.8	+ 0.9%
7	1620 / 1622	1620/49 = 33.1	S_7 = 1609.6	+12.2	+ 0.8%
8	2104 / 2123	2104/64 = 32.9	S_8 = 2100.0	+ 4.0	+ 0.2%

Everything leads us to believe that Galileo dedicated a lot of time to his experiments on the inclined plane and he must certainly have kept in his archive many papers describing the way to proceed and the results obtained. Unfortunately, after the death of Vincenzo Viviani who had taken care of and expanded the Galileo archive, his great grandsons Carlo and Angelo Panzanini looked after the manuscripts with such little care to the point that they (or a servant of theirs) actually sold a number of sheets to the grocer Cioci, who used them to wrap up *mortadella* (boloney)[280] or whatever. All this can explain why only a relic of these experiments has come down to us, Folio 107v.

7.2 *Reconstruction of the experiment of Folio 107v*

The hypothesis we start from is that the inclined plane (fig. 7.4 and 7.5) and the ball are those described by Galileo in the *Discorsi*, and therefore:

1) the plane is about 12 *braccia a terra* long, equivalent to 6.6 m;

2) the groove in the plane is about a finger wide;

3) the distances are measured according to the ancient and traditional division of the Florentine *braccio* into 20 *soldi* subdivided in turn into 12 *piccioli*, each of about 2.3 millimetres (for the *braccio a terra*) or 2.4 millimetres (for the *braccio da panno*).

4) for the ball, which Galileo described as being about the size of a walnut, some commercially produced spheres were used with diameters:

[280] See: *Per l'Edizione Nazionale delle Opere di Galileo Galilei … esposizione e disegno di ANTONIO FAVARO*, Florence,1888, p. 17.

$d_0 = 1''3/16$ (30.160 mm),
$d_1 = 1''\ 1/4$ (31.751 mm),
$d_2 = 1''\ 3/8$ (34.925 mm),
$d_3 = 1''7/16$ (36.125 mm),
$d_4 = 1''1/2$ (38.100 mm).

The museum exhibition[281] *Il Laboratorio di Galileo Galilei* (now at Pavia University) has amongst its pieces of apparatus an inclined plane with a groove, built recently following the description[282] found in the *Discorsi*, and it is with this plane that Folio 107v has been studied.

On the inclined plane the ball always starts from stationary and the space travelled is measured from the position of the ball at the beginning of the motion; which is why the exact motion equation is

$$S(t) = [g \sin \alpha - g_A]\ Kt^2/2\,.$$

In the equation the symbols have the following meaning:
S(*t*): space travelled in time *t*;
g: acceleration due to gravity, which for Padua I suppose to be equal to 9.806 $\mathrm{ms^{-2}}$;
g_A: deceleration due to rolling resistance;
K indicates the numerical value of the expression $[1-(c/d)^2]\ [7/5-(c/d)^2]^{-1}$;
c: width of the channel (~24 mm);
d: diameter of the ball (da ∅ = 30.16 mm a ∅ = 38.10 mm);
α: angle of inclination.

In the experiments the spheres roll resting on the corners of a groove about 24 millimetres wide and we find a decreasing reduction in the acceleration as the diameter grows, due to the values assumed by *K*, which are: $K_0 \approx 0.4783$, $K_1 \approx 0.5103 - K_2 \approx 0.5689 - K_3 \approx 0.5827 - K_4 \approx 0.6013$. (See appendix D for further examination of the effects of the groove.)

The effective acceleration $a_{\text{eff}} = [g \sin \alpha - g_A]K$ is heavily influenced by friction, which is important for very small angles. An approximate check was done on the effects of friction, launching the ball on the plane in a horizontal position, after having inserted at the bottom of the groove, at an appropriate distance, four sensors to detect the times: a deceleration of $g_A = 0.166\ \mathrm{ms^{-2}}$ was found. This method however, for various reasons, is not completely reliable[283]; in any case, the result indicates that g_A cannot be neglected because it is comparable to the effective acceleration $a_{\text{eff}} = 2S_8^T/64 = 0.151\ \mathrm{ms^{-2}}$.

---

[281] More information is available at: http://.www.illaboratoriodigalileogalilei.it

[282] G.G., Vol. VIII, *Discorsi*, pp. 212-213.

[283] The deceleration g_A can be estimated using the motion equation for $n = 8$ and introducing the data obtained into the reconstructions of the experiment. For the sphere with diameter ∅ = 34.925 mm, the figures are: $\alpha_2 = 2.06°$, $S_8 = 4.911$ m, $K_2 \approx 0.5689$ and we obtain $-g_A = \mathrm{g} \sin \alpha_2 - 2S_8/K_2\, t_8^2 = (0.3525 - 0.2698)\ \mathrm{ms^{-2}} = 0.083\ \mathrm{ms^{-2}}$ For the sphere with diameter ∅ = 31.751 mm, the figures are: $\alpha_1 = 2.69°$, $S_8 = 4.710$ m, $K_1 \approx 0.5103$, and we obtain $-g_A = g \sin \alpha_1 - 2S_8/K_1\, t_8^2 = (0.4608 - 0.2956)\ \mathrm{ms^{-2}} = 0.165\ \mathrm{ms^{-2}}$.

Fig. 7.4 Inclined plane 12 *braccia* long.

In order to reconstruct the experiment some necessary information is missing and must be recovered another way. Indeed in the Folio two essential pieces of data are not indicated:

a) the angle of inclination;

b) the unit of measurement of time, which depends both on the length of the pendulum and on the choice between simple oscillations or complete oscillations.

In accordance with the hypothesis that Folio 107v had something to do with the claim «100 *braccia* in 5 seconds» we decided to start from the assumption that the pendulum used by Galileo *beat* a second.

With this choice the only unknown is the angle of inclination α.

The pendulum used to reconstruct the experiment makes on average 20 complete oscillations in 19.88 seconds, with an amplitude that reduces progressively from 20° to 10°. The error of 6/1000 of a second per simple oscillation is comparable to that due to the non constancy of the amplitude.

To determine the angle α the path of 1620 points done in 7 seconds is chosen (the 8 second path was rejected because of conflicting data), placing a barrier across the inclined plane at a distance equivalent to 3.717 m, and varying the inclination until the path takes exactly seven seconds.

We begin with a sphere with a diameter of 1 and 1/4 inches, that is to say 31.75 mm. Following the procedure shown, when the plane is in the position in which the distance of 3.717 m is travelled in 7 seconds exactly[284], the difference in height of the ends of the plane is measured and we find $\sin\alpha_1 = (1.279 - 0.977)/6.66 = 0.0453453$, from which $\alpha_1 = 2.69°$.

Keeping the inclination $\alpha_1 = 2.69°$ fixed, we measure the space travelled in 8 oscillations letting the sphere go when the pendulum passes through the vertical and after the seventh oscillation we insert a foil against which the pendulum strikes when it completes the eighth oscillation. The right distance is reached when the sounds of the pendulum and the sphere striking their respective barriers coincide[285]. In the same way all the other paths are determined ($n = 1, 2,\ldots 6$).

The results are given in the second column of the following table. We use the distance $S_7 = 3.717$ m, with which we determined the angle of inclination, to calculate the ratio $S_7/49 = 0.07586$ and thus to construct the third column. In the fourth column the percentage difference between measured values and calculated ones is given. The discrepancies in percentages between the measured values and the calculated ones are very large and we shall see later that the reason for the differences between the measurements and the theoretical expectations is not a question of precise measurement but rather is due to variations in the width of the groove along the path.

The following table contains the results obtained.

Ø 1"1/4 = 0.03175 m, $K \approx 0.5103$, $\alpha_1 = 2.69°$ (measurements in metres)			
n	S_n	$S_n^T = 0,07586n^2$	$[S_n - S_n^T]/S_n$
1	0.108	$S_1 = 0.076$	+ 29.6%
2	0.371	$S_2 = 0.303$	+ 18.3%
3	0.789	$S_3 = 0.683$	+ 13.4 %
4	1.321	$S_4 = 1.214$	+ 7.5 %
5	2.007	$S_5 = 1.896$	+ 5.5%
6	2.715	$S_6 = 2.731$	– 0.6%
7	3.717	$S_7 = 3.717$	0 %
8	4.710	$S_8 = 4.855$	– 3.1%

The following table gives the same measurements expressed in points, for a comparison with Galileo's data.

[284] In this search for the angle of inclination, a chronometer with hundredths of a second was used instead of the pendulum with the following result (in seconds): 7.03 – 6.97 – 7.01 – 7.06 – 7.03 – 6.95 – 6.93 – 6.99 – 7.10 – 6.99. The average is 7.006 seconds.

[285] The method is fairly similar to that followed by Stillman Drake in *The Role of Music in Galileo's Experiments*, Scientific American, Vol. 235, 1975, pp. 98-104.

$\varnothing$ 1" 1/4 = 31.75, $K \approx 0.5103$, $\alpha_1 = 2.69°$ (measurements in points)			
n	S_n	$S_n^T = 33.063n^2$	$[S_n - S_n^T]/S_n$
1	47.07	$S_1 = 33.1$	+ 29.6%
2	161.7	$S_2 = 132.2$	+ 18.3%
3	343.9	$S_3 = 297.6$	+ 13.4 %
4	575.8	$S_4 = 529.9$	+ 7.5 %
5	951.4	$S_5 = 826.6$	+ 5.5%
6	1287.0	$S_6 = 1190.3$	– 0.6%
7	1620.1	$S_7 = 1620{,}1$	0 %
8	2052.9	$S_8 = 2116.0$	– 3.1%

A. Di Lieto calculated the value of p and of the percentage error in the measurements in meters obtaining: $p = 0.0786$, d$p = 0.0025$ and thus d$p/p \approx 3\%$, which is about 10 times greater than the percentage error found in Galileo's data.

Passing on to the sphere with a diameter of 1 and 3/8 inches = 34.925 mm, the inclination necessary to travel 3.717 m in 7 seconds is arrived at by the procedure followed for the previous sphere but this time using the pendulum. Measuring the heights of the ends of the plane, we calculate $\sin \alpha_2 = (1.231 - 0.992)/6.66 = 0.0361862$, from which we obtain the angle $\alpha = 2.06°$

Keeping the inclination $\alpha = 2.06°$ fixed, as in the previous experiment, the space travelled in 7 oscillations is determined and then the other paths (n = 1, 2,...6 and 8) each time making the sphere bang into the barrier to coincide with the bang of the pendulum at the n-th oscillation. The distances so determined were inserted into the second column of the table that follows.

The ratio $S_7/49 = 0.07586$ is used to construct the third column, containing a possible theoretical expectation. In the fourth column the percentage difference between the measured values and the percentage calculated in the third column is given. The percentage differences between the measured values and the calculated ones are very large here too.

The fifth and sixth columns refer to the measurement of the space actually travelled, taken by a video camera[286]: note that checking with a video camera verifies the great precision of the measurements made with the pendulum, in contrast with their apparent irregularity and distance from our theoretical expectations (third and fourth columns).

[286] To determine the times the filmed sequence was downloaded from the video camera to a computer, so that the time was superimposed; to determine the space travelled a measuring tape was fixed along the groove before filming. The position reached by the sphere each time was measured by stopping the image after n = 1, 2, ...8 seconds. The start position is not in the video camera's field of view, but the moment of departure is marked by a sharp blow struck simultaneously with the release of the sphere and is then read on the time superimposed in the computer. All the results are the average of 6 measurements checked on the computer, reviewing 6 successive repetitions of the experiment. In determining the start time there is an uncertainty estimated of the order of 1/20 of a second.

Fig. 7.5 An inclined plane 12 *braccia* long.

The statistical analysis of the measurements gives the following result: p = 0.0796 , dp = 0.0025 , dp/p ~ 3 %. For the data obtained with the video camera we have: p = 0.0791 , dp = 0.0024 , dp/p ~ 3%.

Instead the difference $\Delta S_n/S_n = [S_n - S_n^{\text{videocamera}}] / S_n$ varies from –0.1% to +0.8% in the interval between n = 3 and n = 7, a result that confirms the truthfulness of Galileo's data.

∅ 1″ 3/8 , $K_2 \approx 0.5689$, $\alpha_2 = 2.06°$ (measurements in metres)					
n	S_n	$S_n^T = 0.07586n^2$	$[S_n - S_n^T]/S_n$	$S_n^{\text{videocamera}}$	$\Delta S_n/S_n$
1	0.114	$S_1 = 0.076$	+ 33.3%	0.104	+ 8.8%
2	0.399	$S_2 = 0.303$	+ 24.3 %	0.393	+ 1.5%
3	0.784	$S_3 = 0.683$	+ 12.9 %	0.785	– 0.1%
4	1.313	$S_4 = 1.214$	+ 7.5 %	1.311	+ 0.15%
5	1.968	$S_5 = 1.896$	+ 3.7%	1.981	– 0.7%
6	2.766	$S_6 = 2.731$	+ 1.3%	2.766	0%
7	3.717	$S_7 = 3.717$	0 %	3.688	+ 0.8%
8	4.911	$S_8 = 4.855$	+ 1.1 %	4.824	+ 1.8%

The following table gives the same measurements expressed in points:

$\varnothing$ 1″ 3/8, $K_2 \approx 0.5689$, $\alpha_2 = 2.06°$ (measurements in points)					
n	S_n	$S_n^T = 33.063n^2$	$[S_n - S_n^T]/S_n$	S_n videocamera	$\Delta S_n/S_n$
1	49.7	$S_1 = 33.1$	+ 33.4 %	45.3	+ 8.8%
2	173.9	$S_2 = 132.2$	+ 24.0 %	171.3	+ 1.5%
3	341.7	$S_3 = 297.6$	+ 12.9 %	342.1	– 0.1%
4	572.3	$S_4 = 529.9$	+ 7.4 %	571.4	+ 0.16%
5	857.8	$S_5 = 826.6$	+ 3.6 %	863.4	– 0.7%
6	1205.6	$S_6 = 1190.3$	+ 1.3 %	1205.6	0%
7	1620.1	$S_7 = 1620{,}1$	0 %	1607.5	+ 0.8%
8	2140.5	$S_8 = 2116.0$	+ 1.1 %	2102.6	+ 1.8%

It was not difficult to identify the causes of the irregularity of the downward path along the inclined plane; the most important of these is the non constant width of the groove and in consequence the variations along the path of the correction K due to rolling. The table that follows contains the measurements of the width c, taken every 50 cm (the second measurement is the width at the ball's starting position).

metres	c (mm)	metres	c (mm)	metres	c (mm)	metres	c (mm)
0.0	23.0	1.5	24.0	3.5	23.3	5.5	23.7
0.22	23.6	2.0	23.7	4.0	23.3	6.0	24.2
0.5	23.9	2.5	23.5	4.5	23.3	6.5	23.9
1.0	24.5	3.0	23.3	5.0	23.4	6.66	

From the formula $K = [1 - (c/d)^2]\ [7/5 - (c/d)^2]^{-1}$ with $d = 0.0349$ we obtain average values for K, along the partial paths. The percentage difference between maximum and minimum $(0.5808–0.5639)/0.58 = 0.03$ is the same as the ratio $dp/p \sim 3\%$ found in the measurements on the inclined plane.

Position	c_m	$(c_m/d)^2$	K_m
0.22–0.5	0.02375	0.445719	0.5731
0.5–1.0	0.02420	0.480817	0.5648
1.0–1.5	0.02425	0.482806	**0.5639**
1.5–2.0	0,02385	0.467010	0.5713
2.0–2.50	0.02360	0.457270	0.5757
2.5–3.0	0.02340	0.449553	0.5791
3.0–3.5	0.02330	0.445719	**0.5808**
3.5–4.0	0.02330	0.445719	0.5808
4.0–4.5	0.02330	0.445719	0.5808
4.5–5.0	0.02335	0.447634	0.5800

A second important cause is the irregularity of the edges of the groove, which at some points appear chipped with lack of material and this induces jumps and swerves in the progress of the ball, which loses contact with the groove and thus increases velocity. A more complete study should take into account the possible variation in friction varying with the velocity. The combined effect of the imperfections can be seen in the discrepancies in the measurements compared to the values calculated with the equation of uniformly accelerated motion. There is no doubt that with a better groove the results of the measurements with the pendulum would be closer to the theoretical ones, just as the actual measurements are close to those checked with the video camera. Galileo must have realised the importance of the evenness of the groove and that is why he had it cut with great accuracy and protected it with vellum:

> In a wooden ruler, or measuring rod, about 12 *braccia* long, and half a *braccio* wide in one direction and 3 fingers in the other, a small channel a little wider than a finger was cut into that lesser width; having made it very straight, and cleaned and smoothed it, and having fixed inside it a piece of vellum scraped and polished as much as possible[287] [...]

Only by following the reconstruction of the experiment on Folio 107v and accurately analysing the results obtained, is it possible to appreciate the meaning and value of the words that Galileo devoted to the groove, as the great experimenter informed and warned his readers and those who intended to follow in his footsteps. Nothing can bear witness to the truth and reality of his experiments more than what has been done in this reconstruction, contrary to all those doubting scholars who describe him as a pure theoretician and attribute to him mental processes, even ridiculing the precision of his experiments, as Alexandre Koyré did.

---

[287] G.G., Vol. VIII, *Discorsi*, pp. 212-213.

8. Why «100 *braccia* in 5 seconds»?

The distance travelled on the inclined plane in 5 seconds, which for Galileo was 824 *piccioli*, together with the angle of inclination $\alpha = 2.06°$, obtained with a sphere with a diameter $\varnothing = 34.9$ mm, are the experimental results that led him to make the statement «100 *braccia* in 5 seconds». We have to justify however why we have concentrated our observations with spheres around this diameter. The reason for this is that Galileo suggested using spheres of these sizes when he wrote in the *Discorsi*[288]:

> I use an exquisitely round bronze ball, not larger than a nut; this is rolled [*tirata*] on a metal mirror held not vertically but somewhat tilted, so that the ball in motion runs over it and presses it lightly. In moving, it leaves a parabolic line, very thin, and smoothly traced. This [parabola] will be wider or narrower, according as the ball is rolled higher or lower. From this, we have a clear and sensible experience that the motion of projectiles is made along parabolic lines, an effect first observed by our friend, who also gives a demonstration of it. We shall all see this in his book on motion at the next [*fourth*] meeting. To describe parabolas in this way, the ball must be somewhat warmed and moistened by manipulating it in the hand, so that the traces it will leave shall be more apparent on the mirror.

Guglielmo Libri found in Paris[289] an autograph manuscript by Guidobaldo del Monte, which has the title *Meditatiunculae Guidi Ubaldi e marchionibus Montis Sanctae Mariae de rebus mathematicis* (Meditations of Guidi Ubaldi del Monte on mathematics)and he published some extracts from it in his *Histoire des sciences mathématiques en Italie, depuis la renaissance des lettres jusq'a la fin du dixeptième siècle* (History of mathematical sciences in Italy after the renaissance of liberal arts up to the end of the XVII century) Paris,1838-41, to be precise in Vol. IV, pp. 369-398. Amongst these extracts, I quote one in particular, on page 236 of the Paris manuscript, because it has attracted the attention of many people:

> If a ball is fired from a crossbow or with artillery, or by hand, or with another instrument, over the line of the horizon, it travels the same journey when falling as when rising and the figure is that made by a slack cord, bent down under the horizontal line, being the one and the other natural and violent and it is a line in aspect similar to a parabola and hyperbola (fig. 8.1) and

[288] G.G., Vol.VIII, pp.185-186.

[289] In the *Bibliothèque Royal, suplément latin N° 1058* (now: *Bibliothèque Nationale de Paris, Manuscript, Catalogue No°. Lat. 10246*).

Fig. 8.1

Fig. 8.2

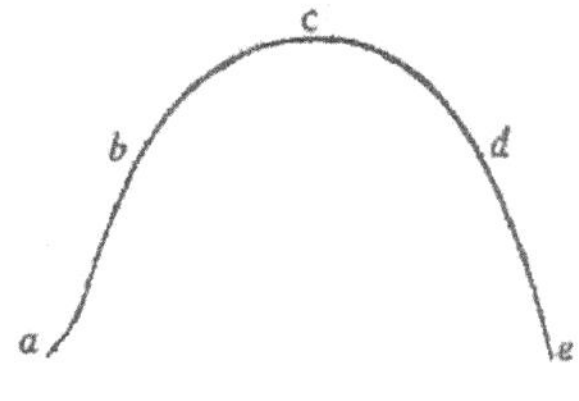

Fig. 8.3

> this was seen better with a chain than with a cord because the cord *a b c* when *a c* are near to part *b* is not drawn close as it should be, because the cord remains stiff in itself (fig. 8.2). As a chain or small chain does not. The experiment of this motion can be done by taking a ball stained with ink, and rolling it on the plane of a board, which should be almost perpendicular to the horizon, so that even though the ball bounces as it moves it makes points however as it travels, from which it is clearly seen just as it rises so also it descends, and it is reasonable thus because the violence that it has acquired in moving upwards makes it happen that in falling it travels similarly overcoming the natural motion in coming down, because the violence that it overcame from *b* to *c*, being conserved, ensures that from *c* to *d* it is equal to *c b* and, descending (fig. 8.3), since the violence is gradually lost, ensures that from *d* to *e* is equal to *b a*, since there is no reason which shows that from *e* towards *d* the violence is totally lost, because although it is continuously being lost towards *a* nevertheless some always remains, which is the reason why towards *e* the weight never travels in a straight line.

The resemblance between this passage by Guidobaldo and the passage in the second day of the *Discorsi*, published thirty years later, is remarkable, especially because Galileo continued his analysis with a detailed description of the way to draw a parabola using a thin chain hanging from two nails fixed to a wall, equidistant from the horizon, «so that marking with points on the wall the path that the chain makes, we shall have described a whole parabola, which with a perpendicular, hanging midway between the two nails, is divided in equal parts».

The resemblance however is not surprising. Galileo had been corresponding with Guidobaldo since 1588; then, after being called to Padua, he met him both at Pesaro, the habitual residence of the Marquis del Monte, and at Montebaroccio, his country residence, on which occasions they were able to carry out some experiments together.

We have seen that the question of the motion of a body thrown upwards had been raised by Brother Paolo Sarpi on 9 October 1604; we recall Sarpi's very important declaration, which concerns Galileo: «so you lately claimed and invented that through the same points it will come back down as those it went up through», that is to say that the velocity with which a projectile leaves is equal to that with which it returns, independently of the path, in a straight line if launched vertically or a parabola if not launched vertically.

Even if we cannot be absolutely certain who first thought of the experiment of launching a sphere *upwards* on a *metal mirror* or on a *board*, to trace the parabolic trajectory, the fact remains that Salviati, (*i.e.* Galileo) had «an exquisitely round bronze ball, no larger than a walnut» to do the experiment with.

A little later, in the *Discorsi*, urged by Simplicio to «bring some experiment of which they say that you have many, which in several cases agree with the conclusions shown», Salviati answered with the well known passage that begins: «in a ruler, ... a very hard bronze ball was made to descend ...».

When we arrive at this point in our reading it is natural to think that the very hard bronze ball descending on the inclined plane is the same as the exquisitely round bronze ball, no larger than a walnut, mentioned a little earlier and the considerations that follow confirm this.

Galileo repeated several times in the *Dialogo* in 1632 that a mobile travels, falling, 100 *braccia* in 5 seconds.
The first time he introduced the question as follows[290]:

> SALVIATI: [...] Getting back to our calculation, already begun, of the time in which a heavy body would fall from the Moon's orbit all the way to the centre of the Earth, and in order not to proceed arbitrarily or at random, but with a rigorous method, let us first seek to make sure by experiments repeated many times how much time is taken by a ball of iron, say, to fall to Earth from a height of one hundred yards [*braccia*].
> SAGREDO: And taking for this purpose a ball of deteminate weight, the same as that for which we shall make the computation of the time of descent from the Moon.
> SALVIATI: That makes no difference at all, for a ball of one, ten, a hundred, or a thousand pounds [*libbre*] will all cover the same hundred yards [*braccia*] in the same time.

And a few lines later he clarifies[291]:

> SALVIATI: [...] let us suppose we want to make the computations for an iron ball of one hundred pounds [*libbre*] which in repeated experiments falls from a height of one hundred yards [*braccia*] in five seconds.

After a few more lines we find how to do the calculations[292]:

> SALVIATI: [...] Therefore having, as I said, by careful experiment observed that such a moving body falling from a height of 100 yards [*braccia*] covers this in 5 seconds, let us say: if 100 yards [*braccia*] are passed in 5 seconds, 588 000 000 (for that is 56 radii of the Earth)[293]) would be covered in how many seconds?

---

[290] G.G., Vol VII, *Dialogo*, p. 249.

[291] G.G., Vol VII, *Dialogo*, p. 250.

[292] G.G., Vol VII, *Dialogo*, p. 251.

[293] Galileo estimates the distance between Earth and Moon to be 56 times the radius of the Earth (588 000 000 / 56 = 10 500 000 *braccia* = 5781.61 km, which is 10% less than the average value r = 6.372 km). The average distance, measured with radar, is estimated today to be about 384 400 km, *i.e.* about 60.28 times the Earth's radius.

The statement, often repeated, astonished Mersenne, so much so that he actually denied that Galileo had really carried out the experiment[294]; indeed, since H = 100 *braccia* is 55 metres, a value for the acceleration constant g follows which is less than half the precise value: $g = 2H/t^2 = 110/25 = 4.4\ ms^{-2}$.

Galileo explained to Baliani how he arrived at the claim "100 *braccia* in 5 seconds" [295]:

> The length of this channel, or rather of the inclined plane, is the proportional mean between the perpendicular elevation of that plane and the length of all the perpendicular space that in the same time would be passed through by the falling mobile: as, for example, assuming that the channel is 12 *braccia* long, and its perpendicular elevation is half a *braccio*, one *braccio* or two, the space travelled in the perpendicular will be 288, 144 or 72 *braccia*, as is demonstrated [...]

His reasoning can be explained better with some formulae. Let us follow Galileo's reasoning: let L be the space travelled on the inclined plane in time t = 5 s, H the difference in height between the beginning and end of the path L, h = 100 *braccia* the space travelled in free fall in the same time. On the plane the effective force is reduced by a factor H/L and the following relationships hold:

$$h = gt^2/2,$$
$$L = g(H/L)\ t^2/2.$$

Eliminating the common factor $gt^2/2$, we obtain

$$H = L^2/h.$$

So L, the length of the inclined plane, is the mean proportional between the elevation h of the plane and the height of free fall H = 100 *braccia* which happens over the same time.

In reality, in Galileo's experiments the sphere rolls, touching the channel in two points, and as we have seen it is necessary to introduce the rolling factor K to obtain theoretically Galileo's experimental results: the precise formula of the experiment on the inclined plane, *unknown to Galileo*, is

$$L = [g(h/L) - g_A] K\ t^2/2.$$

We have seen that in the experiment in the inclined plane, described in Folio 107v, the sphere travelled in 5 seconds the distance L = 824 points, *i.e.* L = 3.433 *braccia*. From Galileo's formula the height H follows immediately, because the elevation h is obtained directly from the angle of inclination: $h = L\sin\alpha = 0.035946L = 0.1234$ *braccia*.

$$H = L^2/h = 95.5 \textit{ braccia}.$$

---

[294] MARIN MERSENNE, *Harmonie Universelle*, Livre II, *Du Mouvement de Corps*, p. 112. We shall see later in chapter 10.

[295] G.G., Vol. XVIII, pp. 76-77.

Comparing this result with the «100 *braccia* in 5 seconds» we find a difference of just over 4%, an extraordinary result which we could easily make exact simply by narrowing the groove very slightly or using a ball with a slightly greater diameter, changes that lead to a reduction in the angle of inclination and hence an increase for *H*.

But – let us be clear – Galileo certainly carried out other experiments, as well as the one in Folio 107v. For example, he may have fixed another value for the angle and measured the space travelled in 5 seconds. With that ball and that plane the experiment however must always lead to the same result: «100 *braccia* in 5 seconds».

Folio 107v is another proof that Galileo had already established his law on motion experimentally in the first years of the "new century".

Without worrying too much about making the discovery official with a publication, Galileo spoke of it around. Only decades later, in the second day of the *Dialogo sopra i due massimi sistemi del mondo*, would he make the enunciation of the law public[296]:

> [...] something which has been unknown to all philosophers down to our time. It was first discovered by our friend the Academician, who, in some of his yet unpublished writings, shown in confidence to me and to some other friends of his, proves the following. The acceleration of straight motion in heavy bodies proceeds according to the odd numbers beginning from one.

Therefore the theoretical error of supposing that the average velocity grows with the space travelled was soon overcome by Galileo [297]; and a note of his, which begins with the word «*mirandum*» which can be translated as *marvellous, wonderful, extraordinary*, an exclamation that reveals an enthusiasm rare in Galileo's notes and which certainly marks the moment of the discovery, also dates back to these years. In a folio fragment, which has a watermark that exists only in the letters written at Padua, we read (fig. 8.4):

> Extraordinary. Perhaps the motion along the perpendicular *ad* is swifter than along the inclined *ab*? It seems so; equal spaces are travelled more quickly along *ad* than along *ab*; however, it also seems that it is not; indeed, having traced the horizontal *bc*, the time for *ab* is to the time for *ac* as *ab* is to *ac*; so along *ab* and along *ac* we find the same moments of velocity: Indeed that is the same identical velocity with which, in different times, different spaces are travelled, which have the same proportion of times. The moments of the velocities of that which falls from above are between themselves like the roots of the distances travelled, precisely in their *subduplicated* ratio of them[298].

---

[296] G.G., Vol. VII, *Dialogo*, p. 248.

[297] Favaro dated back to the first decade of the XVII century a brief chapter in Galileo's own hand with the title *De motu accelerato*, where we read: «So we can understand how a mobile, even if very heavy, descending in natural motion starting from stationary, passes through all degrees of slowness, without ever lingering in any, but according to the succession of the instants, acquires new and greater degrees of velocity. I can put forward many other experiments which confirm the same thing, which I put in my Research in Mechanics, as a more appropriate place»; G.G., Vol. II, p. 264.

[298] G.G., Vol. VIII, p. 375. The fragment is in Folio 164v of Ms. 72. G.G.N.M.: «Little star encircled with crown.

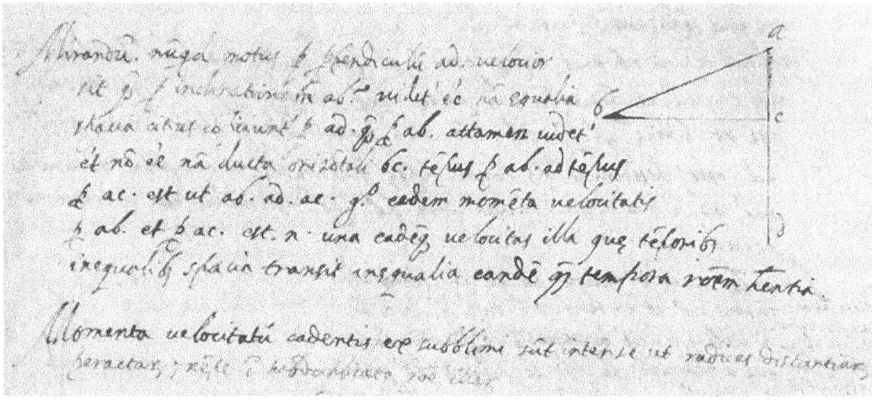

Fig. 8.4 Ms. Gal. 72, Folio 164v.

These are very concise notes valid for motions that start from stationary, where Galileo noted down some remarkable results.

1) If the inclined *ab* is equal to the vertical *ad*, certainly the time taken to travel *ab* is greater than that taken to travel *ad*, and this can be seen by drawing a circumference of which *ad* is the vertical diameter. According to the theorem of chords the circumference will cut *ab* at an intermediate point and the time to travel the first part of *ab* will be equal to that to travel *ad*.

2) The times t and t'' to travel *ab* and *ac* are proportional to the paths. This is a result that he had found before 1604.

3) The proportion between final velocities and the square roots of the heights of the falls follows from the proportion between velocity and time. If, for example, the times to travel *ac* and *ad* are t_{ac}^2 and t_{ad}^2, their ratio is $ac / ad = (t_{ac} / t_{ad})^2$ and if the final velocities (= moments of the velocities) v_{ac} and v_{ad} are like t_{ac} and t_{ad} their ratio is $v_{ac} / v_{ad} = (ac/ad)^{1/2}$

In this fragment the velocities are proportional to the time: $v_{ca} = ct_{ac}$ e $v_{ad} = ct_{ad}$

The fragment dates back to before 1608: when he returned to Florence, Galileo brought with him everything he had discovered about local motion, that is to say the second half of the *Discorsi*. The treatise was already sketched out, as he wrote to Antonio de' Medici in February 1609 and as he told Baliani. We know from the letter, already quoted, that the Genoese scholar wrote to him in 1615[299]:

> [...] and you can imagine that I remained with extreme curiosity to know the true reason for all those conclusions, so many and so beautiful, of the velocities of motions. However it is best for me to have patience, and pray the Lord God that he grant you your full health as soon as possible, so that, as well as a thousand other fine things, you can publish at the

Drake's identification: Watermark type 5. Drake's description: Mountains below cross in circle 12 mm; overall height 45 mm». See G.G., Vol. VII, *Dialogo*, pp. 48-50, for the development of this idea.

[299] G.G., Vol. XI, p. 186.

earliest the treatise that you told me you had sketched out; and if it does not displease you to give me some inkling by letter, I would consider it a great favour.

Amongst his acquaintances whom he informed of his results on motion, Galileo had also included – naively – Baliani, who then tried to attribute the discovery to himself. He had also been equally generous to others, as can be deduced from what was written to him from Naples, on 24 may 1604, by a certain Brother Costanzo Da Cascio, who signed himself «of the Observantist Friars Minor Reformed»[300]:

Later, when I were there in Padua[301], I remember that I asked how it could be proved that two bodies of a same kind and shape, equal or unequal, had the same velocity of motion in the same medium; and you granted two reasons to me, by means of which an adversary would be led to two inconveniences. Now, since so much time has passed, I have forgotten them, and since they are necessary to me for a certain purpose of mine, I pray you to deign to indicate them to me again; and if you have any other mathematical demonstration about this proposition, you would do me a most great favour if you sent it to me.

Conclusion: if the remnants of his letters and notes had not survived, we would never have known and been able to prove that his great result, published in 1632 in his *Dialoghi sopra i due massimi sistemi*, had been discovered before 1604. But how long before?

---

[300] G.G., Vol. X, pp.108-109.

[301] He had gone to Padua to visit the Saint, that is to say the church of St. Anthony.

9. Before 1607: Parabolic trajectories*

The disappointment of not having recognised that Baliani was a false friend who wanted to steal from him an old discovery of his[302] was not his first such disappointment. This misfortune had also occurred six years earlier with a true friend like Bonaventura Cavalieri, who published the important law on parabolic motion in his *Specchio Ustorio* (The Burning Glass; or A Treatise on Conic Sections) before Galileo and announced it to him in a letter, which he dated 31 August 1632. The story is this: some months earlier, towards the end of February, Cavalieri, having received the *Dialogo*, spotted that it contained nothing about the trajectory of projectiles[303]. Galileo's embarrassing silence on parabolic motion forced Cavalieri to cover himself by announcing to Galileo that there were discoveries by Galileo in his *Specchio ustorio*[304]:

* The final date of 1607 is established by the death of Guidobaldo del Monte: «Since Sir you have always been so affectionate towards the person of Sir Guid'Ubaldo my father, I cannot fail to inform you, although with infinite sorrow, of what it has pleased the Majesty of God to decide for him. So you should know that for the past two months he has suffered such a grave infirmity bed bound that finally the day before yesterday, on the feast of Epiphany, at 20 hours and a quarter, he passed from this life to a better one, Divine Will having thus disposed». Letter from Alessandro Del Monte to Galileo on 8 January 1607, G.G., Vol. X. pp. 166-167. The perhaps premature dating of the discovery to around 1592 was proposed by Jürgen Renn, Peter Damerow, Simone Rieger, and Michele Camerota in *Hunting the white elephant. When and how did Galileo discover the law of fall, op. cit.*

---

302 In 1638 Baliani published his *De motu naturali gravium solidorum*, where, amongst other things, he declared that he had already discovered the isochronicity of pendulums and the dependence of their periods on the square root of their length in 1611. Galileo had begun to mistrust his intentions, after Baliani's letter to Benedetto Castelli dated 20 February 1627, when he wrote: «.... On other occasions I made a treatise on the motions of solids, and of their greater or lesser velocity on more or less declined planes ... without finding it, one proposition I did succeed, in my opinion, in demonstrating ... that the bodies of natural motion increase their velocities with the proportion of 1, 3, 5, 7, ... » (G.G., Vol. XIII, p. 348). Baliani had distorted Galileo's law on motion, but his intentions were clear.

303 On 22 March 1632 Cavalieri wrote to Galileo about the *Dialogo*: «Now I saw it, rather I devoured it, so to speak, with my eyes; and indeed I feel in me, in the many times that I have begun to read it, the effect I remember I felt reading the "Furioso" (Ariosto's poem), which wherever I start to read it, I cannot find the end: so it happened to me in your Dialogues. I cannot yet say I have read them all, but have wandered here and there plucking with great greed the flowers of such an enchanting garden, as much as my many engagements have allowed me». The dedication of the *Specchio ustorio* «To the Most Illustrious Worthy Lords» is dated 19 August, while the licence to print the book is dated 7 January, issued by F. Girolamo Longhi, General of the Jesuati Brothers of St. Jerome. On 18 May he announced it to Galileo as follows: «Now, since I had a booklet about parabolic, hyperbolic and elliptical mirrors, on the occasion of thanking these Lords for bringing me back, done for 7 years with an increase of 100 *scudi* a year, I decided to print it, dedicating it to the Regiment».

304 G.G., Vol. XIV, p. 378.

> I touched somewhat on the motion of projectiles[305], showing that it should be in a parabola, excluding any surrounding impediment, supposing your principle of the movement of heavy bodies, that it becomes swifter according to the increment of odd numbers continued from unity, stating however that I learnt much that I deal with on this subject from you, producing also myself a reason for that principle. I refer the reader however to the book that we are waiting for from you on the subject of motion, which all desire soon to be made public, to be able to enjoy such precious and marvellous finds and such rare and necessary doctrine.

Galileo believed he had been cheated and perhaps for the first time realised the risk of plagiarism that his great intellectual generosity had exposed him to[306]. He wrote on 11 September to Cesare Marsili, a friend of them both who, like Cavalieri, lived in Bologna[307]:

> I have letters from Father Buonaventura, advising me that His Fatherhood has newly printed a treatise on the burning glass, in which on a certain occasion he says he has inserted the proposition and demonstration of the line described by projectiles, proving that it is a parabolic line. I cannot hide from Your Illustrious Sir how this information was little to my taste, in seeing how the primacy of a study of mine more than 40 years old, much of which was conferred to the said Father with generous confidence, must now be taken away from me, and the glory that I so earnestly desired and promised to myself after having toiled so long plucked away; because truly my first understanding, that moved me to speculate on motion, was the discovery of that line, although once discovered is then not very difficult to prove, nevertheless I, who have proved it, know how much I toiled to find this conclusion: and if Father Buonaventura had, before publication, informed me of his intention (as perhaps civil manners required), I would have begged him so hard to allow me to print my book first, after which he could add all the finds he wished. I shall wait to see what he produces; but certainly a great thing would be needed to temper my disgust, and those of my friends who have heard of it, who to my greater mortification have thrown in my face that I trust too much. My star leads to me having to fight, and even with loss, that which is my own.

In the work by Renn and others quoted before[308], Galileo's indication of the parabola as «a study of mine more than 40 years old» is considered credible and is considered a confirmation that their backdating of the discovery of parabolic trajectories to 1592 is correct. It is more probable that Galileo, not yet having *tempered* his disgust, in the agitation with which he wrote

---

305 In chapter XXXVIII, *Della cognitione del Moto,* pp. 151-162.

306 Galileo felt no resentment towards his friend, and chose to quote his work in the *Discorsi*: «Salviati: As to Archimedes and the effects of his mirror, all the miracles that are read in other authors are rendered credible to me by reading the books of Archimedes himself, long ago studied by me with infinite astonishment. And if any doubt lingered, the book lately published about the burning glass [*Specchio ustorio*] by Father Buonaventura Cavalieri, which I read with admiration, is enough to put a stop to all difficulties for me» (G.G., VIII, pp. 86-87).

307 G.G., Vol. XIV, p. 386.

308 JÜRGEN RENN, PETER DAMEROW, SIMONE RIEGER, and MICHELE CAMEROTA, *Hunting the white elephant. When and how did Galileo discover the law of fall, op.cit.*

to Marsili became slightly muddled, putting together the discoveries in the *De motu* and the Paduan discoveries, and it would have been closer to the truth if he had written «thirty years», which is already a sufficiently long time to wish not to be cheated.

Ten days later Cavalieri wrote him a letter, full of excuses and explanations, attaching the *incriminated* pages[309]:

> The sorrow that you show having felt (As the Most Illustrious Gentleman Cesare Marsili has informed me) because I touched on something of the parabolic line described by projectiles in my Burning Glass, was certainly not as great as mine on hearing that you were offended by what I did, more through excess of reverence than anything else. What I said on motion I said as a disciple of yours and of Father Benedetto, and so I protest, as you can see from the sheets attached here, having learned from you both, I can say, what little I know. It is true that you may say perhaps that I should have explained rather more clearly that the thought of that same parabolic line belonged to Your Most Excellent Sir; but you must know that the doubt that I had of perhaps not agreeing totally with your conclusion made me not dare to ascribe to you, with specific words, that which you might then have to reject as something not yours; it made me, I say, report the general words said on page 152, where I again name Father Benedetto, not because I put him as author in part of the things that I add but because he too taught me part of those things[310], having seen experiments carried out by him with other scholars, from whom I also heard the same conclusion: in other words it seemed to me that the conclusion and the fact that you were its author were so well known, that there could be no doubt that I could falsely claim it as my own. And if with others I used the courtesy, as with Master Mutio Oddi, of writing to him before printing I know not what that had passed between him and me, much more so would I have done with you (if I had thought that you would take heed of this), as one whom I esteem, honour and love so much for his many virtues and for the infinite favours that I have received from you. And if you, in teaching me, had indicated to me not to make known such and such thoughts, I would in no way have done so; for moreover, in declaring them to others and putting them forward as yours, I thought I had played the part of a good disciple, showing myself at least to understand, if not to imitate, your wonderful efforts that you make in discovering the secrets of nature.
> I also add that I thought that you had written of this somewhere, since I have not had the good fortune to see all your works; and hearing it made so public, and for such a long time that Oddi told me, ten years ago, that you had made some experiment with Lord Guid'Obaldo dal Monte, made me believe it greatly: and this too made me careless in not writing to you about it earlier, considering in reality you did not care at all, indeed that you would rather be pleased that a disciple of yours, on such an opportune occasion, showed himself to be a follower of your doctrine, which however he confesses to have learned from you.
> In other words, despite what I say in my defence, if you still see an error it is surely not out of malice. See what you wish me to do to satisfy you, for I am most ready to do it. I have only

[309] G.G., Vol. XI, pp. 394-395.

[310] He had studied at Pisa with Castelli from 1616 to 1620, and this statement provides a *terminus ad quem* for the discovery of parabolic motion.

given out a few copies here in Bologna; in the meantime I shall not let others go out until the matter is settled, if it can be, to your satisfaction: because I shall either defer giving out further until you have printed your work on motion, or until you can print it with the antedate, or I shall have the two sheets reprinted, eliminating that which you deem prejudices you, or I shall place in the margin on page 164, line 22, if you think that I agree with you, these words for greater declaration, that is: *Conclusion of Sir Galileo Gal.ei*, or finally that I burn all the copies, so that together with them shall be destroyed the reason, as far as possible, of having given disgust to my Sir Galileo, so that he might say to me like Caesar: *Tu quoque, Brute, fili!*; while I have always reputed it my great fortune to have known you and to be able to honour and serve you, enjoying the precious fruits of your eminent doctrine, and therefore having, at every chance that presented itself to me, never failed to exalt out loud, even unto the stars, the divinity of your genius. Tell me freely therefore which of the above things would give you greatest satisfaction that I do, and most readily at once I shall perform it. [...] I send the enclosed sheets, so that you may see the way in which I put forward your doctrine; thus you will understand more clearly that which I did not know how to say in a few words in my past letter, the cause of the greatest regret for you and me. I shall send the whole booklet as soon as convenient.

If Cavalieri, as Muzio Oddi bore witness, attributed to Galileo the authorship «of some experiment» on the parabola, which he states he did together with Guidobaldo, the letter that Galileo wrote to Antonio de' Medici assures us that the discovery of the parabolic trajectory dates back to at least 11 February 1609[311]:

My brother-in-law also orders me to write to Your Excellency something new about my studies, that being your wish; which I receive as a most great favour, and it stimulates me to speculate more than normal. So I inform Your Excellency that after my return to Florence I was busy with some contemplations and several experiments regarding my treatise on mechanics; which I hope will mainly be composed of new things, not touched on by others in the past. And just recently I finished finding all the conclusions, with their demonstrations, regarding the strengths and resistances of pieces of wood of different lengths, thicknesses and shapes, and how much weaker they are in the middle than at the ends, and how much greater weight they will support if this is distributed all along the wood rather than in one place, and what shape it should have in order for it to be equally strong throughout: which knowledge is most necessary in constructing machines and all manner of buildings, nor is there any who has studied it. Now I am studying some questions that remain for me on the motion of projectiles, many of which belong to artillery fire: and also recently I have discovered this, that placing the piece in some place raised above the plane of the countryside, and aiming it levelled correctly, the shot fired from the piece, impelled by much or very little powder or even by just enough to make it come out of the piece, always declines and descends towards the ground with the same velocity, so that in all the levelled shots, the ball lands on the ground in the same time; and this whether the shots are very long or very

[311] G.G., Vol. X, pp. 228-230.

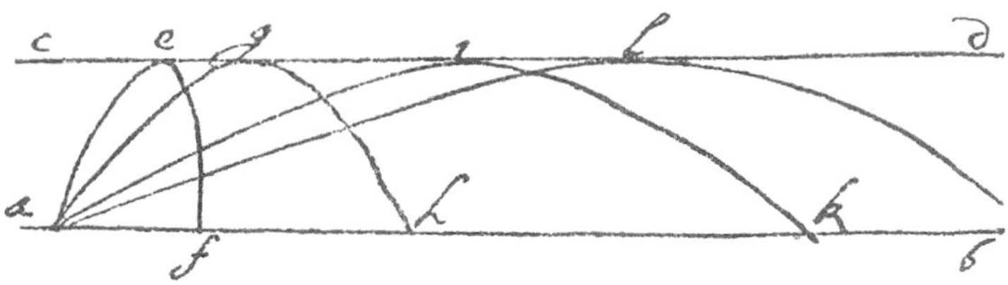

Fig. 9.1

short, or even if the ball only comes out of the piece and falls straight down in the plane of the countryside. And the same happens in elevated shots, which are all sent in the same time, even if they rise to the same perpendicular height: as, for example, shots *aef, agh, aik, alb,* contained between the same parallel lines *cd, ab*, are all sent in the same time (fig. 9.1); and the ball takes as much time to travel the line *aef*, as in *aik,* and in every other; and in consequence their halves, that is to say the parts *ef, gh, ik, lb*, are travelled in equal times, that respond to the level shots. In the matter of waters and other fluids, a part still intact, I have similarly discovered great properties of nature; but the time is too short for me to be able to write of them now, since I must send many other letters. So I postpone to a better opportunity, telling Your Excellency 3 or 4 conclusions and effects seen and already proved by me that perhaps surpass in wonder the greatest curiosities so far sought by men. But that is enough for now.

The experiment that follows, all concentrated on parabolic motion, had been carried out the year before.

10. Before 1610: The velocity acquired in descent is proportional to the square root of the height

Another very important document which gives the results of experiments carried out on the inclined plane by Galileo was made known not long ago by Stillman Drake and immediately became the subject of research for many scholars. I refer to the experiment described in Folio 116v of Ms. Gal. 72 of the Galileo *fonds* of the *Biblioteca Nazionale* in Florence, a folio that has the "countermark C1" symbolized by "mountains 20 × 17″, one of the watermarks present in paper used in Padua and that Stillman Drake dates back to 1608[312].

In Folio 116v (fig.10.1) Galileo calculated the final velocity that, according to the law of uniformly accelerated motion, a sphere should have descending along the inclined plane which ends at a certain height H from the floor, and he compared it with the real velocity obtained by measuring the distance the sphere arrived at on the floor. This is possible because the sphere found, at the end of its path along the inclined plane, a *straightener*, a short curved path that impressed on it a horizontal direction.

The flight from the plane to the floor followed a parabolic trajectory, which Galileo drew, marking the horizontal distance reached, which is a function:

(a) of the velocity with which the sphere left the *straightener*;
(b) of the height H of the *straightener* compared to the floor.

Galileo indicated this «table height» as $H = 828$ *punti*[313] [1.9 *metres*]. He certainly chose this height in order that the sphere, released to descend (with zero initial velocity) from a position y_0

312 Stillman Drake, *op. cit.*, on p. XXV, comments the dating thus: «During the years before 1608 Galileo's extant letters are not numerous. Mountain countermarks occur frequently in his account book [G.G., Vol. XIX, *Ricordi autografi*, pp. 130-175] from 1600 on ... Watermarks on Florentine notes ... differ widely from the Paduan marks, which are also found frequently in notarial records and on paper used in books printed at Padua while Galileo lived there». Folio 116v, according to this convincing analysis, undoubtedly dates back to the Paduan period. For the watermark, the recent revision describes it as: «Crown, form 1».

313 For the value of the *punctus* see R. Vergara Caffarelli, *How long is Galileo's punctus?* at the web address: http://www.illaboratoriodigalileogalilei.it, in the part devoted to *Scritti e pubblicazioni su Galileo*, where I suggest that *punctus* is a synonym for *picciolo* and is 1/240 of a Florentine *braccio*, *i.e.* about 2.3 mm for the *braccio a terra* and 2.4 mm for the *braccio da panno*, contrary to the common opinion amongst historians (Stillman Drake, Thomas Settle, Roland H. Naylor, James Maclachlan, David K. Hill, Winifred L. Wisan, Jürgen Renn, Peter Damerow, Simone Rieger *etc.*) who assign a value to the *punctus* of about 0.94 mm on the basis of the distance of the points marked on the *Galilean compass* in the *Istituto e Museo di Storia della Scienza* in Florence and the drawing on Folio 166r of the Ms. Gal. 72, also reproduced in G.G., Vol. VIII, *Frammenti*, p. 420. From an analysis of Folio 107v (see chapter 7) it can be seen that Galileo had already used the *picciolo* in his measurements.

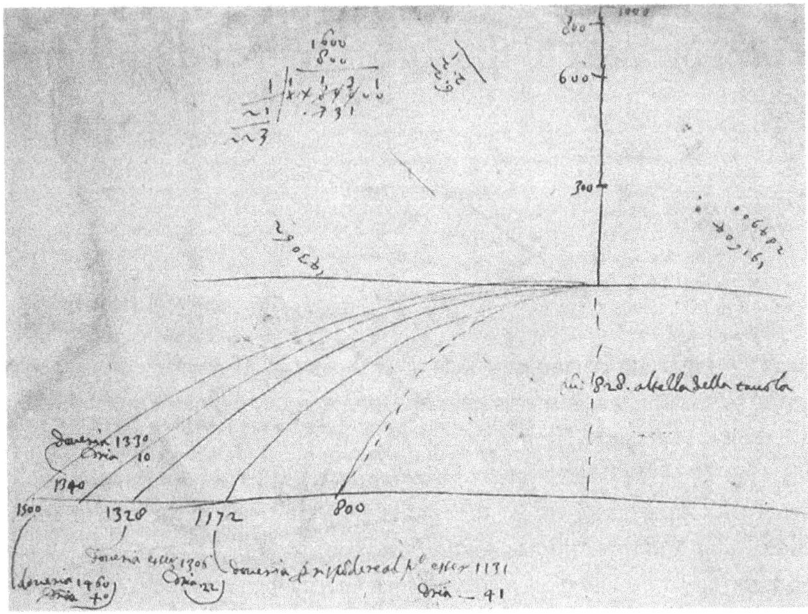

Fig. 10.1 Upper part of Folio 116v.

on the plane that is 300 *punti* higher than the *straightener*, hit the floor after leaving the inclined plane, having travelled a horizontal distance of x_0 = 800 *punti* from the beginning of the parabolic trajectory. Obviously the choice was made with the aim of simplifying the calculations in which a *rolling factor* K, which depends on these two distances, intervenes.

The reason for introducing the factor K is the rolling of the sphere: the conservation of energy, because of the rolling and the groove (with width c) on which the sphere (of diameter $d > c$) rested does not lead to the usual simple formula $v_n^2 = 2gy_n$; instead, the correct expression $K(g - g_A/\sin\alpha)$ has to be introduced in place of the g (see appendix D)

and so the velocity reached at the end of the descent along the plane is

$$v_n^2 = 2\, y_n\, K(g - g_A/\sin\alpha).$$

Later we shall see that the value of the angle of inclination is restricted to within the interval $20.3° \leq \alpha \leq 22.4°$
Given that $g_A < 0.166$ ms^{-2}, the correction $g_A/\sin\alpha < 0.5$ ms^{-2} can be neglected compared with g[314].

In each flight, from the moment at which the ball leaves the inclined plane until it reaches the ground, the time is always the same: $t = (2H/g)^{1/2} \approx 0.62$ seconds. In this time the horizontal distance x_n travelled by the sphere is

$$x_n = v_n t = v_n\,(2H/g)^{1/2}.$$

[314] See p. 147.

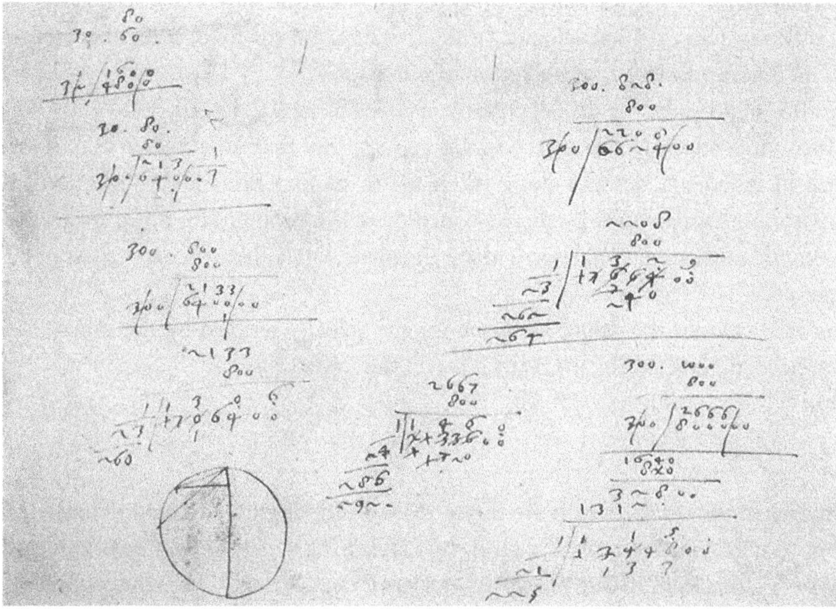

Fig. 10.2 Lower part of Folio 116v.

Introducing the velocity v_n, a function of the difference in height y_n on the inclined plane, $v_n = (2Kgy_n)^{1/2}$, we obtain

$$x_n = (2Kgy_n)^{1/2}\,(2H/g)^{1/2} = (4\cdot K\cdot H\, y_n)^{1/2}.$$

We have decided to carry forward this reasoning, using modern formulae which, as we have often said, is a brief and valid procedure to avoid mistakes and to convince ourselves of the accuracy of Galileo's measurements. Looking at the calculations made in Folio 116v (fig. 10.2) we can see that Galileo knew the laws that are summarised by the formulae that we have used. We shall see this better later on.

Galileo found K by using the start values $x_0 = 800$ when $y_0 = 300$. Continuing to use these formulae, we write

$$800 = (4\cdot K\cdot H\cdot 300)^{1/2},$$

from which we obtain

$$(4\cdot K\cdot H)^{1/2} = 800/(300)^{1/2}.$$

Isolating a dimensional constant K, we get $K = 0.644$. We now find all the values of x, *i.e.* of the horizontal distance between the end of the board and the point of impact, from the equation

$$x_n = 800\,(y_n/300)^{1/2}.$$

We have indicated by y_n the vertical height from which the sphere descends along the plane: this height determines the final velocity. In the lower part of the folio, using this formula, Galileo made all the calculations that we summarise in a table.

In fig.10.1, four heights for the fall onto the inclined plane are marked, 300 - 600 - 800 - 1000, but five trajectories are drawn because the value $y_3 = 828$, not marked in the vertical, is included.

Galileo included this descent along the plane to remind himself that the result disagrees strongly with his theory, which predicted (when there is no rolling) for a space travelled in uniform horizontal motion, after a descent along the plane with a difference in height of 828 *punti*, double the value $x_3 = 1656$ *punti*.

In the final column the values are given for the velocity reached by the sphere descending along the inclined plane, at the moment it leaves the *straightener*:

$$v_n = x_n\,(g/2H)^{1/2} = 1.61\,x_n.$$

The results in the third column are very good, considering the "accidents" present, and it is interesting to note that the numbers given by Galileo show that he was able to measure large distances with a precision of one *punto*.

Difference in height on the inclined plane	«should be to respond to the first ...»	Experimental result	Velocity in m/s [at the *straightener*]
$y_0 = 300$	used to find K	800	$v_0 = 2.95$
$y_1 = 600$	$x_1 = 800(600/300)^{1/2} = 1131.4$	1172	$v_1 = 4.32$
$y_2 = 800$	$x_2 = 800(800/300)^{1/2} = 1306.4$	1328	$v_2 = 4.90$
$y_3 = 828$	$x_3 = 800(828/300)^{1/2} = 1329.0$	1340	$v_3 = 4.94$
$y_4 = 1000$	$x_4 = 800(1000/300)^{1/2} = 1460.6$	1500	$v_4 = 5.53$

We can easily find out the diameter of the sphere used by Galileo in this experiment.

Rewriting the expression $K = [1 - (c/d)^2][7/5 - (c/d)^2]^{-1} = 0.644$ as a function of c/d we find

$$(c/d)^2 = (1 - K7/5)/\,(1-K),$$

$$d/c = 1.902.$$

For the width of the channel we can use $c \approx 24$ mm, which seems a reasonable estimate for the expression «a little wider than a finger»[315]. With this value, the diameter of the sphere used in the experiment is

$$d \approx 46 \text{ mm}.$$

[315] We recall the description of the plane given by Galileo: «In a wooden beam or rafter about twelve *braccia* long, half a *braccio* wide, and three inches thick, a channel was rabbeted in along the narrowest dimension, a little over an inch wide and made very straight; so that this would be clean and smooth, there was glued within it a piece of vellum, as much smoothed and cleaned as possible...».

Bear this result in mind because we have seen that Galileo also used a smaller sphere[316] and that having two different ones to roll down the inclined plane may have caused him some serious confusion.

The data of the experiment allow us to determine the inclination:

the plane is 12 *braccia* long, in other words 2880 *punti*. If the height 1000 *punti* is also the height of its upper edge, we have

$\sin \alpha_{Min} = 1000/2880 = 0.347$, and thus $\alpha_{Min} = 20.3°$.

The most probable value is that of a whole number, $\alpha = 20°$, given Galileo's tendency always to use round numbers. Since $(2880 \times \sin 20°) = 985$, the fifteen *punti* that are missing are provided by the straightener added at the top of the plane and we thus know the size of its radius, just over 5 cm.

It cannot have been easy to carry out the experiment if we consider that the lower edge of the plane is already at a considerable height (H = 828 *punti* = 1.9 meters) and so the upper edge is about 1900 *punti* from the ground, or 4.3 metres high, if not more. We can wonder whether such a large angle is really necessary in order to verify the theorem of the final velocity: it is probable that Galileo first tried with smaller angles, but nothing remains of those experiments. The result, obviously, was always unsatisfactory and that is why he raised the plane as far as possible, taking it as close as possible to the vertical, to see if he could reduce the differences that way and luckily Folio 116v, on which he jotted down the results, has come down to us.

The theorems brought into question by the experiment are numerous and it would require too much space to give them all here; we simply recall a single proposition from the *Quarta Giornata* (Fourth Day) which is particularly significant[317]:

Proposition VI
Given the sublimity and the altitude of a semiparabola, to find its amplitude.

> Let *dc* be a horizontal line and *ac* a vertical to it, in which are given the altitude *cb* and the sublimity *ba*; it is required to find in the horizontal *cd* the amplitude of the semiparabola which is determined by the sublimity *ba* and the altitude *bc*. The mean proportional between *cb* and *ba* is to be taken, of which the double is put as *cd*: I say that *cd* is the required amplitude. This is manifest from the preceding [corollary] [fig.10.3]

Anyone interested will find it useful to read a few pages of the *Discorsi* that precede this Proposition; here we just make some clarifying comments on the figure, which is very similar to the figure in Folio 116v:

---

316 G.G., Vol XIX, *Ricordi autografi – conti col costruttore* (accounts with the builder): on p. 132: «On 5 July 1599 - To the founder, for two balls £ 4 . - - »; later, on p. 145 to Marcantonio Mazzoleni: «on 7 September [1609] he had for a ball and foot £ 24. - -». These are the only documented purchases, which could however also be for balls for pendulums.

317 G.G., Vol VIII, *Discorsi* , p. 294.

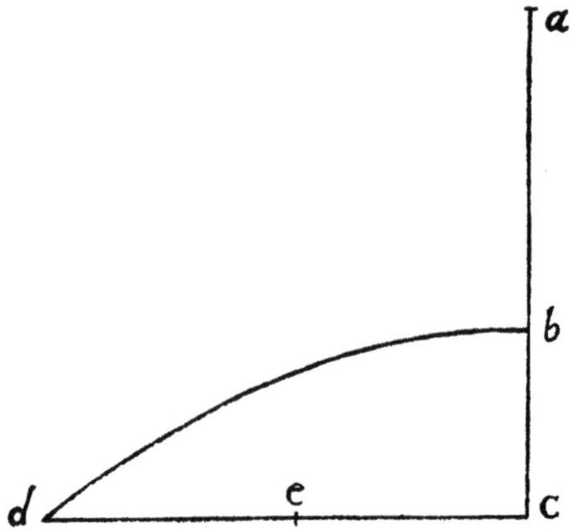

Fig. 10.3

The semiparabola *bd* is the trajectory of a mobile that begins to fall from *b*, with initial velocity directed horizontally.

The segment *cb* is the height of the semiparabola.

The segment *cd* is the amplitude of the semiparabola.

The segment *ba*, the continuation of *cb*, was called the sublimity by Galileo and represents the height from which the mobile is made to descend with uniformly accelerated motion, starting from stationary. The trajectory of the mobile is deviated at *b*, becoming horizontal, and it is supposed that the degree of acquired velocity is not altered. The following motion is composed of two motions, a uniform horizontal one and a naturally accelerated one that begins from stationary at point *b*.

It is obvious that if *cb* is equal to *ba*, the mean proportional *cd* is exactly their double.

Unfortunately, it is not possible to change the trajectory from vertical to horizontal without a considerable reduction in velocity but Galileo knew that the final velocity did not depend on the path, and so he resorted to the inclined plane and invented the *straightener*. In this discussion however, Galileo realised that, when he dropped the sphere from height *ba* = 828 *punti*, equal to the height of the table, contrary to his expectations, the mobile did indeed travel along a trajectory that was parabolic, but it met the horizontal at a distance *cd* of 1340 *punti*, less than double *cb* = *ba* = 828 *punti*. When he met with the subject in the *Discorsi*, however, he made no reference to the difficulties met with in his experimental verification.

11. Before 1610: Launching from the inclined plane without a straightener

Another sheet in Ms. Gal. 72 has attracted the interest of scholars[318]; it is Folio 114v, which is closely linked to Folio 116v, which we have just presented.

Indeed if we compare Folio 114v (fig. 11.1) with Folio 116v, it is obvious that the situations described in the two folios resemble each other very closely, even if the content of Folio 114v is not as detailed as the other since it is reduced to the essentials: there is the sketch of a plane and if we measure the angle of inclination in the drawing we find that it is around 20°, as in the experiment in Folio 116v (fig. 10.1); the parabolic trajectories ending on the floor are drawn, as is the height of the board, just as in the other folio, even if the height is not indicated here, maybe because, I suppose, it is the same as in Folio 116v.

The fact that the folio has been used for calculations of another kind makes us think that it is only a provisional note of measurements, written down elsewhere and the way they were worked out has been lost.

It is therefore natural to think that the two folios refer to a single piece of research which Galileo carried out on the same inclined plane to which he attached or removed the *straightener*, keeping the same height from the ground without changing the inclination, probably in order to compare the results. For this purpose he again used the same sphere, the larger one with a diameter of 46 mm (and so we must take into account the groove with the correction factor $K = 0.644$). We must reconstruct the experiment starting from Galileo's data, but now the analysis is more difficult, because the duration of the flight from the end of the plane to the ground is never the same: it depends on the vertical component of the velocity arrived at on the plane at the moment of separation, which varies with the starting height.

---

318 Bibliography: according to G.G.N.M.: DAMEROW P. *et al.*, *Exploring the Limits of Preclassical Mechanics,* New York, 1992, p. 202; DRAKE S., *Galileo at Work: His Scientific Biography*, Chicago-London, 1978, p. 484, 132; *Galileo: Pioneer Scientist*, Toronto, 1990, pp. 114-115, 121-122, 124-127; NAYLOR R.H., *The Role of Experiment in Galileo's Early Work on the Law of Fall*, Annals of Science, vol. 37, 1980, p. 562; NAYLOR R.H., *Galileo's Theory of Motion: Processes of Conceptual Change in the Period 1604-1610*, Annales of Science, Vol. 34, 1977, p. 388; DRAKE S. and MACLACHLAN J., *Reply to the Shea-Wolf Critique,* Isis, Vol. 66, 1975, pp. 401, 403; NAYLOR R.H., Galileo: *Real Experiment and Didactic Demonstration*, Isis, Vol. 67, 1976, pp. 402-407, 410, 415; NAYLOR R.H., *Galileo: the Search for the Parabolic Trajectory*, Annals of Science, Vol. 33, 1976, pp. 153-172; HILL, D. K., *Dissecting Trajectories: Galileo's Early Experiments on Projectile Motion and the Law of Fall*, Isis, Vol. 79, 1980, pp. 658-668; NAYLOR R.H., *Galileo's Theory of Projectile Motion*, Isis, Vol. 71, 1980, pp. 550-570.

Fig. 11.1 Folio 114v.

The sphere, after travelling a space S_n ($n = 0, 1, 2,\ldots, 6$) along the plane, leaves the board and begins its flight, and in this precise instant the module of the velocity arrived at is given by

$$v_n^2 = 2\,K(g \sin\alpha - g_A)\,S_n \approx 2Kg \sin\alpha\, S_n = 2Kg\,h_n\,.$$

We have neglected in these steps the insignificant correction g_A due to friction.

Galileo released the ball starting from ever higher points $h_0, h_1, \ldots, h_6$. The points are not chosen at random (or alternatively, at distances which are not always equal to each other, as in Folio 116v where the heights from the ground are however all stated) but must be set at regular distances because Galileo accurately measured and recorded only the horizontal distances X_n from the end of the plane to the point where the sphere hit the floor. There must therefore be an agreement between the regularly growing heights $h_n = (S_0 + nS)\sin\alpha$ the sphere is launched from and the distances X_n arrived at:

$$\begin{array}{lcll}
X_0 = 253 & \leftrightarrow & h_0 = S_0 \sin\alpha, & \\
X_1 = 337 & \leftrightarrow & h_1 = h_0 + h & = (S_0 + S)\sin\alpha, \\
X_2 = 395 & \leftrightarrow & h_2 = h_0 + 2h & = (S_0 + 2S)\sin\alpha, \\
X_3 = 451 & \leftrightarrow & h_3 = h_0 + 3h & = (S_0 + 3S)\sin\alpha, \\
X_4 = 495 & \leftrightarrow & h_4 = h_0 + 4h & = (S_0 + 4S)\sin\alpha, \\
X_5 = 534 & \leftrightarrow & h_5 = h_0 + 5h & = (S_0 + 5S)\sin\alpha, \\
X_6 = 573 & \leftrightarrow & h_6 = h_0 + 6h & = (S_0 + 6S)\sin\alpha.
\end{array}$$

The sphere, released from a point that is distant S_n from the end of the plane, acquires the velocity v_n given by

$$v_n = (2Kg \sin\alpha\, S_n)^{1/2}.$$

The trajectory of the sphere, when it leaves the plane, is a parabola described by the equations

$$y(t) = v_n\, t + (g/2)t^2,$$
$$x(t) = \cos\alpha\, v_n\, t.$$

The vertical space travelled during the time of flight t_n is

$$H = \sin\alpha\, v_n\, t_n + (g/2)t_n^2.$$

In the same time t_n the distance X_n of the point of arrival is given by

$$X_n = \cos\alpha\, v_n\, t_n\, .$$

Substituting t_n and v_n into the equation of the vertical component of motion, we find that, as in the previous case, the relationship does not depend on the acceleration of gravity g:

$$H = X_n \operatorname{tg}\alpha + (g/2)\, [X_n/(v_n \cos\alpha)]^2$$
$$= X_n \operatorname{tg}\alpha + (g/2)\, (X_n)^2 /(\cos^2\alpha\, 2Kg \sin\alpha\, S_n)$$
$$= X_n \operatorname{tg}\alpha + (X_n)^2 /[4 \cos^2\alpha \sin\alpha\, K(S_0 + nS)].$$

Reordering, we obtain

$$S_0 + nS = (X_n)^2 / 4K\,(H \sin\alpha \cos^2\alpha - X_n \sin^2\alpha \cos\alpha).$$

So Galileo decided to continue the experiment described in Folio 116v, removing the *straightener* but without changing the position of the plane, with the angle of inclination of 20°, which creates a height difference of about 1000 *punti* between the ends of the inclined plane which is about 12 *braccia* long, *i.e.* 2880 *punti*. Removing the *straightener*, the point of separation is slightly higher so the distance from the ground is a little bigger than 828 *punti* and we can unhesitatingly assume that H is exactly three *braccia* and a half, $H = 840$ *punti*, because Galileo was very accurate in positioning the inclined plane, with distances that he could reproduce easily. Introducing the quantities used in the previous experiment:

$K = 0.644$,
$H = 840$ *punti,*
$\alpha = 20°$,

in the numerical coefficients in the last equation we obtain

$$4K\,H \sin\alpha \cos^2\alpha = 653.5,$$
$$4K \sin^2\alpha \cos\alpha = 0.283,$$

and the equation we have to examine is

$$S_n = S_0 + nS = (X_n)^2 / (653.5 - 0.283\, X_n).$$

With the distances X_n ($n = 0, 1, 2,\ldots,6$) we can obtain directly the distance S_0 between the first starting point and the end of the board and six values for the constant distance $S = S_n - S_{n-1}$ between successive starting points ($n \neq 0$):

$$S = \{[(X_n)^2 / (653.5 - 0.283\, X_n)] - S_0\}/n.$$

The results are given in the following table:

X_n	Distance $X_n - X_{n-1}$	Distance $S = S_n - S_{n-1}$
$X_0 = 253$		$S_0 = 110$
$X_1 = 337$	84	$S_1 - S_0 = 93.5$
$X_2 = 395$	58	$S_2 - S_1 = 89.0$
$X_3 = 451$	56	$S_3 - S_2 = 92.3$
$X_4 = 495$	44	$S_4 - S_3 = 91.8$
$X_5 = 534$	39	$S_5 - S_4 = 91.5$
$X_6 = 573$	39	$S_6 - S_5 = 93.0$

It is obvious that Galileo set the starting points at a constant interval equal to 90 *punti* (*i.e.* 3/8 of a *braccio*). The small discrepancies that we have found are mainly due to the difficulty of measuring the distances X_n, accurately because the ball arrives obliquely to the ground and it is more difficult to establish the point of impact exactly.

To make sure that this is the correct solution let us reverse our analysis, starting from the hypothesis that the starting points are exactly $S = 90$ *punti* apart. Now the unknowns are the X_n and the equation which must be resolved is

$$(X_n)^2 + 0.283\, X_n(110 + 90n) - 653.5\, (110 + 90n) = 0.$$

Once again we collect the results in a table for $n = 0, 1, 2\ldots6$:

X_n measured by Galileo	X_n calculated	Difference in *punti*	Difference in mm
$X_0 = 253$	$X_0 = 253$	0	0
$X_1 = 337$	$X_1 = 334$	+ 3	6.8
$X_2 = 395$	$X_2 = 396$	+ 1	2.3
$X_3 = 451$	$X_3 = 447$	+4	9.2
$X_4 = 495$	$X_4 = 492$	+3	6.8
$X_5 = 534$	$X_5 = 531$	+3	6.8
$X_6 = 573$	$X_6 = 566$	+7	16.1

The results are exactly as expected, with the measured distances slightly bigger than the calculated ones because the oblique trajectory leaves a *long mark* on impact and it is difficult to establish where it begins. They are, however minimal differences of a few millimetres: Galileo reached an extremely high degree of accuracy in these experiments on motion.

It is a pity that he left nothing in writing about the method that allowed him to reach such accuracy; we can, however, say what we shall do when we are able to reconstruct his experiment: to be certain of the position of the point of impact to the millimetre we shall arrange a track in front of the inclined plane and we shall slide along it a thin iron crosspiece. For each measurement we shall move the crosspiece until, after a few attempts, the sphere will end its flight right on this small bar.

The final launch occurs at a distance of 650 *punti* from the end of the board, which corresponds to a difference in height of 222 *punti*, *i.e.* about half a metre. At this height we have to add the distance of the board above the ground, $H = 840$ *punti* = 1.93 m. A reasonable height to stop at.

Why did he carry out this experiment? Perhaps in order to see whether the great difference met with in the previous experiment between theoretical expectations and the results of the measurements was due to the *straightener*. Unfortunately there is not the slightest trace of such calculations but, if they did exist, Galileo must certainly have used the equation of motion with $K = 1$:

$$(X_n)^2 - (840 - X_n \operatorname{tg} \alpha)[4 \cos^2\alpha \sin \alpha \, (S_0 + nS)] = 0.$$

We have calculated the solutions for $n = 0$ e $n = 6$, obtaining: $X_0 = 283$ *punti* (instead of 253) and $X_6 = 681.73$ *punti* (instead of 573). Galileo could thus be convinced that the *straightener* is not the cause of the discrepancies; the annotations became useless and for this reason he used the blank spaces on the sheets for other calculations.

I conclude by observing that the data in Folio 116v made it possible to reconstruct the experiment described in 114v: Folios 116v and 114v supplement each other perfectly.

12. The time taken to descend along inclined planes of equal height and the theorem of final velocity

The results of the experiments discussed in the two previous paragraphs confirm the reasonableness of the hypothesis that Galileo posed as a fundamental principle of his whole theory of motion and which he summed up as follows:

> I assume that the degrees of speed acquired by the same moveable over different inclinations of planes are equal whenever the heights of those planes are equal [319].

This principle, already introduced in the first day of the *Dialogo* did not seem obvious to some readers; Galileo knew that and for a long time he tried to introduce it into the theory in a more acceptable form but even the treatment given to it in the *Discorsi* was not found very convincing until, after some unsatisfactory attempts, he managed to find a demonstration, resorting to some arguments from «an ancient treatise on mechanics already written in Padua by our Academic» and to the laws of motion. Galileo himself wrote all this to Benedetto Castelli on 3 December 1639[320].

> I am afraid that it is evident, my Most Reverend Sir, that in philosophy doubt is the father of invention, opening the way to the discovery of the truth. The objections made to me, several months ago now, by this young man [*Vincenzo Viviani*] at present my guest and disciple, against that principle supposed by me in my treatise on accelerated motion, which he was then studying with great application, forced me in that way to think on it, in order to persuade him that the principle could be conceded and was true, in which I finally succeeded, to his great delight and mine, in meeting with the conclusive demonstration, if I am not mistaken, which so far I have revealed to more than one person here. This he has now written out for me, for I find myself deprived totally of my eyes and perhaps I would have become confused in the figures and letters that are needed for it. It is written in dialogue, as recalled to Salviati, so that whenever my Discourses and Demonstrations may be published again, it may be inserted[321] immediately after the exposition of the second proposition of the said treatise, on pages 177 of this edition[322], as a most essential theorem for establishing the sciences of motion that I had promised.

---

[319] G.G., Vol. VIII, *Discorsi*, p. 205.

[320] G.G., Vol. XVIII, pp. 125-126.

[321] G.G., Vol. VIII, *Discorsi*, pp. 214-219.

[322] The pages are those of the Leiden edition of 1638.

Galileo never had any doubts about the validity of the principle because the experiment described so well in Folio 116v shows with great precision that the velocity acquired by the sphere in descent depends solely on the difference in height and not on the angle of inclination, and the drawing itself, in which the various heights are marked along a vertical line, makes this evident. The experiment did highlight the fact that the final velocity arrived at on the inclined plane by a rolling sphere is less than that acquired falling freely through the same difference in height. This partially calls into question another result which compares the times taken by a mobile to fall freely from a certain height to the times necessary to descend along an inclined plane of the same height. We have already spoken of this in chapter 4 when his possible first experiments were analysed on the basis of hints suggested by the *De motu*, but then Galileo did not have available the clear results that he had now. The difficulty presented itself again more seriously in Padua when he began to write the third day, which is the oldest part of the *Discorsi*, and he arrived at theorem III[323]:

> If the same moveable is carried from rest on an inclined plane, and also along a vertical of the same height, the times of the movements will be to one another as the lengths of the plane and of the vertical.

The theorem is immediately followed by a corollary that extends the property to all inclined planes that have the same height:

> From this it is deduced that the times of descent over differently inclined planes of the same height are to one another as their lengths[324].

Galileo gave a first demonstration of this theorem in Folio 151r, which we discussed in chapter 4; here we present a more elaborate version of his, contained in Folio 163v[325] of Ms. Gal. 72:

> The time of the fall along an inclined plane is to the time of the fall along the line of its height as the length of that same plane [*is*] to the length of its height.

And the theorem is followed by the demonstration, also illustrated by a drawing (fig.12.1):

> Let the plane *ba* be inclined with respect to the horizontal line *ac* and its height be the perpendicular line *bc*. I say that the time of the fall with which the mobile moves along *ba* is to the time in which it falls along *bc* as *ba* is to *bc*. Let a perpendicular be raised from *a* to the horizon, let it be *ad*, and let this meet at *d* the perpendicular to *ab*, led from *b*, and let this be *bd*, and around the triangle *abd* let a circle be described. From this I conclude that the times of descent along differently inclined planes are to each other as are their lengths, as long as

[323] G.G., Vol. VIII, *Discorsi*, p. 215.

[324] G.G., Vol. VIII, *Discorsi*, p. 219.

[325] G.G.N.M., Folio 163v; «Little star encircled with crown. Drake's identification: Watermark type 5. Drake's description: Mountains below cross in circle 12 mm; overall height 45 mm».

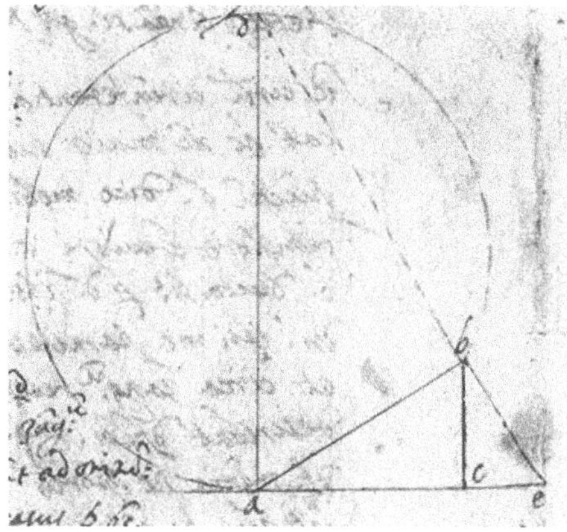

Fig. 12.1 Folio 163v.

their height is the same[326]: since *da*, *bc* are both perpendicular to the horizon, it is clear that the time of the fall along *da* is to the time of the fall along *bc* as the mean between *da* and *bc* is to that same *bc*. Nevertheless, the time of the fall along *da* is equal to the time of the fall along *ba*: but the average between *da* and *bc* is that same *ba*: so the proposition is proven.

The demonstration is very elegant: the construction of the circumference allows Galileo to apply the theorem of chords and establish that the time of the fall along *ab* is equal to the time of the fall along the diagonal *da*; the next step is to find the ratio between the times of free fall along *da* and along *bc*. The statement that «the time of the fall along *da* is to the time of the fall along *bc* as the mean between *da* and *bc* is to that same *bc*», *i.e.* as the square root of the product of *da* times *bc* is to *bc*, is none other than the content of the 2nd corollary of the 2nd theorem in the third day of the *Discorsi*[327], which can be proved extremely easily by substituting the distances by the squares of the times according to the law of motion. The final step is the relationship $(da \cdot bc)^{1/2} = ba$, which follows straight from the similarity of the triangles *abd* and *bca*.

It is not easy to understand the reasons that led Galileo in the *Discorsi* to prefer to this nice demonstration another one that in my opinion is less rigorous and which was first drafted here in Folio 179r[328], a completely different proof which is certainly more intuitive and striking, as witnessed by the numerous underlinings in the manuscript, probably by Galileo himself. The same theorem is considered in Folio 164r[329], again from his Paduan period, with an important addition:

---

[326] G.G., Vol. VIII, *Discorsi*, p. 219.

[327] G.G., Vol. VIII, *Discorsi*, p. 214.

[328] G.G.N.M., Folio 179v: «No watermark could be identified by the project group. Drake's identification: Watermark type 8. Drake's description: XX below crossbow; overall height 50 mm».

[329] G.G.N.M., Folio 164r: «Little star encircled with crown. Drake's identification: Watermark type 5. Drake's description: Mountains below cross in circle 12 mm; overall height 45 mm».

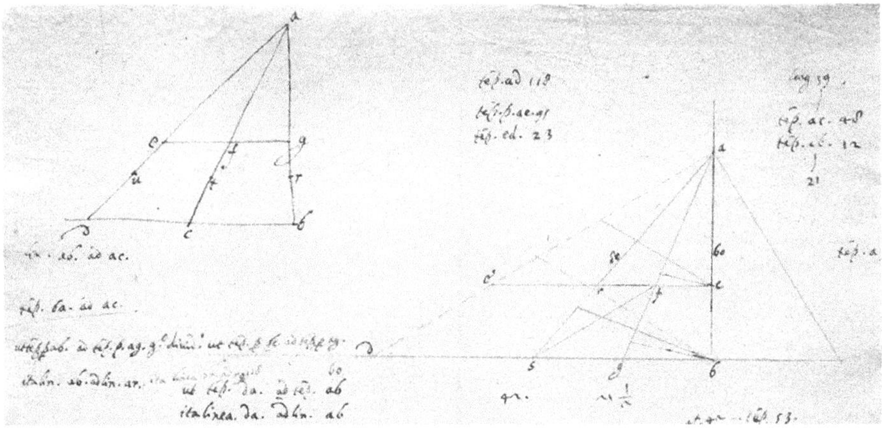

Fig. 12.2 Part of Folio 174r.

From this then it follows that the times of the falls along *bc* and *ba*, both if *b* is the beginning and boundary of the motion and if the motion comes first but from the same height, keep the same ratio between themselves, exactly the ratio that there is between lines *bc* and *ba*.

The theorem is written down in this form in the *Discorsi* as Theorem X, Proposition X. The demonstration we can read in the *Discorsi* is fairly complex and elegant at the same time. A document on the same theme is contained in Folio 179v.

From all these references the importance that Galileo gave to the theorem of the ratio between the lengths of the inclined planes and the times taken to travel over them is obvious, because he brought into play the possibility of carrying out a crucial experiment.

In Folio 174r[330] of Ms. Gal. 72 (fig. 12.2), also prior to 1610, Galileo took care to illustrate the theorem in a practical way with an example: a vertical path and three other paths with different inclinations which start from the same point and have the same height, with a measurement which is indicated by the number 60, which as usual he did not associate with any precise unit, indeed this measurement of the vertical distance also represents graphically the time necessary to travel it in free fall. In order to distinguish the measurements of time from the measurements of distance we shall write, for example, 60^*L for the distance and 60^*T for the time.

In this folio we see a sort of table that correlates the length of some straight trajectories (identified in the drawing by the letters at the furthest points), and the corresponding travel times. The four paths are cut at the height $cb = 21^*L$ by a horizontal plane; as well as the whole path there are thus two other paths and two other times, which are given in the following table:

[330] G.G.N.M., Crown, form 1. Drake's identification: Watermark type C1. Drake's description: Mountains 20 × 17 mm.

Length	Time	Length	Time
ab 60*L	60*T	*ad* 118*L	118*T
ac 39*L	49*T	*ae* 76*L	97*T
cb 21*L	11*T	*fs* (=) *ed* 42*L	23*T
ag 66*L	66*T	*as* 80*L	80*T
af 43*L	54*T	*ar* 52*L	65*T
fg 23*L	12*T	*rs* 28*L	15*T

In the first and third columns a total of twelve distances are given and in particular the lines *ab*, *ag*, *as*, *ad* are the lengths of the vertical path and of the three inclined planes; in the second and fourth columns we find the corresponding travel times. As we have already said the time of the first path travelled «*temp. ab* = 60» is numerically equal to the measurement «*long. ab* = 60», thus introducing an arbitrary choice of the unit of time; all the other travel times are a consequence of this choice.

Let us calculate, for example, the time required to travel the inclined plane *ag* which is 66*L long, using the law of motion $s = K \sin \alpha\, t^2$:

$T(ag) = (ag/\ K \sin \alpha)^{1/2}$.

Introducing $ag = 66$, $\sin \alpha = ab/ag = 60/66$ and the constant K which is obtained from the equation for the vertical path: $K = ab\ /\ T^2(ab) = 1/60$, we find

$T(ag) = 66^* T.$

The choice of making the time numerically equal to the measurement of the length for the vertical path brings with it equality between the numerical values of the paths and of the times for the three inclined planes also. In this example the proportionality introduced in the theorem X between times and length becomes equality. The calculation of the intermediate times is very easy and one example is enough.

The time necessary to arrive from *a* to *c* is calculated this way:
given that $t_{ac}/t_{ab} = (ac/ab)^{1/2}$ and, $t_{ab} = 60$, $ab = 60$ and $ac = 39$, we obtain $t_{ac} = (60 \times 39)^{1/2} = 48.37$. Galileo rounded up the result and wrote $t_{ac} = 49$ (we would have written 48).

We can propose the following interpretation of Folio 174r: Galileo studied the results of one of his experiments trying to isolate some of its geometrical aspects, to try to understand why in Folio 116v the sphere rolled down the inclined plane travels a shorter distance than predicted. There are arguments in favour of this hypothesis which we put forward helped by a figure very similar to that on the folio in Galileo's hand (fig. 12.3).

To construct the right-angled triangle *adb* only two measurements are required, the values of *ab* and *ad*; the only difference from Galileo's drawing (which we introduce to simplify the calculations), is the value $ad = 120$, rather than $ad = 118$:
$ab = 60$,
$ad = 120$.

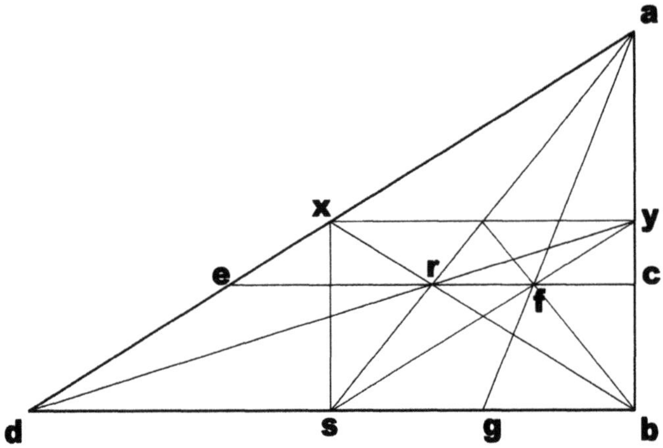

Fig. 12.3

These preliminary data define the angles of the triangle *abd*:

angle *adb* with vertex in $d = 30°$,
angle *dab* with vertex in $a = 60°$,
angle *dba* with vertex in $b = 90°$.

We introduce the three medians of the triangle *abd*: *as*, *bx*, *dy*; the three lines meet exactly at point *r*, which is the centre of gravity of the triangle.

Let us draw the line *ec*, parallel to the base *db*, which passes through the centre of gravity *r*.

With this construction we obtain the following results:

1) the triangle *axb* is equilateral and so $ax = xb = 60$,
2) the triangle *xsb* is right-angled at *s* and has the angle at *b* of 30°,
3) the cathetus *xs* has the value $xs = yb = 30$,
4) we use the following properties of the medians: 2/3 of the median is between the vertex and the centre of gravity, 1/3 between the centre of gravity and the mid point of the opposite side,
5) the right-angled triangles *abs* and *acr* are similar, so we obtain:
$ac = 2/3\ ab = 40$,
$cb = 1/3\ ab = 20$,
6) the right-angled triangles *abd* and *ace* are similar and
$ae = 2/3\ ad = 80$,
$ed = 1/3\ ad = 40$.

All the measurements that follow are a direct consequence of the previous results:
$ab = 60$ (as a hypothesis)
$ad = 120$ (as a hypothesis)
$db = (3)^{1/2}\ ab$,
$sb = (3)^{1/2}\ ab/2$,
$as = (7)^{1/2}\ ab/2 = 79.37$,
$ar = (7)^{1/2}\ ab/3 = 52.91$,
$rs = (7)^{1/2}\ ab/6 = 26.46$,
$rc = 2/3\ sb = ab$.

The line *sy* is parallel to *ad*

$ec = 2\ ab/(3)^{1/2}$,
$er = rc = ab/(3)^{1/2}$,
$ax = xd = ab$.

The line that connects *x* and *y* is parallel to *db*, because *x* and *y* are mid points, and is half of *db*. The line *sy* is parallel to *ad* and so

$sf = de = 40$,
$ef = ds = sb$.

The line *ag* passes through point *f*, which is the centre of gravity of the triangle *asb*.
Making $ec - ef = fc = rc/2 = ab/2(3)^{1/2}$

$gb = sg = fc\ ab/ac = (3)^{1/2}ab/4$,
$xy = (3)^{1/2}\ ab/2$,
$af = (19)^{/2}\ ab/6 = 43.6$,
$ag = (19)^{1/2}\ ab/4 = 65.4$,
$fg = (19)^{1/2}\ ab/12 = 21.4$.

For the times we apply expressions of the following type:

$t_{ac} = (ab\ ac)^{1/2} = 48{,}4$,
$t_{ag} = (af\ ag)^{1/2}\ 53.4$,
$t_{fg} = (fg\ ag)^{1/2}$.

The new table shows results very similar to those in the previous table:

Length	Time	Length	Time
ab 60*L	60*T	*ad* 120*L	120*T
ac 40*L	48.4*T	*ae* 80*L	98*T
cb 20*L	11.6*T	*fs* (=) *ed* 40*L	22*T
ag 65.4*L	65.4*T	*as* 79.4*L	79.4*T
af 43.6*L	53.4*T	*ar* 52.9*L	64.8*T
fg 21.8*L	12*T	*rs* 26.5*L	14.6*T

The table is basically the same as that used by Galileo for the lines *ag* and *as* (the differences are minimal, due partly to the way the numbers are approximated to units), and there is only a slight shift for the line *ad* = 120, because of the different length chosen as the initial datum. Galileo, therefore, constructed fig.12.2 with the criteria that we have followed: the inclined planes *ag* and *as* were not chosen at random: *as* is a median and *ag* is constructed so that *g* is the mid point of *sb*.

But why 118 and not 120, if the figure is arbitrary? This number is also repeated in the less precise sketch on the left hand side of the folio and which has only two inclined lines. The only possible explanation is that *ad* = 118 and *ab* = 60 are quantities linked to an experiment and immediately the inclined plane Galileo had constructed «about 12 *braccia* long» springs to mind. Let us suppose that in the experiment Galileo had raised one end of the plane 6 *braccia* above the other and had chosen the tenth of a *braccio*, that is to say two *soldi*, which are about 55 mm, as the unit of measurement, a reasonable unit of measurement for an experiment in which the space travelled by a sphere on a plane inclined at an angle α, $30° < \alpha < 66.6°$ (the upper limit is given by $\text{tg}\ \alpha = gb/ab = 4/(3)^{1/2}$) has to be measured. The theorem that he wanted to verify is the theorem already discussed of the times proportional to the lengths:

> If the same mobile moves from stationary, on an inclined plane and along the perpendicular, the height of which is the same, the travel times will be to one another as the lengths of that same plane and of the perpendicular.

In the experiment that we are trying to reconstruct, with the plane inclined exactly so that the height is half its length, the time on the inclined plane must be double the time along the vertical: to obtain precise measurements Galileo built a pendulum of such a length that it completed a simple oscillation in the time taken by a sphere to fall along $ab = 6$ *braccia*: it was characterised by the period $T = 0.82$ seconds and the length $L = 67$ cm. Now he could measure the space travelled by the sphere on the inclined plane in two oscillations. To find the space that he really measured, we need to know the diameter of the sphere, determine the factor K and apply the formula

$s = K \sin 30°\ g(2T)^2/2$,

knowing that $6 = gT^2/2$ substituting:

$s = 12\ K$.

It is not difficult to find K because the watermark of Folio 174r is the same as in six other folios of Ms. Gal. 72 identified by the numbers 116, 121, 147, 159, 187. From the wide variety of watermarks and punchmarks we can assume che Galileo had the habit of buying a little paper at a time and that no supply lasted more than a few months. The experiment in Folio 174v is therefore contemporary to the experiment in Folio 116v and we know that in the experiment described in Folio 116v the sphere had a diameter of about 46 mm and that $K = 0.644$. Using this value we arrive at $s = 7.7$ *braccia*, compared to the fraction $ae = 8$ *braccia* of the plane $ad = 12$ *braccia*.

Maybe we have found the clue to the puzzle, that is to say the reason for the drawing. The paths on the inclined planes are reduced by the factor K to about 2/3 of the expected measurement, but this is also the part of the median that lies between the vertex and the centre of gravity. Galileo must have been startled by the consistency of the results and he tried (in vain) to discover whether the figure might suggest to him a reason for this reduction. I often remember a well known passage from *Il Saggiatore*[331]:

> Philosophy is written in this great book that lies continuously open before our eyes (I mean the universe), but we cannot understand it unless we first learn to understand the language and to know the letters in which it is written. It is written in mathematical language, and the letters are triangles, circles, and other geometrical figures, and without these means it is impossible to understand humanly a word of it; without it we wander in vain in a dark maze.

Unfortunately Galileo was wandering through a dark maze and geometry could not help him find the way out.

---

[331] G.G., Vol. VI, *Il Saggiatore*, p. 232.

13. Another comparison between two motions: free fall and descent along a plane. Difficulties due to the rolling of the sphere

When a body descends along an inclined plane (disregarding friction) a very precise relationship between the final velocity arrived at (which does not depend on the angle of inclination) and the difference in height of the path travelled follows inevitably from the law of motion but we have seen, in the experiments in chapters 9 and 10, that Galileo had to introduce a correction because he used a rolling sphere.

We recall that Galileo measured the final velocity by letting the sphere fall to the ground at the end of the inclined plane, using the expedient of straightening its motion in the horizontal direction. As the point of departure is raised ever higher the ball, after completing a parabolic trajectory in the air, hits the ground at an ever farther point: its distance x_n from the plane, measured on the floor, should depend only on the difference in height y_n between the beginning and the end of the path travelled on the plane and on the height H between the end of the plane and the floor. But it does not: we have seen that Galileo was forced to introduce a correction factor K into the relationship

$$x_n = (4K\,H\,y_n)^{1/2}.$$

Galileo found K by shifting the height H between the end of the plane and the floor in such a way that the ball reached the distance x_0 = 800 *punti* when descending along the plane from a difference in height of y_0 = 300 *punti*: he found H = 828 *punti* and with these data he could calculate K.

$$K = (x_n)^2/4\,H\,y_n = 0.644\,.$$

In the surviving notes and in the published works there is no trace of calculations or reasoning aimed at explaining such a crippling contradiction. We can wonder whether Galileo ever studied, at least experimentally, the effect of the sphere's rotation on the translation velocity: If he did, the results were certainly disappointing, as we saw in the previous chapter and as we shall see now, and this may explain why he kept hidden the great difficulty he had come across and it is also not difficult to find a justification for his conduct.

Research today, especially in the field of physics, takes place mainly according to two opposing motivations: a) we try to draw new and relevant consequences from a well established theory, b) we try to put a theory into question with experiments that reveal new and unexpected aspects. Galileo had, instead, the problem of convincing people that his theory was correct and he could not afford to point out its weak points, due to effects that he could not explain, also because in the experiments on the inclined plane the dependence of the acceleration on the diameter of the sphere put an even more fundamental law into doubt.

We have seen that from 1590 Galileo accepted Benedetti's explanation that bodies fall in the same way, independently of their weight: there is no difficulty in verifying the law qualitatively, by dropping bodies that are very different in weight and matter *from a tall tower* because they reach the ground more or less at the same time; but it is rather difficult to measure how their velocity changes over time.

Early in 1604 Galileo explained to Costanzo da Cascio why – these are the friar's words – «two bodies of a same type and shape, equal or indeed unequal, have in the same medium the same velocity of motion» but perhaps he did not tell him everything he had discovered; soon afterwards, towards the end of 1604, we saw that he informed Paolo Sarpi about the law of motion: the space travelled by all bodies in free fall grows with the square of time. Galileo's new idea was to delay the motion, making experiments with the inclined plane: so that he not only verified the law but he was also able to prove experimentally that the theorem of the inclined plane, that is to say the identification of the multiplying factor "sin α" which reduces the force acting on the body, holds even when there is an accelerated motion and not only when there is equilibrium, as occurs on the plane with the pulley[332].

But at a certain moment a difficulty emerged. As long as he let the same sphere descend along the groove in the plane, just changing the angle, this is always true; but if at the same time he let two spheres of different diameters descend, their accelerations would be different: if he put the larger one before the smaller one he would have realised that their distance grows with the passage of time. If he tried to find how much space the sphere travelled on the inclined plane in the time that another fell vertically he would find that the space travelled is less than expected.

We see how Galileo may have come across these difficulties. We know for certain that, as well as the sphere with a diameter of 46 mm he also had a much smaller sphere of about 35 mm in diameter and, having two spheres with different diameters, Galileo may have tried to check whether they descended along the inclined plane with the same acceleration[333], considering that already in the experiment of the measurement of final velocity things had not gone as the theory led him to expect.

So, if the smallest sphere is placed behind the other and they are left free to descend; when the larger one has travelled all along the plane 12 *braccia* long, the smallest will only have travelled 10.6 *braccia*.

For every diameter d_i there is a different value of the rolling factor K_i and the spaces S_i travelled in the same time by the two spheres are regulated by the formula $S_1/S_2 = K_1/K_2$.

---

332 See chapter 3, where I described his plane with a pulley which in his treatise *Le Mecaniche* serves to prove the sine law and the principle of inertia.

333 This comparison is explicitly recalled by Galileo in the *Discorsi* : «I also thought of making the moveable descend along an inclined plane not much raised above the horizontal. On this, no less than along the vertical, one may observe what is done by heavy bodies differing in weight» (G.G., Vol. VIII, p. 128).

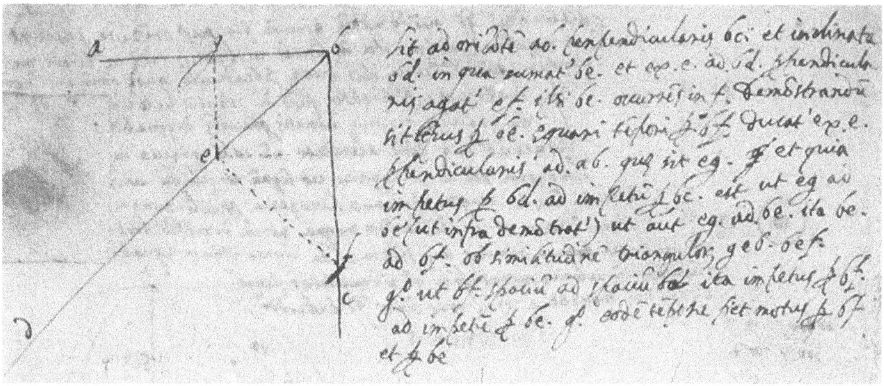

Fig. 13.1 Folio 147v.

If Galileo had discovered that *K* depends on the diameter of the sphere and on the length of the groove, and had found how it depends on these two constants, he could have introduced the result as a phenomenological property, so as to reconcile the experiments on the inclined plane with those in air.

Galileo knew a fairly simple way of studying the relationship between the diameter of the rolling sphere and the factor *K*, by means of the differences found when the chord theorem is applied, to which he had referred in a simple way in the *Dialogo*[334] but which was widely discussed in the third day of the *Discorsi*. In his latest book the theorem of chords is theorem VI of the third day for which he gives – and this is unique – no less than three demonstrations[335], but his first demonstration dated back to his time in Padua, because it is contained in a fragment from that time (fig.13.1)[336].

> Let the perpendicular *bc* and the inclined line *bd*, on which [the line] *be* is taken, be [drawn] to the horizon *ab*, and from *e* let *ef* be drawn, perpendicular to *bd*, and let it meet the said *bc* at *f*:
> It is to be proved that the time along *be* is equal to the time along *bf*. Draw, from *e*, the perpendicular to *ab*, and let it be *eg*: and since the impetus along *bd* is to the impetus along *bc*, as *eg* is to *bc* (as shown below); since, on the other hand, as *eg* is to *be*, so *be* is to *bf*, due to the similarity of the triangles *geb* and *bef*; so, as the space *bf* is to the space *be*, so the impetus along *bf* is to the impetus along *be*: so, the motion along *bf* and along *be* will take place in the same time.

[334] G.G., Vol. VII, *Dialogo*, p. 50.

[335] G.G., Vol. VIII, *Discorsi*, pp. 221-223.

[336] Ms. Gal. 72, Folio 147v. Watermark: Crown, form 1. Drake's identification: Watermark type C1. Drake's description: Mountains 20 × 17 mm.

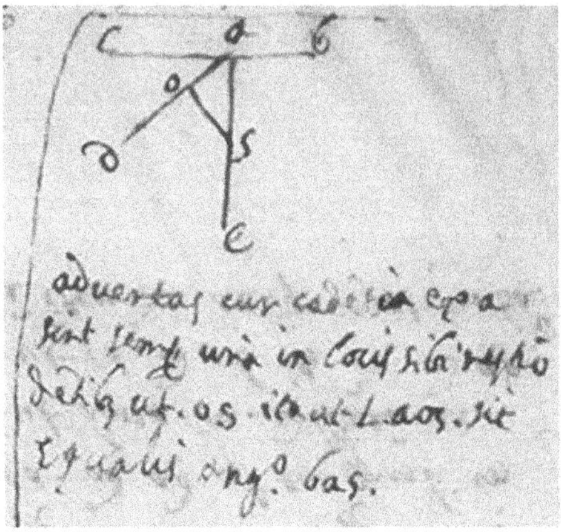

Fig. 13.2 Folio 147v.

In a corner of the same sheet of paper, but written on the back, there is a further observation (fig.13.2)[337]:

> Consider why [mobiles] falling from *a* are always found at the same time in positions corresponding to each other, such as *o* and *s*, such that the angle *aos* is equal to the angle *bas*.

Looking at fig. 13.1, we can write that in the same time t we obtain

$$bf = gt^2/2,$$
$$be = K \sin \alpha g t^2/2,$$

and so we can find $K = be/(bf \sin \alpha)$.

No trace remains of experiments of this type but if he did carry them out he certainly did not succeed in solving the conundrum, because there is practically no chance of guessing the complex relationship that exists between the diameter of the sphere d and the width of the channel c. Perhaps he would have found the constant result $K = 5/7$ if he had hollowed out a wide concave groove in his plane so that the sphere touched at only one point; unfortunately, he built the plane with a narrow groove to guide more accurately the spheres, which always have a diameter greater than the width of the groove, and this complicated everything. In chapter 4 we showed that it is difficult to carry out the direct experiment and that the results are not very conclusive.

We tried to evaluate the difficulty of deducing K from the experiments, using four spheres of different sizes to obtain different values of K. Next to their diameters the corresponding values of K are given:

[337] See below the letter Luca Valerio wrote to Galileo on 18 July 1609.

$A =$ Ø 1″ 3/16 = 30.16 mm $K_A \approx 0.5103$,
$B =$ Ø 1″ 3/8 = 34.92 mm $K_B \approx 0.5689$,
$C =$ Ø 1″ 7/16 = 36.51 mm $K_C = 0.5827$,
$D =$ Ø 1″ 1/2 = 38.10 mm $K_D = 0.6013$.

The precise formula is: $K_A = L/H(\sin\alpha - g_A/g)$ with g_A/g which cannot be totally neglected with respect to sin α. In order to proceed, we neglect g_A/g, simplifying the formula that becomes $K = (L/H)\sin\alpha$. With this simplification an error is introduced of between 10% and 20%. the results of the experiments are given in the two tables that follow: The first table gives the measurements for spheres *A* and *B*, the second table gives those for spheres *C* and *D*.

H	α	sin α	L_A	K_A	L_B	K_B
1.900	10.6°	0.1833333	0.159	0.456	0.174	0.499
1.730	8.3°	0.1443939	0.083	0.332	0.097	0.388
1.548	6.3°	0.1092424	0.060	0.320	0.089	0.526
1.350	4.0°	0.0693939	0.035	0.374	0.053	0.566
average				0.370		0.495
exact value				0.510		0.569

H	α	sin α	L_C	K_C	L_D	K_D
1.900	10.6°	0.1833333	0.187	0.537	0.198	0.568
1.730	8.3°	0.1443939	0.122	0.488	0.140	0.560
1.548	6.3°	0.1092424	0.089	0.526	0.104	0.615
1.350	4.0°	0.0693939	0.058	0.619	0.060	0.640
average				0.543		0.596
exact value				0.583		0.601

The results are better for the two larger spheres because the simultaneous sounds of the impact of the two spheres, one with the ground and the other with the obstacle on the plane, can be more clearly perceived. Obviously it is impossible to derive any dependence on *c* and *d* from these few numbers.

Let us suppose (and it is very likely) that Galileo took measurements; what would he have found? No more than he already knew, that is to say that there is a contradiction between the two types of experiments which he did not know how to resolve.

Galileo, publishing his *Dialogo* in 1632, could still allow himself to put the problem off, but after his sentence and his imprisonment he could only publish the theory of motion which he had arrived at with his experiments on the inclined plane, but he did not give up altogether. We shall see that he continued to study motion up to the end, moving on to a new ingenious mechanism which slowed down the vertical motion and at the same time avoided the difficulties due to rolling, *Galilei's machine*, with which, perhaps, he continued experimenting in view of a new edition of the *Discorsi* to which a fifth day that he was writing would be added.

The sheets of paper collected in Ms. Gal. 72, confirm that Galileo had already obtained nearly all the results of the *Discorsi* before returning to Florence: however he let them settle, probably in the hope of being able to understand the contradictions between his theories and experiments.

14. Before 1606: Experiments on a ship in uniform motion. Long before 1623: Galileo's principle of relativity

Of all the discussions that Galileo had in Rome between the end of 1615 and the beginning of the following year one strikes us as important for the chronology of his writings, his discussion with Francesco Ingoli, secretary of the Congregation *de Propaganda Fide*, whom he had known from the time when Ingoli studied at Padua[338]. In the presence of Lorenzo Magalotti Ingoli claimed, against Galileo, that the opinion of Copernicus was untenable and, following this kind of round table, it was agreed that he would put his arguments in writing and that Galileo would then reply. *De situ et quiete terrae contra Copernici systema disputatio*, was the title Francesco Ingoli gave to his work, which was only distributed in manuscript form.

Amongst other arguments Ingoli presented the following one[339]:

> Many things can be opposed to the daily movement of the Earth, some of them given by Tycho in two astronomical letters against Rothmann, a defender of Copernican opinions, on pages 167 and 188 of his book of *Astronomical Letters*: that is to say about the fall of a lead globe from a very high tower according to the perpendicular, despite being allegedly accompanied by the air, while the opposite should occur, if the Earth moves with a daily motion, even in the northern parallels of Germany, by one hundred and fifty "greater paces" in a second of time [...]

Galileo was unable to reply to Ingoli, who had sent his text at the beginning of 1616, because on 5 March of that year a decree of the Congregation of the Index suspended Copernicus's work *ut corrigeatur* and forbade the teaching of his opinions. This was the outcome of the so-called "first trial of Galileo", concluded on 26 February with the warning issued to him by Cardinal Bellarmino to abandon the aforesaid erroneous doctrine[340].

---

[338] Francesco Ingoli, born in Ravenna on 21 November 1578, graduated in Padua on 27 May 1601 in civil and canonical law. Ingoli's *Disputatio* was never printed. Later Lorenzo Magalotti was made cardinal by Urban VIII. Galileo's reply was known to many, certainly it was read by Monsignor Ciampoli, Father Grassi, Guiducci, Filippo Magalotti, a Scots gentleman who served Cardinal Barberino, Giorgio Conneo, some of Ciampoli's friends, the Prince of Cesi.

[339] G.G., Vol. V, p. 408. Francesco Ingoli, *De Situ et quiete terrae...disputatio.* The *passus maior* (greater pace) corresponds to 5 Rhine feet and is equal to 1.576 metres. The 750 feet velocity at Uraniborg latitude (55°. 54′), where Tycho had his Observatory, corresponds to a velocity of 236 m/s, which is a good approximation of the present value of 262 m/s.

[340] Antonio Favaro, *Galileo e l'inquisizione*, Florence, 1907, p. 17: «Since the most illustrious Cardinal Bellarmino

Eight years later, after the fears raised by the "first trial" had faded, when Galileo, who was already thinking of the *Dialogo,* decided to reply to Ingoli, he could no longer find the text amongst his papers and he had to search around for a copy, which he obtained from Cesare Marsili. Ingoli's text however «had reached many foreign nations and was perhaps even in the hands of heretics», it had certainly already reached Kepler by 1617, through Thomas Mingonius who then transmitted the Linz astronomer's reply[341] to Ingoli.

With the election to the papacy in 1624 of Urban VIII, who was well disposed towards him and to whom he had dedicated *Il Saggiatore*, Galileo, believing the moment to be favourable, conceived the hope that the decree condemning the Copernican system might be abolished. Having failed in this attempt, he allowed himself to believe that he could at least publish his own ideas, and so he wrote his *Letter to Francesco Ingoli in reply to the Disputatio de situ et quiete terrae*[342].

Although Galileo did not go so far as to publish anything, having paid attention to the opinion of many advisers, nevertheless, as Antonio Favaro assures us, this text in the form of a letter «was known in Rome, amongst others also to the Pope and the large number of manuscript copies of this reply that still survive is also proof that it was distributed fairly widely[343]». Galileo was told that Urban VIII knew of it from Giovanni Ciampoli, who wrote to him from Rome on 28 December 1624[344]:

> I read the reply written to Ingoli and I reported much of it to Our Lord who greatly appreciated the example of the riddle and of those heavy bodies judged little suited to motion, with those charming experiments that you put forward.

---

had reported that the mathematician Galileo Galilei, after having been warned by order of the Sacred Congregation [*of the Holy Office*] to abandon the opinion that he had held so far, that the Sun is the centre of the spheres and immobile, and the Earth is instead mobile, he agreed, and was informed of the Decree of the Congregation of the Index, that the writings of Nicolaus Copernicus *De revolutionibus Orbium Caelestium,* of *Didico Astunica in Job*, and of Brother Paolo Antonio Foscarini of the Carmelite Order had been prohibited and suspended respectively; the Most Holy One had ordered that an edict be published by the Master of the Sacred Palace of this suspension, respectively».

[341] *Ioannis Kepleri responsio ad Ingoli disputationem de Sistemate*; in JOHANNES KEPLER GESAMMELTE WERKE, Vol., XX, I. pp. 168-180; München, 1988.

[342] G.G., Vol. VI, pp. 509-561.

[343] ANTONIO FAVARO, *Nuovi studi galileiani*, Memorie del Reale Istituto Veneto di Scienze, Lettere ed Arti. Vol. 24, Venice, 1891, pp. 149-184. The letter to Ingoli was almost certainly known in Paris from 1627. Indeed in September 1627 Mersenne wrote to Luc Holste in Rome: «*Je vous prie aussi de m'escrire s'il est vray ce que le Sieur Piccolomini, apportant le chappeau de cardinal a Msr de Berulle, est veritable, a scavoir si le livre de Galilé a Galileo de Motu Terrae s'imprime avec permission du Pape, qui en a veu et approuvé la demonstration*». See *La Correspondance Du P. Marin Mersenne, édité et annoté par Cornelis de Waard,* Paris, 1945, Vol. I, p. 603 and p. 606, where the editor supposes that the work Ascanio Piccolomini had spoken of was really the *Lettera a Francesco Ingoli*, which may therefore have circulated in Paris from that date. This hypothesis is confirmed by what Cornier wrote to Mersenne on 14 January of 1628: «*Je presse Le Vasseur de faire imprimir sa Sphere de Copernic, qui est le mesme que le mouvement de la Terre de Gallilei. Je luy ay dict que cestui cy le fasoit imprimir en Italie, afin de l'advancer. Il m'a promis d'y travaller bientost; je ne scay s'il me tiendra parolle*».

[344] G.G., Vol. XIII, p. 295.

As is well known, at that time there was the threat of intervention by the Holy Office because of a denunciation of heresy raised with regard to what Galileo had written in *Il Saggiatore*, which failed only due to the intervention of Father Guevara, general of the Minims. Prince Cesi also suggested that he should not deliver the letter to Ingoli, given that Copernicus's opinion was defended in it *ex professo*; and so it was, as we know from Guiducci: «for all these reasons it seems wise to refrain, as I have said, and to leave the question rest a little». But now let us read some passages from it which concern local motion[345].

> This is the discourse: in which unfortunately I spy both of the errors I speak of. However, that the stone falling from the top of the tower moves in a straight line and perpendicular to the surface of the Earth, neither Aristotle nor you gather this, nor can gather it, from anything other than seeing how it moves descending, so to speak, skirting the surface of the tower, built perpendicular above the Earth; so that we see the line described by the stone is also straight and perpendicular. But here I tell you that from this appearance we cannot otherwise infer this except by supposing that the Earth stays motionless while the stone descends, which is then the question that I seek; because if I with Copernicus say that the Earth moves around and in consequence takes the tower with it and we still observe the effect of the stone, we shall say that the stone moves with a motion compounded of the universal daily circular motion to the east and of the other accidental motion directed towards its all, from which it ensues there is one motion inclined to the east; of which the one that is common to me, to the stone and to the tower, in this case to me remains imperceptible and as if it did not exist, and only the other motion can be observed, in which the tower and I are missing, that is to say the movement aproaching the Earth. Here therefore, is the misunderstanding shown clearly, if however I have managed to explain enough.

A little later Galileo added[346]:

> And this indeed is one of such experiments, that of a stone falling from the top of the mast of a ship, which always ends and strikes in the same place, both when the ship is at rest and while it travels fast, and the stone does not go, as they believe (as the ship slips away while the stone comes down through the air), far from the base of the mast towards the stern; in which I was doubly better a philosopher than them, because they, in saying what is actually the contrary, have even added a lie, saying that they have seen that with an experiment, and I have done the experiment, before which the natural discourse had most firmly persuaded me that the effect should happen as indeed it does: nor was it difficult for me to discover their deception, for they, imagining themselves as one who, with the whole ship at rest, was at the top of the mast, and so, with everything at rest, dropped a stone from there, and did not realise then that when the ship was moving, the stone no longer started from rest, since the mast and the man at the top and his hand and the stone also moved with the same velocity as the whole vessel; and again and again they give to me often into my hands minds so

[345] G.G., Vol. V, pp. 544-545.

[346] G.G., Vol. V, pp. 545-546.

> coarse, that it is not possible to get into their heads that if he who is on the mast keeps his arm steady, the stone does not depart from rest. So I say to you, Master Ingoli, that, while the ship is travelling, then the stone also moves with just as much impetus, which impetus is not lost because he who holds it opens his hand and lets it go freely, instead it is indelibly conserved in the stone, so that through this it is enough to follow the ship; and through its own heaviness, no longer prevented by him, it descends below, compounding from both a single motion (and perhaps also circular), transversal and inclined to where the ship is travelling; and so it comes to fall at the same spot of that ship where it fell when all was at rest. From this you could understand that those same experiments put forward by adversaries against Copernicus do much more for him than for them; because if the motion communicated by the ship's movement to the stone, which is indubitably accidental to it, nevertheless is so conserved in it, that the same effect is seen to a hair both in a ship that is sailing and one that is at rest, what doubt can linger that a stone, taken to the summit of a tower, with the same velocity as the whole terrestrial globe, conserves the same velocity when it then falls down? the same, I say, which is not, like that of the ship, accidental to it, but is its natural primary and coeternal inclination.

The only great man who preceded Galileo in understanding the experiment on the ship was Giordano Bruno in a fairly well known passage in his book *Cena de le Ceneri* (The Ash Wednesday dinner), published in London in 1584. Galileo's statement «*and I have done the experiment*» takes us back to the early years of the century, to the discussion, already mentioned, that he had about it in Padua before 1606 with the Jesuit Andrea Eudaemon-Ioannes[347]: it is the explanation of the impossibility of distinguishing the uniform motion of the reference system with experiments within the system, as illustrated a little further on in an unforgettable passage, which the author would then introduce, with only a few differences, into the *Dialogo* . It is the example of what would later be called the Galileian reference system[348]:

> In the largest room available below deck on some great vessel shut yourself in with one of your friends, and make sure that you have flies, moths and similar flying creatures there; take also a large container of water, with small fish in it; place too a pot high up that drips into

[347] Galileo's statement, so clear and precise, of having carried out the experiment was disputed by ALEXANDRE KOYRÉ, *Studi Galileiani,* Einaudi, Turin, 1979, p. 228, who attributed the glory of first carrying out the experiment in 1641 to Gassendi; as did: TULLIO GREGORY, *Gassendi e Galileo, Saggi su Galileo Galilei*, edited by CARLO MACCAGNI, Florence, 1972. pp. 313-314; HANS REICHENBACH, *The rise of scientific philosophy*, Los Angeles, 1951, It. Transl: *La nascita della filosofia scientifica*, Bologna, 1961, pp. 100-101; BERNARD BROCHORT and PIERRE COSTABEL, in *MARIN MERSENNE, Correspondance, publiée et annotée par C. De Waard*, vol. III (1631-1633). *Seconde édition revue et complétée.* In Vol. II of the *Correspondance du P. Marin Mersenne* (Paris, 1945), CORNELIS DE WAARD, on pp. 236-237 made Beeckmann discover the principle of inertia around 1614 and states that in 1619 he applied it to the experiment of the ship «*il l'applique [la loi d'inertie] ancore très nettement à l'interprétation d'un phénomène qui devint classique lorsqu'il eut discuti par Galilées dans son Dialogo de 1632*», and then added: «*Galilée n'a jamais connu le principe sous cette forme. Beeckmann en usa par la suite en plusieurs endroits de son Journal*». The original text is in the *Journal tenu par Isaac Beckmann de 1604 a 1634, publié avec une introduction et des notes par Cornelis De Waard*, The Hague, M. Nijhoff. 1939, vol. I, p. 331. An excusable ignorance for all these authors?

[348] G.G., Vol. V, p. 547-549.

> another one below with a narrow neck: and when the ship is still, observe diligently how those little flying creatures go to all parts of the room with equal velocity, the fish you will see wander indifferently towards any part of the edge of the container, the falling drops will all enter the pot below; and you, if you toss something to your friend, will not have to throw it with more force in one direction rather than another, when the distances are the same; and leaping, as they say, with feet together you will travel equal spaces in all directions. When you have carefully observed all these things, make the ship travel at any speed you like; and (as long as the motion is uniform and not swaying to and fro) you will not espy the slightest change in all these things, nor in any of them, nor indeed from something that there is in yourself can you be sure whether the ship is still or sailing; jumping you will pass the same spaces over the boards as before, nor, since the ship is moving swiftly, will you make greater leaps to the stern than to the bow, even though, in the time that you are in the air, the boards glide in the direction contrary to your jump; and throwing a piece of fruit to your friend, you will not have to throw it with greater strength, to reach him, if he is towards the bow and you towards the stern, than if you were oppositely placed; the drops will fall into the pot below without even one straying towards the stern, although, while the drop is in the air, the ship sails many spans; the fish in their water will not endure more effort in swimming towards the forward rather than the aft part of the container, but with equal ease they will go to take the food that you place on whichever part of the edge of the container that you wish; and finally the moths and the flies will continue flying indifferently in all directions, nor will they ever be reduced to withdrawing towards the part that looks to the stern, almost as if they were tired of keeping up with the swift progress of the ship, from which they will have been separated for a long time, that is to say while they stay suspended in the air; and if you make a little smoke by burning a little incense, you will see it rise and stay there, and like a small cloud move indifferently no more to one side than another. And if you ask me the reason for all these effects I shall reply for now: "because the universal motion of the ship, being communicated to the air and to all those things that are contained in it, and not being contrary to their natural inclination, is conserved indelibly in them"; another time then you will hear detailed answers more widely explained. Now, when you have seen all these experiments, and how these movements, although accidental and random, are shown indeed to be the same when the ship is sailing and when it is still, will you not abandon all doubt that the same must happen around the terrestrial globe, since the air always travels with it ? and even the more so, since that universal motion, which in the ship is accidental, we propose, in the Earth and earthly things, to be natural and proper. Add more, that in the ship we, even if we try a hundred times to make it move and to be still, never however will we able to recognise from internal things what it is doing: how is this possible in the Earth, which we have always had in one same state?

It is impossible to be clearer. The passage needs no comment.

15. The laws of motion: Galileo announces them in the *Dialogo* (1632) and presents them in the *Discorsi* (1638)

In the programme that Galileo announced to the Grand Duke's secretary[349] during the negotiations for his return to Florence, which occurred in 1610, two works of great importance are indicated which were already well advanced. In his letter to Belisario Vinta he describes them as follows:

> The works I have to bring to a conclusion are mainly two books *De sistemate seu constitutione universi*, an immense concept full of philosophy, astronomy and geometry: three books *De motu locali* an entirely new science, since no other, ancient or modern, had discovered any of the numerous wondrous symptoms that I show are in the natural movements and in the violent ones, so I can most reasonably call it a new science and retrieved by me from its first principles: three books on mechanics, two regarding the demonstrations of principles and foundations, and one of problems; and although others have written on this same subject, even so that which has been written until now is not, in quantity or anything else, a quarter of what I write.

The first of the works that he has to «bring to a conclusion», which had a provisional Latin title, would later be written completely in Italian with the title *Dialogo sopra i due massimi sistemi del mondo*. The discoveries he was making with his telescope encouraged him to proceed with his astronomical observations before going on to write the final text and in the meantime, in 1613, he published the *Istoria e dimostrazioni intorno alle macchie solari e loro accidenti* (Letters on sunspots) a fundamental work that reinforced his vision of the cosmos. There was no presentiment of the approaching storm; the *imprimatur* dated 4 November 1612 was accompanied by a highly complimentary opinion from Antonio Bucci, asked for by the Master of the Holy Apostolic Palace Ludovico Ystella Valentini[350]:

> I have examined diligently the three letters on sunspots, which I judge most worthy of publication, not having found anything that is in contradiction with the rules of the Holy

---

349 G.G., Vol. X, pp. 351-352, letter to Belisario Vinta dated 7 May 1610.

350 G.G., Vol. V, p. 74: «... *tres Epistolas de Maculis Solaribus ... diligenter vidi, quas cum nihil, quod sacri Indicis regulis repugnet, immo raram doctrinam, novas ac mirabiles observationes hucusque incognitas, inauditasque facili, ac perpolito stilo explicatas continere invenerim, typis dignissimas iudicavi*».

Index, but indeed that contain an extraordinary theory and marvellous new observations not known before and never seen before, explained in an easy and refined style.

The Decree of the Congregation of the Index of 1616, which banned support for the doctrine that the sun was motionless, for over a decade seemed to him an insuperable obstacle, even though he did not desist from discussing celestial events and in 1623 he wrote *Il Saggiatore*.

As for the other work, the *De motu locali*, which he would then publish with the Italian title *Discorsi intorno a due nuove scienze*, it was much further advanced in its editing: indeed if we examine Ms Gal 72 we see that in 1610 Galileo had already written, in a sometimes more concise Latin than the final version, a quantity of theorems, corollaries, propositions and problems from the third and fourth days of the *Discorsi*. These papers are arranged and gathered together in the following table to document the extent of the work done at Padua.

Third Day

Equable or uniform motion

Theorema	I, Propositio I	Folio 138r	November 1605
Theorema I,	Propositio I	Folio 138v	November 1605

Naturally accelerated motion

Theorema III	Propositio III	Folio 163v	by 1610
Corollarium		Folio 172v	by 1610
Corollarium		Folio 179r	by 1610
Theorema VI	Propositio VI	Folio 151r	by 1610
Theorema VI	Propositio VI	Folio 160r	by 1610
Theorema VI	Propositio VI	Folio 172r	by 1610
Theorema VII	Propositio VII	Folio 172r	by 1610
Problema I	Propositio XIII	Folio 145r	May 1608
Theorema VIII	Propositio VIII	Folio 164v	by 1610
Theorema IX	Propositio IX	Folio 147v	by 1610
Theorema X	Propositio X	Folio 164r	by 1610
Theorema XI	Propositio XI	Folio 164r	by 1610
Theorema XII	Propositio XI	Folio 126r	August 1607
Problema IV	Propositio XVII	Folio 143r	February 1609
Problema V	Propositio XVIII	Folio 143v	February 1609
Problema VI	Propositio XIX	Folio 161r	February 1609
Scolium		Folio 163v	by 1610
Theorema XVI	Propositio XXV	Folio 163v	by 1610
Theorema XVII	Propositio XXVII	Folio 087r	August 1607
Theorema XIX	Propositio XXX	Folio 140r	May 1608
Theorema XX	Propositio XXXI	Folio 127v	May 1608

Theorema XXI	Propositio XXXII	Folio 127v	May 160
Problema XII	Propositio XXXIII	Folio 161v	February 1609
Lemma 1		Folio 172v	by 1610
Lemma 2		Folio 172v	by 1610
Lemma 3		Folio 163r	by 1610
Problema XIV,	Propositio XXXV	Folio 144r	February 1609
Theorema XXII	Propositio XXXVI	Folio 157v	by 1610
Problema XV	Propositio XXXVII	Folio 087r	August 1607

Fourth Day

Parabolic motion «composed of the equable horizontal motion and the descendent natural motion»

Theorema II	Propositio II	Folio 91v	August 1607
Theorema III	Propositio III	Folio 91v	August 1607
Problema I	Propositio IV	Folio 91v	August 1607
Problema	Propositio V	Folio 87v	August 1607
Corollarium		Folio 87v	August 1607
Problema	Propositio VI	Folio 116v	by 1610
Problema	Propositio VI	Folio 114v	by 1610
Theorema	Propositio VII	Folio 86r	by 1610
Theorema	Propositio VII	Folio 111r	August 1607
Theorema	Propositio VII	Folio 90r	by 1610
Theorema	Propositio VIII	Folio 80r	August 1607
Theorema	Propositio VIII	Folio 110r	August 1607
Theorema	Propositio X	Folio 86v	by 1610
Theorema	Propositio X	Folio 110v	August 1607
Problema	Propositio XIII	Folio 110v	August 1607

From what is missing from the small collection of Ms. Gal. 72, we can estimate how rich Galileo's archive must have been. He kept it close to him to the end and we must bitterly regret the lack of care with which his papers were looked after first by his daughter-in-law Sestilia Bocchineri and then by Viviani's heirs.

Galileo had already been working for a few years on the final edition of the "entirely new science"; this is confirmed by a letter from Luca Valerio, a friend from his days in Pisa[351], to whom

[351] G.G, Vol. X, p. 240: «I am that Luca Valerio, your devoted servant, that you knew in Pisa near to the happy memory of Sir Camillo Colonna, when we used to go through those charming and shady fields, in the company of other philosophers, often shouting and arguing together».

Galileo had submitted two principles on which he intended to base the theory of motion[352]; they were the ones that raised the greatest doubts. Valerio reassured him:

> I did not reply earlier to Your Lordship's letter of the 5th of June, which was most welcome to me, because I wished to consider thoroughly the two principles that you deigned to communicate to me. So I say that as principles of a middle science they do not strike me as hard, on the contrary most clear, given that in principles of such sciences it is not necessary that they satisfy at first sight intellects totally lacking in the higher sciences. But a geometrical intellect, with some glimmer of metaphysics, whether natural or acquired, could not doubt the truth of the two propositions as soon as the terms of those propositions had been understood, because it can easily be seen that it is a truth known by itself that if the virtue of the sufficient cause is multiplied, it is necessary that the quantity of the effect be multiplied according to the same multiplication, having removed from it all sort of impediment: because otherwise part of the causal virtue would be useless to it, which involves manifest contradiction; since the causal virtue, as such, refers to the quantity of the effect, and with the quantity of the effect we measure the quantity of the cause, so with regard to extension and intention, as to perfection and nobility: from which, as a geometrician, that same intellect will understand, that the general similarity of the proportions can easily be proved, by means of the reasons usually adduced in many other geometrical matters, and yet not to be inculcated in these middle sciences. So, if the impetus or inclination of the heaviness of the body *A*[(353)] above the inclined plane at the horizon according to angle *B* is supposed to be double the impetus of the same *A* over the inclined plane at the horizon according to angle *C*, greater than angle *B*, and these two different impeti spring from the heaviness of *A*, constrained differently for the production of the impetus because of the different inclinations of said planes, it is seen, as an immediate consequence, that the velocity of the natural motion of *A* over the less inclined plane, will be double the velocity of the motion of the same *A* over that other more inclined plane. So the vigour of the immediate cause of the double velocity, which is the impetus or the inclination to the double velocity, should be double the inclination at the half velocity, according to the greater inclination of the other plane. The second supposition is no less clear to me than the first: thus since the motion of the heavy body *D*, moved along *AC* to the horizon *BC*, is composed of two straight line motions, one parallel to *BC*, mobile towards *BC*, and the other along a perpendicular to the horizontal, this too mobile, it is clear that when *D* is at *C*, it will have acquired as much impetus or inclination to move rapidly, that is the quantity of the effect (as the effect, I say, of that part of the compounded motion made along the mobile perpendicular, equal to the steady *AB*), as it would have acquired if *D* had moved only along the perpendicular *AB*: and this I say in observance of the aforesaid metaphysical principle (fig.15.1).

---

[352] G.G., Vol. X, pp. 248-249, letter to Galileo dated 18 July 1609.

[353] (Note by A. Favaro) In his letter Valerio did not draw the figure recalled, probably because he was referring to a figure that Galileo had sketched in the letter to which he was replying and that has not come down to us. Perhaps the figure corresponded to this one that we add here to facilitate the understanding of the text.

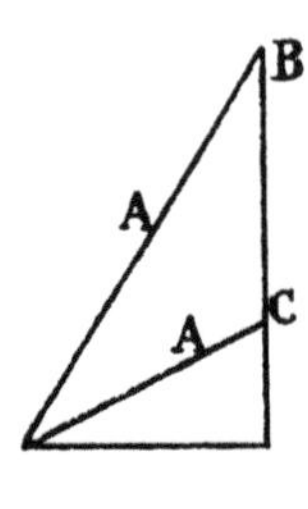

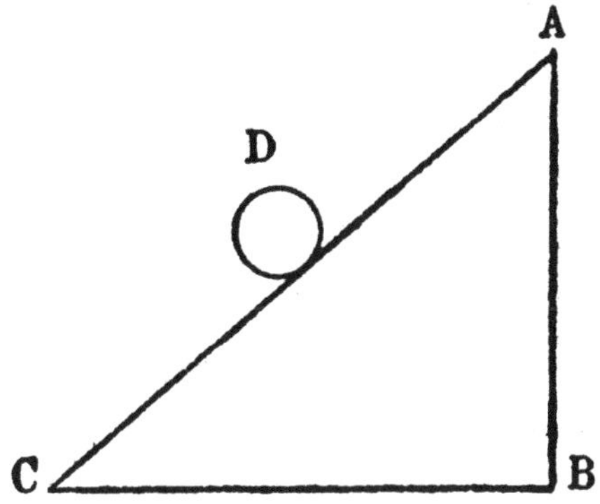

Fig. 15.1

The letter to Luca Valerio is the confirmation that while Galileo was at Padua he had already decided to place two fundamental results of his experiments amongst the principles of the theory of motion:

a) that the ratio between the components of heaviness (*i.e.* between the sines of the angles according to the law of the inclined plane) determines the ratio between motions,

b) that the velocity reached at the end depends only on the difference in height of the inclined plane.

After the admonition from the Congregation of the Holy Office we might have expected Galileo to dedicate all his energies to the treatise on motion; instead, the work remained suspended for twenty-five years because Galileo did not know how to explain the contradictions he had met with in his experiments because of the rolling of the sphere on the inclined plane.

Anyway, with regard to the publication of the first treatise, the situation changed suddenly. With the election to the papacy of Urban VIII, who had always been friendly towards him, Galileo thought he could elude the decree of 1616; so he reverted to writing the *Dialogo sopra i due massimi del mondo*.

The *Dialogo* is a treatise on cosmology, but the reasons that were traditionally opposed to the hypothesis of the Earth's daily rotation refer to situations that involve the local motion of bodies. For this reason Galileo starts the first day enunciating his principles. The strategy is set out by Salviati[354]:

> SALVIATI: [...] it is necessary [...] to proceed to demonstrations, observations, and particular experiments. First we must propound all those that have been put forwards to prove the Earth's stability by Aristotle, Ptolemy, and others, trying next to resolve them. Finally we must produce those by which a person may become persuaded that the Earth, no less than the Moon or any other planet, is to be numbered among the natural bodies that move circularly.

[354] G.G., Vol. VII, *Dialogo*, p. 69.

Following this path Galileo did not feel he was running any great risks, because there was no need to face the contradictions between theory and experiments immediately: he only had to warn the reader that the demonstrations would be made available in his treatise on local motion which was now imminent[355].

SALVIATI: Be content for now that I have removed your incredulity. As for exact knowledge, wait until some other time, when you shall see what our Academic friend has demonstrated concerning local motion. There you shall find it proved that in the time that the one body falls all the distance *CB*, the other descends along *CA* only to the point *T*, upon which falls the perpendicular drawn from the point *B*.

There are four fundamental principles of local motion; we shall examine them one at a time, first presenting them as they appear in the *Dialogo* and then as enunciated (and obviously discussed and proved) in the *Discorsi*.

1) In natural motion the velocity grows in proportion to the time

[*Dialogo*] And since as we have remarked on other occasions the falling body starting from rest acquires always a greater degree of speed as time goes on, according to the time elapsed, [...][356].

[*Discorsi*] I say that that motion is equably or uniformly accelerated which, abandoning rest, adds on to itself equal momenta of swiftness in equal times[357].

2) In natural motion the space travelled grows with the square of the time

[*Dialogo*] The acceleration of straight motion in heavy bodies proceeds according to the odd numbers beginning from one. That is, marking off whatever equal times you wish, and as many of them, then if the moving body leaving a state of rest shall have passed during the first time such a space as, say, an ell [canna], then in the second time it will go three ells; in the third five, in the fourth seven, and it will continue thus according to the successive odd numbers. In sum, this is the same as to say that the spaces passed over by the body starting from rest have to each other the ratios of the squares of the times in which such spaces were traversed[358].

---

[355] G.G., Vol. VII, *Dialogo* , pp. 50-51.

[356] G.G., Vol. VII, *Dialogo*, p. 225.

[357] G.G., Vol.VIII, *Discorsi*, pp. 198 and 202 - 205 where we read: «*Motum aequabiliter, seu uniformiter, acceleratum dico illum [a p. 205: dicimus eum] qui, a quiete recedens, temporibus aequalibus aequalia celeritatis momenta sibi superaddit*».

[358] G.G., Vol.VII, *Dialogo*, p. 248.

[*Discorsi*] If a moveable descends from rest in uniformly accelerated motion, the spaces run through in any times whatever are to each other as the duplicate ratio of their times; that is, are as the squares of those time[359].

3) *In natural motion the theorem of average velocity holds both for the inclined plane and for free fall.*

[*Dialogo*] The impetus (that is, the degree of velocity) the ball is found to have acquired when it arrives at the point *A* is such that if the ball continued to move uniformly with this same speed, without accelerating or being retarded, it would travel twice the length of the inclined plane in a time equal to that of its descent along the incline[360].

[*Dialogo*] [...] the falling body, ever acquiring new speed according to the ratio already mentioned, wherever it may be in the line of its motion it will have such a degree of velocity that were it to continue to move uniformly with this, then in a second time equal to that of its previous descent it would traverse twice the distance already passed over[361].

[*Discorsi*] The time in which a certain space is traversed by a moveable in uniformly accelerated movement from rest is equal to the time in which the same space would be traversed by the same moveable carried in uniform motion whose degree of speed is one-half the maximum and final degree of speed of the previous uniformly accelerated motion[362].

4) In natural motion the principle of final velocities holds

[*Dialogo*] SALVIATI: [...] I know that you will make no question of granting that the acquisition of impetus is measured by the departure of the movable body from the point of origin and its approach toward the centre to which its motion tends. So will you not put an end to your difficulty by conceding that two equal movable bodies, descending by different lines and without any impediment, will have acquired equal impetus whenever their approaches to the centre are equal?
SAGREDO: I surely believe it would [363].

[*Discorsi*] I assume that the degrees of speed acquired by the same moveable over different inclinations of planes are equal whenever the heights of those planes are equal[364].

---

[359] G.G., Vol.VIII, *Discorsi.*, p. 209 THEOREMA II. PROPOSITIO II. The text is: «*Si aliquot mobile motu uniformiter accelerato descendat ex quiete, spatia quibuscunque temporibus ab ipso peracta, sunt inter se in duplicata ratione eorundem temporum, nempe ut eorundem temporum quadrata*».

[360] G.G., Vol.VII, *Dialogo*, p. 52. This enunciation of the theorem refers to motion on an inclined plane.

[361] G.G., Vol.VII, *Dialogo*, p. 252. This enunciation of the theorem refers to motion in free fall.

[362] G.G., Vol.VIII, *Discorsi*, p. 208. «*Tempus in quo aliquod spatium a mobili conficitur latione ex quiete uniformiter accelerata, est aequale tempori in quo idem spatium conficeretur ab eodem mobili motu aequabili delato, cuius velocitatis gradus subduplus sit ad summum et ultimum gradum velocitatis prioris motus uniformiter accelerati*».

[363] G.G., Vol. VII, *Dialogo*, p. 47.

[364] G.G.,Vol.VIII, p. 205. «*Accipio, gradus velocitatis eiusdem mobilis super diversas planorum inclinationes acquisitos tunc esse aequales, cum eorumdem planorum elevationes aequales sint*».

Galileo, by bringing forward his results on motion in the *Dialogo* in 1632, offered ideas, cues for reflection and subjects of discussion to various characters gravitating around Marin Mersenne – I refer above all to Descartes, Roberval and Fermat, who were not to prove very benevolent towards him – but this choice still brought him luck, because it was through Thomas Salusbury's English edition of the *Dialogo* that Newton became acquainted with Galileo's reasoning. For the great British scientist what he read in the *Dialogo*, without having known[365] the *Discorsi*, which he read later in the 1699 Latin version, was enough for him to attribute the first two laws of motion to Galileo. If we reflect on the relationships that the four laws announced by Galileo have to each other, we can understand why Newton attributed the primacy to Galileo.

If the theory of proportions made it impossible – at least on paper – for Galileo to fuse together the laws he had discovered, Newton had no such hesitation and this is what he read in the *Dialogo*:

Galileo's first two "laws" can be represented by expressions in which two constants g and g' appear

(1) $v(t) = g\,t,$

(2) $H(t) = g'\,t^2.$

The third "law" is described by an expression in which double the height H is numerically equal to the product of the velocity $v(t)$ reached at the end of the accelerated motion by the time t taken to fall from height H,

(3) $2H(t) = v(t)t\,.$

Since for the (1) $v(t) = gt$, the (3) can be written

(4) $H(t) = gt^2/2$

equalling (4) to (2) we obtain

(5) $g' = g/2\,,$

[365] I. B. Cohen questioned the possibility that Newton was aware of the *Discorsi* and put forward the thesis that: «the *Prima Lex* of Newton's *Principia* was derived directly from the *Prima Lex* of Descartes' *Principia*, as I have been able to document by identity of language as well as of concept ... As to the Second Law, considered as a mathematical relation between an impulse and the resulting change in momentum (defined as the product of mass and vector velocity), which is the form in which it appears in Newton's *Principia*, surely there can be no valid claim that this might have been known to Galileo». See: *Newton attribution of the first two laws of motion to Galileo* in «*Atti del Simposio Internazionale di Storia, Metodologia, Logica e Filosofia della Scienza " Galileo nella Storia e nella Filosofia della Scienza"*», pp. XXV-XLIV.

and so, to sum up, the content of his first three "laws" is contained in two universally known mathematical formulae:

(6) $$v = g\,t\,,$$

(7) $$H = (1/2)g\,t^2\,.$$

Moreover with (6) and (7), eliminating the time, we can arrive at the expression that expresses the velocity acquired as a function only of the height of the fall:

(8) $$v(t)^2 = g^2t^2 = 2gH(t).$$

The relationship (8) also provides the proof of the theorem of final velocities, because on an inclined plane with angle φ, in place of g we must put $g\sin\varphi$ and in place of H we must consider $H\sin\varphi$. Now, from (6) and (7) we can eliminate not only the time but also $\sin\varphi$, and thus show that the final velocity, both over an inclined plane and in free fall motion, is a function only of the difference in height $(2gH)^{1/2}$ (when there is no rolling or friction).

It remains to determine how much Galileo, who in his verbal expressions often showed that he was capable of going well beyond the limits of the theory of proportions, had this in mind.

16. Before 1610: The constant-flow chronograph

There are experiments in which it seems obvious that Galileo used his constant-flow chronograph; traces were found, for example, in Folios 115v and 189v of Ms. Gal. 72; they are however sheets of paper without watermarks and therefore cannot be dated.

Galileo presented his new method of measuring time explicitly in the *Discorsi*[366]:

> As for the measurement of time, a large bucket full of water was hung, attached above, which through a narrow pipe, welded to the bottom of it, poured a thin trickle of water, which was collected in a small tumbler for all the time that the ball descended in the groove and in its parts: then the drops of water, thus collected, were weighed with most accurate scales from time to time, giving us with the differences and proportions of their weights the differences and proportions of the times; and this with such accuracy, that, as I have said, such operations, repeated many times over, never differed by a perceptible moment.

This procedure presented considerable advantages compared to the pendulum: the measurement of time is continuous and is as precise as the scales allow it to be, so that the space can be chosen arbitrarily and the time taken to travel it can be measured, while with the pendulum the situation is reversed, the time is fixed in units of oscillations of the pendulum (simple or complete) and the space travelled is measured. Galileo sent a more detailed description of the «constant-flow chronograph» to Giovan Battista Baliani, in a letter dated 1 August 1639, when he explained to him that he had not measured the acceleration of the natural motion directly, but had deduced it from the acceleration observed on the inclined plane. Initially, he referred to the pendulum, which remained the fundamental instrument for comparison with sidereal time, but then he went on to describe the new apparatus[367]:

> [...] It remains for us now to find the quantity of the time of the descents along the groove. This we shall obtain from the admirable property of the pendulum, which is to make all of its vibrations, large or small, in equal times. We seek, *pro una vice tantum*, that two, three or four curious and patient friends, having set a fixed star against some steady sign, taken a pendulum of any length, count its vibrations for all the time of the return of said fixed star to the first place; and this will be the number of vibrations of 24 hours. From the number of these we can find the vibrations of any other larger or smaller pendulums as we see fit; so

---

[366] G.G., Vol. VIII, *Discorsi* , p. 213.

[367] G.G., Vol. XVIII, pp. 76-77.

that if, for example, the vibrations counted by us in the 24 hours had been[368], for example, 234567, taking another shorter pendulum, with which one counted, for example, 800 vibrations while the other counted 150 of greater ones, we would already have by the golden rule the number of vibrations of all the time of the 24 hours: and if with these vibrations we wished to know the time of the descent along the groove, we could with the same ease find not only the minutes, seconds and thirds, but fourths and fifths, and as much as we like. It is true that we could proceed to more exact measurements having seen and observed what the flow of water is through a thin pipe, because collecting it, and having weighed the quantity that passed, *e.g.*, in a minute, we could then, by weighing the amount that passed during the time of the descent along the groove, find the most exact measurement and quantity of that time, using mainly a scale so precise that it moves at a sixtieth of a grain [...]

The photograph (fig.16.1) shows the reconstruction of Galileo's chronograph, a piece of equipment[369] that we started to use in 1992: in this, the large vessel which Galileo spoke of is a cylindrical container with a diameter of 240 mm and a height of about 200 mm. Underneath a tap is fixed in which small pierced cylinders can be inserted, to obtain «a thin trickle of water».

When the level of the water is about 170 mm and the diameter of the hole of the reducer is 2 mm, 4.2 grams of water pour out every second which, weighed on a scale «so precise that it moves at a sixtieth of a grain», *i.e.* a milligram, ensure the theoretical possibility of distinguishing 1/4200 of a second; naturally, the time to be measured must be of only a few seconds, so as to leave the height of the water in the container practically constant (or the outflow has to be compensated by the inflow of an equal quantity). As to precision, it all depends on the possibility of making the beginning and the end of the event to be measured coincide with the duration of the collection of the water. In the case of measurements of the time of descent of a sphere on an inclined plane, the operator can let the sphere go with one hand, checking the beginning of the motion and with the other hand place the tumbler at the same moment under the flow of water, almost simultaneously. It is more difficult to make the end of the motion coincide with the end of the collection of the water. This operation, which depends on the experience and reflexes of the operator, leads to a fluctuation of the order of 1/10 of a second.

In a series of 59 measurements taken on a plane with an inclination of 2.5° and a groove 25 mm wide, along which sensors had been fitted, using a steel sphere with Ø = 30.16 mm, in a path of 2 305 mm checked electronically, we found that on average the time measured with Galileo's chronograph was $T_C = 5.42$ s ($\sigma_n = 0.07$) while the time measured electronically by the sensors was $T_E = 5.28$ s ($\sigma_n = 0.02$).

---

368 Note that 234567 is a number deliberately taken at random, (or rather, it is taken from the series of natural numbers). In 24 hours there are 86 400 seconds and for an ideal pendulum that beats each second the length is L_c = 0.248 m (complete oscillations) or L_s = 0.993 m (simple oscillations), with small variations according to the latitude. Instead the length of a pendulum which corresponds to a period of 84 600/234567 ≈ 0.37 s, is l_c = 0.034 m (complete oscillations) or l_s = 0.135 m (simple oscillations).

369 The experiments described here were carried out in August 1992 and were recorded in a film presented at the IX conference of the European Physical Society (Florence, 14-17 Sepember 1993). The film is called *Gli esperimenti di Galileo sul moto naturale* (Galileo's experiments on natural motion) and can be seen on the internet at the following link: http://www.illaboratoriodigalileogalilei.it/film1.html

Fig. 16.1

The electronic time is systematically less than that of the chronograph because the sensors set off the electronic chronograph when the sphere interrupts the ray of light that keeps them active and this operation always happens a little later than the beginning, and a little sooner than the end, of the motion.

In principle Galileo's chronograph is at least 100 times more precise than a clock with a pendulum, even if this precision was made useless by the inability to set the beginning and end of events clearly; the first machine that was able to compete with it was Hipp's chronograph, invented in the middle of the 19th century. Hipp ensured the theoretical possibility of reading a thousandth of a second, just like the water clock, but it had the advantage of being able to interrupt its course extremely rapidly by means of an electromagnet.

This invention of Galileo's was also set aside by his successors, indeed mocked by historians[370], until Thomas Settle[371] in a memorable paper showed in 1961 that «with a simple but ingenious device Galileo could obtain relatively precise time measurements».

[370] The champion of them all is A. Koyré; see: *An experimentum au XVII siècle: la determination de G*, XXII Congrès International de Philosophie des Sciences, Paris, 1952 : «*Il est juste de reconnaître son immense mérite. Mais il est juste aussi d'attirer l'attention sur l'invraisemblable pauvreté des moyens expérimentaux dont il dispose. Une boule roulant dans une rigole "bien polie", un seau d'eau avec un petit trou d'où elle s'écoule dans un petit récipient que l'on pèse ensuite pour mesurer le temps (Ctésibius avait déjà des appareils bien meilleurs): quelle accumulation de sources d'erreur et d'inexactitude! Comme on comprend bien que Galilée évite, tant qu'il peut, de donner des chiffres; et que, lorsqu'il les donne, ils sont grossièrement inexacts*». Even more vent is given to Koyré's sarcasm, which frankly is not in very good taste, in the English edition of his work: *An experiment in measurement*, Proceedings of the American Philosophical Society, Vol. 97 (1953) pp. 222-237.

[371] Thomas B. Settle, *An Experiment in the History of Science*, Science, Vol. 133, 6 January 1961.

17. Galileo overcame the difficulty due to rolling by carrying out experiments with a new machine*

On returning to Tuscany after the painful events that led to the ban of his unfortunate *Dialogo*, Galileo began to work on the final version of the work that he had so often announced, the *Discorsi e dimostrazioni matematiche intorno a due nuove scienze*, a title chosen by the editor which did not correspond to the title wanted by the author, who was not able to have it changed however[372]:

> It is with surprise and dismay that I have been struck by the liberty taken by Master Elzevier in transforming the title of my book, reducing it from noble, as it deservedly should have been, to over mundane, not to say plebeian [...]

He devoted himself to the first two days, dedicated to the resistance of materials and the qualitative aspects of motion (vacuum, pumps, pendulums, sound, motion in fluids, scales etc.).

He had already written the mathematical formulation of the laws of motion (essentially definitions and theorems) at Padua and he had written it in Latin: the elderly scientist decided not to change language but here and there he added a certain number of explanations and connections in Italian dialogue form. So while he was completing the third and fourth days at the same time he began to study the old problem of the force of percussion.

If he had not brought to Florence the long inclined plane with which he had carried out his experiments at Padua[373], at Arcetri Galileo ordered another equally important instrument to be built: a new and simple piece of apparatus, consisting of a cord passing through a pulley fixed up high, to the ends of which two equal weights were attached. Galileo wrote that the weights

* A knowledge of Galileo's text on percussion is certainly useful to understand this last part better.

---

[372] G.G., Vol. XVII, p. 370, letter to Elia Diodati, August 1638.

[373] It is only with an effort that three men can move a few metres the inclined plane (built according to the description we read in the *Discorsi*) which is now part of the *Laboratorio di Galileo Galilei*. We can imagine the difficulty that Galileo would have had to face, not to mention the expense, if he had taken his plane to Florence; besides, a large vehicle would have been needed to transport it unharmed over the roads at that time: we do not wish to suggest that it would have been impossible, because he must have taken with him his clothes, papers, books, some paintings and some furniture he wanted to keep; in other words, he must have organised a house move but for that very reason he must have tried to limit the expense; to ship these household goods he may perhaps have chosen a sea route. While leaving the plane behind he may have thought that he could rebuild it, if necessary, once he had arrived and was settled in town, with less expense than that of transporting it, and besides, there is no evidence, direct or indirect, that the plane, a significant and visible object, had been noticed in Florence.

were of 100 *libbre* (pounds), about 34 kg: they were probably less heavy but he preferred, as he so often did, to give a round number[374].

This apparatus was a development[375] of another machine, the inclined plane with a pulley at one end, used in his Mechanics to prove the fundamental theorem of the inclined plane and for the principle of inertia.

In the new machine the bodies moved vertically and the only object that rotated, and then only slowly, was the pulley, a negligible mass compared to the others hanging from the cord.

As usual, the most precise information is to be found in his correspondence: Galileo, soon after returning to Arcetri, in January 1634, communicated his first results on the force of percussion to Niccolò Aggiunti, who in turn wrote to him on 1 February[376]:

> Your Excellency's proposal about percussion is truly marvellous, and once it is proved it brings with it no less admirable consequences, one of which appears to me to be this: that any even slight percussion will have infinite force, because, having proposed any very great weight, we could find such a resistance in which a slight percussion will work no less than the pressing heaviness of the great weight proposed. I confess that, although some probable conjecture that the business happens as you say had passed through my mind, nevertheless I felt at the same time difficulties and doubts arise and swarm on so many sides, that I was as if stunned and senseless, and no life sign remained to me other than an immense desire to recover from this stupidity; so I therefore feel the greatest passion at not being able to come and receive sense and life from your mouth. Unavoidable occupations oblige me to stay here; but I swear to Your Excellency that I, although far away, am daily with you, for I do not believe at all that a single day passes without you being talked of in this house, and with incredible relish.

A few notes on the subject by Niccolò Aggiunti survive, probably the consequence of discussions that took place at Arcetri during the summers of 1634 and 1635, when Aggiunti, free from lessons, could go and visit him. I transcribe a few passages from these papers[377], because in them correct use is made of the concept of inertial mass as the quantity of material, which acts in dynamic processes differently from the weight, because this is a concept that many erroneously believe was not known to Galileo:

> Percussion operates with the velocity and with the power of the matter in which the said velocity is impressed and so, if they fall from the same height, two unequal bodies of the

[374] It may also be that legal multiples of the *libbra* (pound) existed then, used to weigh large quantities; in which case the indication of 100 pounds would be naturally explained.

[375] In the following paragraph it will be described how Galileo had the idea of the pulley, which happened more or less at the time when he was finishing the first day of the *Discorsi*.

[376] G.G., Vol. XVI, p. 31.

[377] See: Antonio Favaro, *Niccolò Aggiunti*, in *Amici e corrispondenti di Galileo Galilei*, Atti del R. Istituto Veneto di Scienze, Lettere ed Arti, A.A. 1913-14 – Tomo LXXIII, Vol. XII, pp.1-77 and Raffaello Caverni, *Storia del Metodo Sperimentale in Italia*, Vol. IV, pp. 186-189.

same material, such as two unequal iron balls, they shall strike unequally, and the impact of the larger ball shall be greater, although both descend with the same velocity.
[...] That the velocity, without the weight, operates and has force is [...] manifest in violent percussions, because since the violent percussion is made upwards by the heavy body, and since the inclination of the body is downwards, the effect therefore of the percussion cannot derive from the weight, that is to say the propensity downwards, but rather from the velocity impressed on it upwards. Finally this is manifest too in the middle, or rather horizontal, percussion in which, since the body moves parallel to the horizontal, the effect that results from that movement will not come from its weight, that is to say from its inclination to the centre, but from the sideways impulse, or horizontal, which the weight or rather the downward motion does not hinder, but neither does it operate nor cooperate.
The same velocity, in greater and lesser quantities of matter, works more or less powerfully, according to the proportion of the matter.
[...] moreover, I say that if there are two mobile solids *b*, *a* of equal velocity in the horizontal *cd*, made of the same matter but of unequal quantities of that matter, then the momentum of one to the momentum of the other is as the quantity of matter of one to the quantity of matter of the other.

Unfortunately Aggiunti died young on 6 December 1635 and with him Galileo lost his most valid assistant for his new research into percussion, which still continued however. The experiments with the new machine confirmed to him that in his experiments in free fall the value of the acceleration is greater than that obtained on the inclined plane: probably he even arrived at a fairly good value for the constant g, but this statement is the outcome of an investigative process that I would now like to expound.

The first clue is very concrete because it was entrusted to a writing in Galileo's own hand: with a view to a new edition Galileo had ordered a copy of the *Dialogo* bound with some extra pages for his annotations, inserted at the beginning and end of the book and after each day. Galileo only used the first of the eight pages inserted between the first and second days, penning in a firm hand a brief exchange of remarks between Simplicio and Sagredo, and here there is the correction of the old affirmation: "100 *braccia* in five seconds"[378]:

SIMPLICIO: Please put it down to my lack of practice in the mathematical sciences if I say freely that your arguments, based upon "greater ratios" and "lesser proportions" and other terms which I do not sufficiently well understand, have not removed my doubt – or rather my incredulity – that a heavy ball of lead, weighing some 100 pounds [*libbre*], leaving its state of rest and being let fall from on high, must pass through every gradation of slowness when one may see it to have moved more than 100 yards [*braccia*] in four[379] pulse beats.

[378] G.G., Vol. VII, *Dialogo* , p. 54.

[379] The manuscript page inserted between the pages of the first edition of the *Dialogo* was published for the first time in the Padua edition of 1744 with the number "four" written out in full, as it was in all the following editions, but it is 4 in the autograph page.

We should do a few calculations: how much could «more than100 *braccia*» be? Let us add a couple of *braccia*, say 56 metres; for the four pulse beats we can consider 70 pulses per minute (the standard heart beat is 72 beats per minute), so 4 beats correspond to about 3.4 seconds.

With a height of fall of H equal to 56 metres in the time 3.4, the new measurement of the constant becomes $g = 9.7\ ms^{-2}$, an excellent result for «the acceleration used by nature in the motion of its descending bodies ».

What led Galileo to add this passage? To start with, from the literary point of view he had to create an occasion to insert the correction without disturbing the text too much and so he resorted to Simplicio's incredulity «that a heavy ball of lead ... must pass through every gradation of slowness», but it is a rather artificial opportunity because Sagredo had already put forward the same doubt two pages earlier and the point had already been amply discussed[380]:

> SAGREDO: So far I follow you; nevertheless it seems remarkable to me that a cannon ball (for such I imagine the falling body to be) which is seen to fall so speedily that in less than ten pulse beats it will pass two hundred yards [*braccia*] of altitude[381], should be found at so small a degree of velocity during its motion that, continuing to move at such a rate without further acceleration, it would not have passed the same distance in a whole day.

In these pages Galileo, using the inclined plane and the principles of motion that he was gradually expounding, explained with great accuracy – but on the basis of unproved principles – how it was possible that «the heavy body, departing from rest, passes descending, through all the degrees of slowness preceding any degree of velocity that it acquires».

Perhaps someone had pointed out to him that his reasoning was difficult to follow. Perhaps Galileo himself realised that it was necessary to explain his concept more intuitively, and so he added the example of the cannon ball, fired perpendicularly, which before stopping passed through every gradation of slowness, which it then passed through again in the opposite direction when descending.

Once again he used Simplicio[382]:

> SIMPLICIO: Please put it down to my lack of practice in the mathematical sciences if I say freely that your arguments, based upon "greater ratios" and "lesser proportions" and other terms which I do not sufficiently well understand, have not removed my doubt [...]

So far it was a normal text correction but Galileo took the opportunity to introduce the new measurement of acceleration:«one may see it to have moved more than 100 *braccia* in four pulse beats».

---

380 G.G., Vol. VII, *Dialogo* , p. 46.

381 «... in less than ten pulse beats it will pass more than two hundred *braccia* of altitude» may be a blunder deliberately put into mouth of Sagredo, who still had no idea of the real time, or perhaps it is an oversight. If, starting from rest, according to Galileo, a mobile travels 100 *braccia* in 5 seconds, in 10 pulse beats, *i.e.* 8.6 seconds, it should travel about 350 *braccia*.

382 G.G., Vol. VII, *Dialogo*, p. 54.

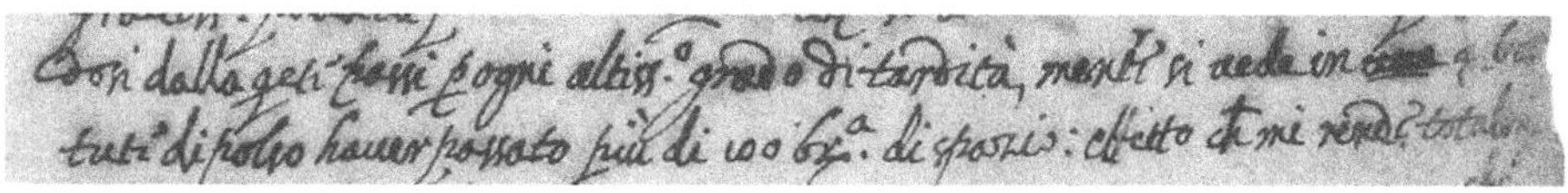

Fig. 17.1

Simplicio, however, could have no idea how much time a ball needed in order to fall from 100 *braccia* and more, because Salviati, the only one of the three speakers who knew and illustrated Galileo's discoveries, would say so much later. So why did he put the correction in the first day? Why did he not make the correction directly where "five seconds" was written, putting a four instead of the five? Probably because he would have had to change the calculations of the time taken by a ball to travel from the concave of the Moon to the centre of the Earth. He needed that calculation to correct Giorgio Locher, a student of his adversary Father Scheiner for whom the time was considerably more than six days, while Galilei had calculated: «3 hours, 22 minutes and 4 seconds». The correction would have made the difference even greater: 2 hours, 41 minutes and 39 seconds; but Galileo preferred to let the old and new measurements coexist; he could always return to them and clarify everything in the *Discorsi* that he was writing.

A second clue concerns the autograph writing of the insertion, which we were able to examine because it is reproduced in a facsimile edition[383] (fig.17.1). Examining it closely we saw that a word had been cancelled before the "4" in the phrase «in 4 pulse beats». We asked Achille Cantamessa, in charge of the *Biblioteca del Seminario Vescovile* (Library of the Diocesan Seminary) of Padua, for information and we received an exhaustive reply[384]:

> After your request I was able to examine Galileo's autograph text and I can reply that the word you asked me about (which already shows traces of cancellation in the original) has not been transcribed, to my knowledge, in any of the modern critical sources available to us. However I have reason to believe that it is not "*circa*", as you suggested, because the usual dot on the "*i*" is missing, nor indeed "*cinque*" (five), which would take up more room on the line. From a handwriting comparison with other portions of text analogous to the *ductus* of this word, I believe that we should rather read "*una*" (one) cancelled by the Author who then corrected it to "4 pulse beats".

So Galileo was therefore about to write: «one pulse beat», a fantastic statement that could easily be placed in Simplicio's mouth like the 10 pulse beats Sagredo talked of just a little earlier, but while writing he realised that instead he could put the precise figure, so he cancelled "*una*" and then wrote "4" and immediately afterwards he also increased the space to be travelled: "more than 100 *braccia*" In our investigative process the change, which is so clearly intentional, considerably reinforces the theory that Galileo had already measured *g* with his new machine.

---

383 Florence, Olschki, 1999.

384 I thank Prof. Don Riccardo Battocchio, the Director of the Library, for his kindness in sending a digital copy of Galileo's page and for authorising its publication, and Dr. Achille Cantamessa for his scrupulous examination of the fragment and his helpful comment.

A third clue is the hesitation with which Galileo repeated the statement «100 *braccia* in 5 seconds» in his letter to Giovan Battista Baliani dated 1 August 1639, written a few years after the correction to his copy of the *Dialogo*. In fact, his is not a spontaneous statement, but he spoke of it because he had to reply to Baliani who a month before had asked him this question[385]:

> With regard to what you say you have written about the vibrations of the pendulum made during the same time and about the observation of heavy bodies that descend with equal velocity, I have seen nothing else other than what you write in the Dialogues of the System. In those you say Sir something, about that which I hoped you would give a more distinct account of here, that is to say of having observed that the heavy body descends by natural motion through a hundred *braccia* in five seconds of an hour; I hoped, I say, that you would state by what reasoning you made sure that it is five seconds, and above all where, on Folio 175[(386)], you give a separate account of other experiments carried out on similar matter.

In his reply Galileo was cautious, distancing himself from the statement made seven years before[387]:

> [...] although then wishing to find out if that which I wrote about 100 *braccia* in five seconds is true, it was found false, because in order to show the extreme clumsiness of he who wrote and assigned the time of the fall of the cannon ball from the lunar orb, it matters little whether the five seconds of the 100 *braccia* are correct or not.

Perhaps this might have been the justification that Galileo would have inserted in a new edition of the *Discorsi*, which should have contained the two remaining days not in the Leiden edition of 1638. It is not by chance that in the first four days of the *Discorsi*, the only ones that Galileo succeeded in consigning to his editor in time, there are no examples from which it is possible to deduce the time of free fall.

The logical place to speak of the correction – «one may see it to have moved more than 100 braccia in 4 pulse beats» – should have been immediately after the writing on the force of percussion, because it is in the experiments with his machine that a much more precise value for g was probably obtained.

We say *probably* because his last writing was unfinished, or it did not come down to us intact. We can suppose from the judgement given by Viviani[388], who spoke of a new science,

---

[385] G.G., Vol. XVIII, pp. 69-70. Baliani's letter is in reply to a letter dated 20 June from Galileo, who sent him a copy of the *Discorsi* without the foreword, who contested – so it seems from Baliani's reply – his priority with regard to the isochronicity of the pendulum and the law of motion. The letter, which Baliani cannot much have liked, is the only one (as chance would have it) from their correspondence that has not come down to us.

[386] Baliani indicated the page of the Leiden edition of 1638; the same can be read in: G.G., Vol. VIII, *Discorsi*, pp. 212-213.

[387] G.G., Vol. XVIII, p. 77.

[388] In *Opere di Evangelista Torricelli*, Faenza, 1919, Vol IV, pp. 21-23, Viviani's opinion is recalled, according to whom the final day «should comprise the account of various of Galileo's old experiments carried out by him to investigate

putting it on the same level as the study of the resistance of materials and the study of motion, that Galileo had much more in mind than what he wrote on the force of percussion.

The writings he did leave, indeed, offer a glimpse of a vast field: because the experiments on his machine, when the suspended masses are slightly different, lead to the obvious distinction between inertial mass and gravitational mass and because his experiments on *tearing* [*strappata*] would be followed by the dynamics of collisions, which for a century and more would be studied by scholars of the *new sciences*; a field that perhaps he thought he would be able to explore more than he was actually able to.

As happens in investigations without direct testimony, clues become a reason for certainty if they are verified by reliable reconstructions. To see whether Galileo could have measured g with his new machine, we made a few quantitative experiments; whether Galileo did them, or had them done, remains a matter of opinion. We can only claim that they were very easy to do.

Indeed, using the methods that Galileo used to study motion on the inclined plane, adding[389] a small mass m to one of the two equal masses M hanging from the cord, we found:

a) That on the new machine too the space $s(t)$ travelled in the successive units of time grows like odd numbers *ab unitate*.

b) That, measuring the time taken to travel a prefixed space s by the mass to which are then added, successively, a series of masses which are different from each other but always small: m_1, m_2, m_3 we always obtain[390] $m_i t^2 \approx$ constant for $i = 1, 2, 3, \ldots$

c) Observe that the motion is slow and this can be explained by the way in which gravity operates on a body because, according to Galileo, the continuous action could be likened to successive impulses that are accumulated in the heavy body, instant after instant, because of the acting force mg on the body. The body, is then made up of the group of suspended bodies which move as one, and which acquires a total momentum $(2M + m)v(t)$ which increases continuously with time[391]:

> The momentum of a body in the act of impact is nothing but a composite and aggregate of infinitely many momenta, each of them equal only to a single moment [*al solo momento*], either internal and natural *per se*, as it is that [moment] of its own absolute weight which it eternally exercises when placed on any resistant body, or else extrinsic and violent, as is that [momentum] of the moving power [forza]. Such momenta go accumulating during the time of [naturally accelerated] motion of the heavy body from instant to instant with equal increments, and are stored therein in exactly the way that the speed of a falling body goes increasing; for as in the infinitely many instants of a time, however short, a heavy body goes ever passing through new and equal degrees of speed, always retaining those acquired in the

the infinite force of percussion, of which Galileo himself believed that after long vigils and applications he had arrived at the true principles and foundations on which he could construct a new third science and show with geometrical progression stupendous properties beyond common imagining».

389 Later we shall see that in this experiment three different values of m are used: 0.3 kg - 1 kg - 1.5 kg, giving respectively $g = 9.17\ \mathrm{ms}^{-2}$, $g = 9.62\ \mathrm{ms}^{-2}$, $g = 9.50\ \mathrm{ms}^{-2}$.

390 We recall that in the experiments discussed by Galileo the initial velocity is zero; moreover, the space $s(t)$ and the counting of the time are measured from the point and at the moment at which the motion begins.

391 G.G., Vol. VIII, *Discorsi*, p. 344.

previously elapsed time, so also in the moveable those momenta (either natural or violent, conferred to him by nature or art) go conserving [themselves] and compounding from instant to instant etc..

Galileo's reasoning concerns the effect of a pile driver of mass M (which is its *internal* momentum) falling under the action of the force weight Mg and which after a time t reaches the velocity v_t and acquires the momentum Mv_t through the effect and accumulation of successive external momenta $Mg\Delta t$. The verbal description of this process of *additamento* (addition) is very clear and we can represent the increase in momentum that occurs at time t during a minute interval of time Δt symbolically by the following relationship:

$$Mv_{(t+\Delta t)} = Mv_t + Mg\Delta t.$$

In uniformly accelerated motion the mass M is present in both terms of the equation and is therefore eliminated, which is why Galileo did not speak of mass in the *Discorsi*. In the *giornata sesta* dedicated to the study of the force of percussion, in which Galileo's machine and the experiments that he carried out with this apparatus come into play, the force acting on the body of mass $M_T = (2M+m_i)$ is only that of the excess weight $m_i g$ and the previous expression becomes

$$M_T v_{(t+\Delta t)} = M_T v_t + m_i g\Delta t$$

We know of course that this equation belongs to Newton, but how else can we explain the expression: «such momenta go accumulating during the time of [naturally accelerated] motion of the heavy body from instant to instant with equal increments, and are stored therein in exactly the way that the speed of a falling body goes increasing". It is usually said that Galileo did not possess the correct concept of gravity as the mutual attraction between bodies, perhaps giving a restrictive interpretation of the famous passage in the *Dialogo*[392]:

SALVIATI: [...] I say that that which makes the Earth move is a thing similar to whatever moves Mars and Jupiter, and which he believes also moves the stellar sphere. If he will advise me as to the motive power of one of these movable bodies, I promise I shall be able to tell him what makes the Earth move. Moreover, I shall do the same if he can teach me what it is that moves earthly things downward[393].
SIMPLICIO: The cause of this effect is well known; everybody is aware that it is gravity.
SALVIATI: You are wrong, Simplicio; what you ought to say is that everyone knows that it is called "gravity". What I am asking you for is not the name of the thing, but its essence, of which essence you know not a bit more than you know about the essence of whatever moves the stars around. I except the name which has been attached to it and which has been made a familiar household word by the continual experience that we have of it daily. But we do not really understand what principle or what force it is that moves stones downward, any more than

[392] G.G., Vol. VII, *Dialogo*, pp. 260-261.

[393] Isaac Newton succeeded, taking up his suggestion.

we understand what moves them upward after they leave the thrower's hand, or what moves the Moon around. We have merely, as I said, assigned to the first and more, specific and definite name "gravity", whereas to the second we assign the more general term "impressed force" [*virtù impressa*], and to the last-named we give "spirits" [*intelligenza*], either "assisting"[*assistente*] or "abiding" [*informante*], and as the cause of infinite other motions we give "Nature".

This thought should not be separated from another one which follows a few pages later and which confirms Galileo's concept of gravity as mutual attraction[394]:

SALVIATI And I shall say that I believe that heavy things exist prior to the common centre of gravity; hence it is not a centre (which is nothing but an indivisible point and therefore incapable of acting) that attracts heavy materials to itself, but simply that these materials, cooperating naturally toward a juncture, would give rise to a common centre, this being that around which parts of equal moments are arranged. From this I suppose that the large aggregation of heavy bodies being transferred to any place, the particles which were separated from the whole would follow; and if not impeded, they would penetrate wherever they might find part less heavy than themselves. But upon arriving where they met with heavier material, they would descend no farther. Therefore I think that in the cavern full of air, the entire vault would press inward, and would sustain itself upon that air by force (*violentemente*) only when the hardness of this vault could not be overcome and broken under its weight. But I believe that detached stones would get down to the centre and would not float above upon the air. Nor may it be said from this that they do not move toward their whole, all the parts being moved toward the place where the whole would go if it were not hindered.

Galileo tried to keep these concepts in mind when he thought of experiments with his machine: the ceiling of the room is like that of a cave, and to it the pulley is fixed; the two masses M attached to the ends of the rope are like the weights in equilibrium on a pair of scales and the pulley bears an overall weight $2Mg$, whether the two weights are still or whether they move with uniform velocity, because their centre of gravity is still. If now we add a small mass m to one of the two masses M, but the pulley is blocked, it will bear a weight $(2M+m)g$; if the pulley is then released, an accelerated motion begins with the mass M that rises and the mass $M+m$ which descends, and the pulley returns to bearing a weight of $2Mg$ because the mass m in motion *has no weight*, as Galileo had always claimed.

Galileo's concept became clearer when he considered horizontal motion, in which case the force of gravity does not intervene, as, for example, we can read in the thoughts presented at the end of the *Giornata aggiunta*[395]:

He who shuts the bronze doors of San Giovanni will try in vain to close them with one single simple push; but with a continual impulse he goes impressing on that very heavy movable body such a force that when it comes to strike and knock against the jamb, it makes the

394 G.G., Vol. VII, *Dialogo*, pp 270-271.

395 G.G., Vol VIII, *Principio di Giornata aggiunta*, p. 345.

> whole church tremble. From this one sees how there is impressed in moveables – and the more, the heavier these are – and how there is multiplied and conserved in them the force that has been communicated to them over some time, etc.

Galileo returned to this question in a fragment published by Favaro at the end of the *Discorsi*[396]:

> [...] Having weighed anchor, the sails were spread to the wind and the ship sailed forth: where the strength of the wind does not suddenly impart the greatest velocity to the ship, but successively and over time, it happens in the beginning that it is found to be motionless, and then moment by moment it works on the mobile continuously affected by greater velocity. Nor must we set any difference between the impulses given at intervals and that given by continuous force, because just as between the interrupted impulses no variation must be considered if sometimes in 10 minutes of time 20 oar strokes or 30 or 100 or 1000 are made, so neither can any alteration occur between them and the continuous impulse, since the latter is none other than a most frequent multitude of impulses, or rather infinite impulses, within the same time. So it is not enough that the mobile, the medium and the faculty are always the same, to introduce such a speed; but since the mobile departs from rest a succession of time is required.
> In this same way I think that the matter proceeds in natural mobiles, starting from rest, where by some impediment they had been delayed: because, since the medium is always the same, the mobile too and also the moving heaviness, nevertheless this heaviness works at first on a mobile not used to any motion, but then works on a mobile affected by velocity; so, since this virtue works in the same way, it moves more, because it increases motion on a mobile that it finds in motion.

From these writings it is obvious that it was Galileo who suggested to Niccolò Aggiunti the ideas on collisions that I mentioned at the beginning of this chapter and not vice versa. In his *Discorsi* Galileo described very well how the *eguale additamento* (equal addition) occurs during what we have called minute intervals of time Δt, suggesting a process very similar to the limit passage discussed in the example of the sailing ship in which he declared that the ship driven continuously by the wind and the ship moved forward by oar strokes were equivalent; in this case however he was dealing with a reduction, since the motion was directed upwards[397]:

> SIMPLICIO: But if the degrees of greater and greater tardity are infinite, it will never consume them all, but will move forever while always slowing down – something that is not seen to happen.
> SALVIATI: This would be so, Simplicio, if the moveable were to hold itself for any time in each degree; but il merely passes there, without remaining beyond an instant. And since in

[396] G.G., Vol. VIII, *Discorsi (frammenti)*, pp. 441-442. The note is in Viviani's hand but underneath the fragment we can read a comment written by Viviani «I have the original of this».

[397] G.G., Vol. VIII, *Discorsi*, pp. 200-201.

any finite time [*tempo quanto*], however small, there are infinitely many instants, there are enough to correspond to the infinitely many degrees of diminished speed.

To pass from Galileo's law: the spaces travelled in any times, … are to each other as the squares of the times»[398] (*spatia quibuscunque temporibus ab ipso peracta, sunt inter se …ut eorundem temporum quadrata*) to the equation for a heavy body falling from stationary: $s = gt^2/2$, it is sufficient to change the plural to the singular and to make the constant of proportionality explicit, setting it equal to $g/2$. It is true that Galileo clung when he could to the use of proportions but we believe that when he was thinking and writing, he thought and wrote in terms of relationships between non-homogeneous quantities[399]. From all of this we feel authorised to write that the same law on the inclined plane at an angle α becomes:
$s = \sin\alpha\, gt^2/2$.

In the case of Galilei's machine the new accelerating factor $gm_i/(2M+m_i)$ must be put in place of $g \sin\alpha$:

$$s = [m_i/(2M+m_i)\,]gt^2/2.$$

This equation is, for the system of two masses tied and suspended from the pulley, the integral of Newton's equation.

From what has been written so far it is clear that Galileo discovered experimentally the essential difference that exists between inertial mass and gravitational mass: indeed in his machine the motion is slowed down as on the inclined plane but it was not the partial support of the plane that held it back but the overall inertial mass ($2M + m$), while the moving force is generated by the small excess of mass m. It is really unforgivable that when the editor Manolessi asked for all possible unpublished writings for the collected works of Galileo that he was printing in Bologna, Viviani in 1655 did not give him the *Giornata aggiunta* to publish, although he had it available and knew it well.

To recapitulate, Galileo, even if he did not linger to discuss the cause of this slowing-down because he had another aim: percussion, knew the following facts:

a) that the cause of the accelerated motion is the difference between the suspended masses,

b) that the slowing is due to the total mass to be moved.

Later we shall give a detailed description of the machine and the experiments.

---

[398] G.G. Vol. VIII, *Discorsi*, pp. 209.

[399] There is a considerable difference between what he thought and calculated and what he wrote: when he calculated the time of the fall of the mobile from the concave of the Moon, Galileo multiplied the distance from Moon to Earth by the square of the time for travelling 100 *braccia*, then divided by 100 *braccia*, and finally extracted the square root. By doing this he revealed, unintentionally, that for him the rules of proportions are only a requirement for rigour of presentation, and they needed him first to divide the distance from Moon to Earth by 100 *braccia*, in order to have a dimensionless quantity, then he could multiply the result by the square of the 5 seconds necessary to travel 100 *braccia* and finally extract the square root. See G.G., Vol. VII, *Dialogo*, p. 251.

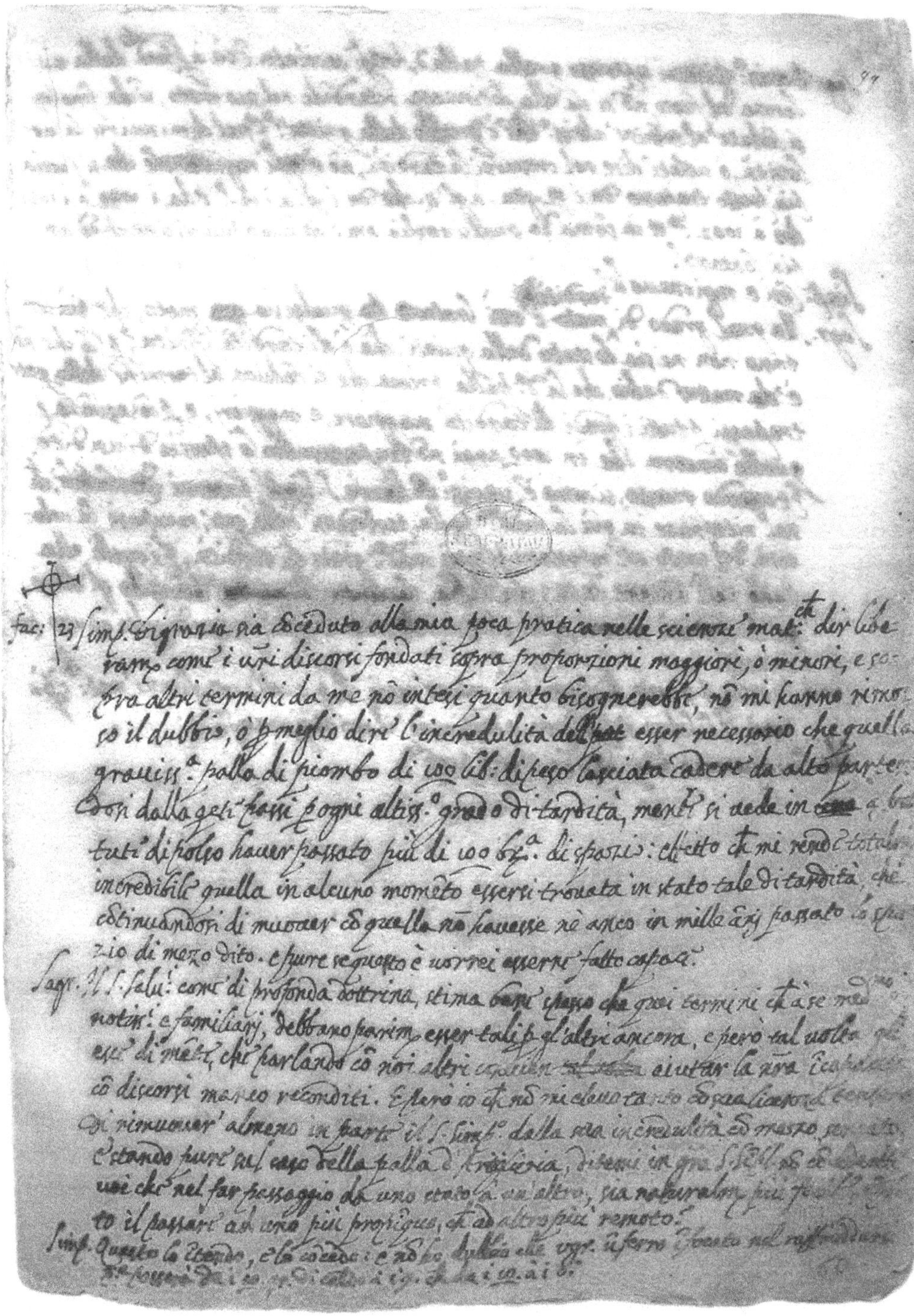

Galileo's manuscript inserted in his personal copy of the *Dialogo*, now at the *Bioblioteca del Seminario Vescovile* in Padua.

18. The conception of Galilei's machine: The "vertical plane"

The other book that we have nearly finished writing, of which this one is like a rib detached for an independent life of its own, is dedicated mainly to the last day of the *Discorsi*, published for the first time in the Florence edition of *Le Opere* (1718) with the title *Giornata sesta del Galileo della forza della percossa da aggiungersi ai Discorsi, e alle Dimostrazioni Matematiche intorno alle due nuove scienze appartenenti alle meccaniche, ed ai movimenti locali* (Galileo's sixth day on the force of percussion to be added to the Discourses and to the Mathematical Demonstrations of the two new sciences belonging to mechanics and local movements).

Rarely read, often not included in the editions of the *Discorsi* and in its translations, this brief treatise on the force of percussion deserves to be better known and studied.

The question is almost inevitable: when did Galileo begin to think of a sort of "vertical plane", that is to say a piece of apparatus that would delay motion like the inclined plane, but without the complications of rolling?

Probably the new apparatus occurred to him when, drafting the first day of the *Discorsi* – in around 1634 – he arrived at the point when Salviati wanted to convince Simplicio that the fall velocity of two stones does not change even if they are joined together. And at this point he wrote[400]:

> SALVIATI: [...] Note that one must distinguish heavy bodies put in motion from the same bodies in a state of rest. A large stone placed in a balance acquires weight with the placement on it of another stone, and not only that, but even the addition of a coil of hemp will make it weight more by the six or seven ounces that the hemp weighs. But if you let the stone fall freely from a height with the hemp tied to it, do you believe that in this motion the hemp would weigh on the stone, and thus necessarily speed up its motion? Or do you believe it would retard this by partly sustaining the stone?

It is the same reasoning we came across in the *De motu*. In the case with the added hemp coil, the scales rotate, but very slowly, and then, at the end, friction stops it with the new centre of gravity plumb below the suspension of the arm. Already in the *Dialogo* Salviati had observed the obvious phenomenon of the scales with equal arms, in which one weight lifts the other only if there is a difference between them, however small[401].

---

[400] G.G., Vol. VIII, *Discorsi*, p. 108.

[401] G.G., Vol. VII, *Dialogo*, p. 240.

SAGREDO: I believe it to be exactly so, and it is for this reason that two equal weights in a balance are seen to remain steady and in equilibrium, the heaviness of one weight resisting being raised by the heaviness with which the other, pressing down, seeks to raise it.
SALVIATI: Very well. So to have one raise the other, it would be necessary to add weight to the one pressing down, or subtract weight from the other.

If a few ounces are added to one of the two weights on scales that are bearing two equal weights, the scales will slowly start to rotate. Unfortunately, it is an accelerated rotational motion, analogous to the motion of a pendulum or of the sphere in the riddle and is of no use in order to study the motion of natural fall, because the weights attached to it follow curved paths. Galileo, however, always bore in mind the unsolved problem of rotation and it may actually have been while reflecting on scales that he recalled what he had written at Padua about the pulley in his old treatise on mechanics[402]:

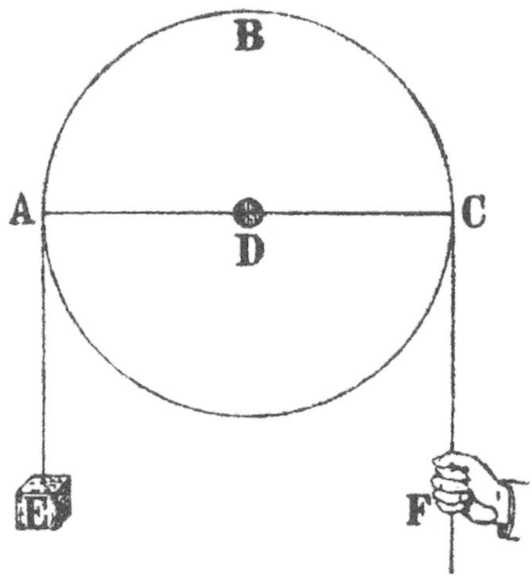

Fig. 18.1

[...] take a pulley *ABC*, made of metal or hard wood, free to move around its axis, which passes through its centre *D*, and around this pulley let the cord *EABCF* be placed, from one end of which let the weight *E* hang, and from the other let us understand there to be the force *F* [fig.18.1]: I say, the weight is borne by a force equal to itself, nor does the pulley *ABC* gain any benefit from the force applied at *F* with regard to moving or sustaining the said weight. Except that if we understand two lines to be drawn from the centre *D*, which is at its point of support, to the circumference of the pulley at points *A*, *C*, at which the hanging

[402] G.G., Vol. II, *Le mecaniche*, pp.172-173.

> cords touch the circumference, we shall find scales with equal arms, since the semidiameters *DA*, *DC*, which determine the distances of the two suspensions from the centre and support *D*, are equal; so it is manifest that the weight hanging from *A* cannot be supported by a lesser weight hanging from *C*, but rather by an equal one, because such is the nature of equal weights, hanging from equal distances: and even though, when the force *F* is moved downwards, the pulley *ABC* spins around, the disposition and respect that the weight and the force have of the two distances *AD*, *DC* do not change however; indeed the pulley, when spun around, becomes a pair of scales similar to *AC*, but perpetuated.

What Galileo is saying is clear: The properties of the pulley are very similar to those of the scales, because the pulley is equivalent to scales with equal arms which always remain parallel to the horizontal plane, even if the weights attached are unequal and move. The cord is wrapped around the upper semi-circumference of the pulley and detaches itself at two exactly opposing points, *a* and *c*, which are the ends of the diameter *AC* parallel to the horizon. If we turn the pulley, two other points a' and c' of the cord replace *a* and *c*, as the ends of a new diameter $A'C'$ of the pulley, which is still parallel to the horizon.

If the weights are equal, the pulley stays still like the scales, but it can also spin if one of the weights is pushed. The constancy of the velocity of the cord and of the angular velocity of the pulley corresponds to the equilibrium of the scales. When the weights are different, the correspondence becomes closer: only the motion is possible, since both the scales and the pulley have an angular acceleration. The two weights, as the pulley turns, contrary to what happens with the scales, now travel vertical trajectories, as in the previous case of inertial motion, and it is possible to have a motion that is both uniformly accelerated and arbitrarily slow.

This was, very probably, the route followed by Galileo in eliminating the distorting effects of rotation.

19. A description of Galilei's machine and of the experiments that can be carried out on it

The machine that we built is of large proportions (about 3 metres high) but of simple construction, consisting of a pyramid structure with a square base and sides made of stainless-steel tubes with a square cross-section, fixed together as required (fig. 19.1).

Fig. 19.1 Galilei's machine.

The structure consists of a solid bicycle wheel frame with a diameter of 42 cm, supported by a chassis fixed above the pyramid structure. The wheel was modified, creating a groove[403]. Two weights[404], M_1 (on the left) and M_2 (on the right) of a mass equal to 20.732 kg, are linked together by a steel cable 4 mm in diameter. The cable passes through the groove of the wheel and has the correct length to allow the system of coupled weights to run fully in both directions. For safety reasons two parallel steel tubes act as guides for each of the weights, in which two holes were made for the tubes to pass through. A crosspiece, with a screw at the centre, is fixed below the weights to add further loads in some experiments (fig.19.2).

At the centre of the machine there is a vertical rod, 2.6 metres long, to which a scale with millimetric divisions is fixed which serves to measure the space travelled by M_2.

At the base of M_2 a small rod is fixed, jutting out towards the millimetric scale, for a precise reading of its position (fig. 19.3). Along the vertical rod some sliding brass bridges are placed which hold parchment paper markers: they serve to indicate the passage of the mass M_2 in the experiment on the principle of inertia and in the measurement of the acceleration of gravity. At the front of the structure a pendulum was applied (fig. 19.4) which intercepts a parchment paper marker.

The pendulum, made from a plumb line, completes a full oscillation in about a second (40 oscillations in 41.3 seconds).

Fig. 19.2 Weights M_1 and M_2.

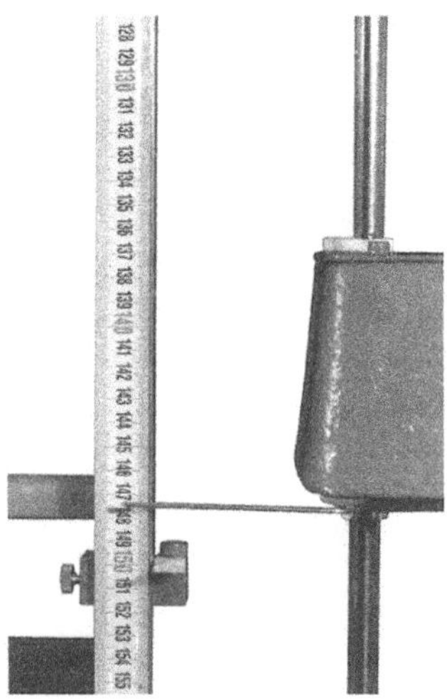

Fig. 19.3 Rod.

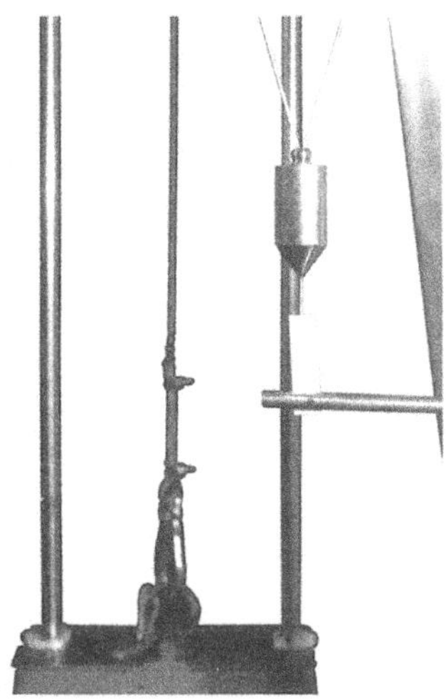

Fig. 19.4 Pendulum.

403 The original weight of the wheel was 1.180 kg, but when the groove was applied it became 3.028 kg; the contribution of the ring part to the enertia effects of the combination of the masses in motion has been calculated to be M_{wheel}= 1 kg in the wheel without the groove and M_{wheel}= 2.8 kg with the groove.

404 The two masses used in the machine were originally two proved and tested weights of 20 kg, used with large commercial scales. The modifications and the additions for the purposes of this machine led them to have the final mass indicated here.

19.1 *First experiment: verification of the law of inertia*

The experiment is based on the following steps[405]:

> SALVIATI: [...] I want you to imagine a solid weight of, say, 1000 pounds [*libbre*], placed on a plane that sustains it. Next, I want you to think of a rope tied to this weight and led over a pulley fixed high above. Here it is evident that when force is applied by pulling down on the end of the rope, it will always meet with quite equal resistance in raising the weight; that is, the opposition of 1000 pounds [*libbre*] of weight. For if from the end of the rope there were suspended another weight, equal to the first, equilibrium would be established; and being raised up without support from anything below, they would remain still; nor would this second weight descend and raise the first unless given some excess of weight.

And a few pages later he added[406]:

> [...] And in this same way the two equal weights, hanging from the ends of the rope, will be at rest when placed in balance, and if impetus downward[407] shall be given to one, it always conserve [*sic*] this equably. Here it is to be noted that all this things would follow if there were removed all external and accidental impediments, as of roughness and heaviness of rope or pulley, of friction in the turning of these about the axle, and whatever others there may be of these. [...] Now it is evident that this degree of speed will not go on increasing when its cause of increase is taken away, this being the weight of the descending body itself; for its weight no longer acts when its propensity to descend is taken away by the repugnance to rising of its companion of equal weight. Hence the maximum degree of speed will be conserved, and the motion will be converted from one of acceleration to uniform motion.

In this experiment the principle of inertia is verified in a more general form than with the horizontal plane: on each of the two masses hung from the cable the resultant of the forces is zero, so each of them remains still or, if put into motion, moves with constant velocity.

Five small bridges are used, marked with a yellow sticker, which hold parchment paper markers which are brushed against by the small rod sticking out from M_2. The distance that separates two successive markers along the vertical rod is the distance that M_2 travels in every complete oscillation of the pendulum. The velocity is imparted by a mass of lead m_{Pb} (m_{Pb} = 0.884 kg) which runs along the outer guide tube of mass M_2 and is held still above by a thread, which passes through a pulley and is attached to a stop on the side structure (fig. 19.5).

---

[405] G.G., Vol.VIII, *Della forza della percossa. Principio di Giornata aggiunta*, pp. 332-333.

[406] G.G., Vol.VIII, *Della forza della percossa. Principio di Giornata aggiunta*, pp. 336-337.

[407] Note that Galileo said "downwards" because that way the weight pushed downwards raises the other weight, since the resultant of the force of gravity remains zero. Here the cord only has the task of communicating the "impetus" instantly to the other weight.

Fig. 19.5

Initially m_{Pb} lies on the mass M_2 and imparts a constant acceleration to the system. M_2 and m_{Pb} descend together for 0.24 m. At the end of this path the thread tautens, M_2 frees itself of the weight m_{Pb} and the system has acquired a velocity whose variations, if any, are examined.

Carrying out the experiment

Because of the way that the experiment was designed, two people are required: the first operator checks the time, striking with a hammer (fig. 19.6) at every passage of the pendulum through its marker; the second operator checks the passages of M_2 through the equidistant bridges, signalling them with the hammer that he too has available.

1) The first operator (the operator, in other words, who observes the pendulum) brings M_1 down by pulling the steel cable, so as to raise M_2 to the departure point A, marked by a small bridge. As it rises M_2 meets the mass m_{Pb} and begins to raise it upwards.

2) The second operator gives a push to the pendulum which begins to oscillate.

3) The first observer starts to strike with the hammer at every passage of the pendulum through its marker and lets the cable go in coincidence with a passage, thus starting the accelerated phase of the experiment.

4) The system acquires growing velocity during the first stretch of the descent of M_2, until the moment when the thread that m_{Pb} is tied to tautens and the lead weight becomes detached from M_2.

5) The length of the thread of m_{Pb} is adjusted so that it always becomes detached exactly in coincidence with the end of an oscillation of the pendulum, and the striking of the hammer marks the beginning of the constant-velocity motion. This way the same uniform velocity can always be imparted to the system, and we can study the motion of M_2, on which the resultant of the forces has become zero throughout the path still available.

6) The position of the second bridge is found by trial and error until the small rod of M_2 passes through it exactly after one oscillation of the pendulum.

7) The positions of the first and second bridges are read on the measuring rod; their distance will be that used to set the distances of the other bridges.

9) Observe that the passages of M_2 through the later markers occur synchronised with the later oscillations of the pendulum. Indeed the blows struck by the hammers sound in unison.

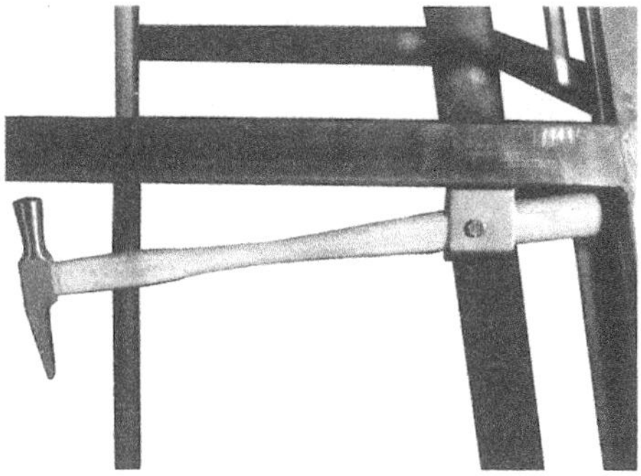

Fig. 19.6 Hammer.

Result

The excellent synchronicity of the hammer blows highlights the constancy of the velocity. The five oscillations of the pendulum last 5.16 seconds all together. The space travelled is 1.675 m and therefore the velocity $v = 0.32$ m/s.

Control

The velocity acquired by the system of total mass $M_T = 44.7$ kg descending for 0.24 m with an overweight of $m = 0.884$ kg is $v = [4.7\ m/(M_T + m)]^{1/2} = 0.30$ m/s.

Could Galileo have done it?

The experiment that we have illustrated proceeds with the same methodology already followed on the inclined plane to prove the law of odd numbers; in this case it is the law of inertia that is verified. We cannot know if Galileo carried out the experiment in this way but it is probable that somehow he checked the truth of this fundamental law which he proclaimed decisively: «if impetus downward shall be given to one, it always conserve this equably».

Galileo also became aware of the braking effect of friction, as shown by the words he puts in Sagredo's mouth[408]:

> Hence I shall say, still dubiously, that it is true that the weight of 100 pounds [*libbre*][409] of the falling body will suffice to raise the other, which also weighs 100 pounds, as far as to equilibrium, even without its being endowed and supplied with speed; [to so this] the excess of a mere half-ounce [*mezza oncia*] will suffice. But I also think that that equilibration will be made very slowly [...]

Galileo said that after the addition of half an ounce, which corresponds to 14 grams, he observed a process of "equilibration", that is to say a very slow descent that ended in equilibrium, in

[408] G.G., Vol. VIII, *Della forza della percossa. Principio di Giornata aggiunta*, p. 334.

[409] Twelve *once* (ounces) = one *libbra* (pound) = 0.3395 kg.

rest. This observation of his is of considerable interest because it assures us that the friction present in "his machine" was not very different from the friction observed in today's machine, which is completely cancelled out by an increase in weight of about 100 grams, added to mass M_2. In the machine the friction varies according to whether the guide pipes are more or less lubricated and are more or less parallel.

19.2 *Second experiment: measurement of $g \approx 9.4\ ms^{-2}$*

On the same central rod there are other sliding bridges, with red markers, set at growing distances. They serve to measure the acceleration. The later distances are obtained from the distance travelled in the first oscillation of the pendulum, multiplying it by the square of the following whole numbers. In a preparatory experiment with an accelerating mass of 0.3 kg, the space travelled in the first oscillation is 0.029 m, the spaces travelled in the following units of time by mass M_2 were: 0.029 - 0.087 - 0.145 - 0.203 - 0.261 - 0.319 - 0.377- 0.435.

We recall that the period of the pendulum is $T = 1.03$ s. The experiment takes place exactly like the first one, with the two operators striking their hammers at the passages through the markers. A good result is again found, through the excellent synchronicity of the blows.

Let us follow the steps of the *Giornata aggiunta* that concern this experiment:

> [...] nor would this second weight descend and raise the first unless given some excess of weight [410].
> [...] the operation of its heaviness in raising the other [weight] is nil, this being opposed by the resistance of equal heaviness in that other, which clearly would not be moved without the addition of some small weight[411].

A mass m_i is added to the mass M_2 on the right-hand side, the other mass M_1 descends to the lowest point. Mass M_1 is released: if m_i is much less than M_t a uniformly accelerated motion is observed.

First method

The markers along the path are used and also the pendulum to beat the seconds.

With a mass $m_0 = 0.3$ kg the space travelled in 9 oscillations was 2.549 m, and therefore the space travelled in the first oscillation was 2.549/81 = 0.0315 m. The difference compared to the previous experiment is due to the greater friction present. The friction varies each time and it has to be counterbalanced by an additional weight of M_2.

---

410 G.G. vol. VIII, *Della forza della percossa. Principio di Giornata aggiunta*, p. 333.

411 G.G. vol. VIII, *Della forza della percossa. Principio di Giornata aggiunta*, p. 335.

The markers are placed according to the distances

0.031 - 0.126 - 0.283 - 0.503 - 0.786 - 1.133 - 1.542- 2.014 – 2.549.

Observe the perfect coincidence of the passages through the markers with the oscillations of the pendulum. The motion is uniformly accelerated, with the acceleration

$a = 2 \times 2.549/81 = 0.0629\ ms^{-2}$.

The value of g follows directly from the value of a. I introduce the total mass M_T
$M_T = M_1 + M_2 + M_{wheel} + M_{cable} + \mu_{friction} = 44.7$ kg.
where $M_1 = M_2 = 20.732$; $M_{wheel} = 2.8$ kg; $M_{cable} = 0.\ 285$; while $\mu_{friction} = 0.155$ kg is the mass added to M_2 in this experiment to cancel out the deceleration due to the friction.

$g_0 = (m_T + m_0)\ a/m_0 = (44.7 + 0.3)\ a/\ 0.3 = 150\ a$,

$\boxed{g_0 = 9.44\ ms^{-2}}$.

Second method

These experiments were done when the wheel did not yet have the groove, with a cable of Ø3 mm and for a fall path $S = 2.384$. The time required to arrive at the end of the run is measured and the acceleration a of the motion equation is determined (knowing the space S):

$S = (1/2)\ at^2$.

The experimental value of g, acceleration of gravity, is calculated from the expression:

$g = (M_t + m_i)\ a/m_i = 2S\ (M_t + m_i)/m_i\ t^2$.

The total mass in motion is $(M_t + m_i)$, with $M_T = 42.814$ kg, because in these experiments $M_{wheel} = 1$kg; $M_{cable} = 0.\ 250$; $\mu_{friction} = 0.100$ kg.

$g_i = 2 \times 2.384\ (42.814 + m_i)\ /\ m_i\ t^2$.

First experiment: $m_1 = 0.5$ kg

$g_1 = 413/t^2$,

measurements of t_1: {6.74; 6.69; 6.73; 6.79; 6.74; 6.76; 6.69; 6.73; 6.63; 6.62},
average value $t_1 = 6.71$,

$\boxed{g_1 = 9.17\ ms^{-2}}$.

Second experiment: $m_2 = 1$ kg

$g_2 = 209/ t_2^2$,

measurements of t_2: {4.69; 4.63; 4.64; 4.67; 4.69; 4.69; 4.62; 4.61; 4.68; 4.65 },
average value $t_2 = 4.66$,

$$\boxed{g_2 = 9.63 \text{ ms}^{-2}}.$$

Third experiment: $m_3 = 1.5$ kg

$g_3 = 211/t^2$,

measurements of t_3 = {3.88; 3.90; 3.91; 3.79; 3.84; 3.81; 3.83; 3.86; 4.84; 3.84},
average value $t_3 = 3.85$ s,

$$\boxed{g_3 = 9.52 \text{ ms}^{-2}}.$$

The measurements $g_1 = 9.17$; $g_2 = 9.63$; $g_3 = 9.52$ obtained with the second method are consistent with each other and their average coincides with the value $g_0 = 9.44$ obtained following the first method.

This is probably by chance but the coincidence is nevertheless of a certain interest and significance.

Could Galileo have done it?

We know that Galileo considered the fact that on his machine masses of 100 *libbre* (pounds), hanging from the two ends of a cord, can be put into motion by adding a small mass to one of them; we cannot say, however, whether he took precise measurements or whether his observations were only qualitative.

We do not exclude the possibility that Galileo, repeating what he had already done on the inclined plane, may have measured the space travelled on the machine according to multiples of a unit of time (oscillations of the pendulum) and may have proved, once again with great precision, that the space grows «like the odd numbers *ab unitate*».

The first method that we have illustrated, in which a mass $m_0 = 0.3$ kg was added and the markers were placed at distances that grow like odd numbers, serves to illustrate in an incisive way and continuous form what Galileo perhaps did more easily by moving a marker from time to time, exactly as on the inclined plane.

It is possible, however, that he did not need a methodical verification: his experience with experiments on the inclined plane was sufficient to assure him that the motion on the machine is uniformly accelerated: the fact that that the velocity grows uniformly can be perceived directly. If he had had the inclined plane with him, he could have compared the various passages on the plane and on the machine, inclining the plane by an angle of 0.38° for the added mass of 0.3 kg and by an angle of 2° for the added mass of 1.5 kg. The plane would become the clock of the machine and from a spectacular point of view it would have been truly interesting to observe the coincidence between the 8 passages on Galilei's machine and the passages over the 8 sensors inserted in the groove of the inclined plane: the blows struck by the hammers and the bells linked to the sensors would ring out in unison.

The situation is in part similar to that of the inclined plane, but in part it is also different: on the machine too the acceleration is much less than that of a body in free fall, but the reduction cannot be explained by the reduction of the force caused by the support of the inclined plane. the only explanation available is suggested by the great mass of the whole system which has to be put into motion. If the overweight is increased the acceleration increases noticeably.

We have seen what happens if we add increasing masses: m; $2m$; $3m$. We can see immediately that the time to travel the space S diminishes rapidly. How? It is not difficult to notice, as the table shows, that the product $m_i t_i^2$ is virtually constant: $m_i t^2 \approx 22\ \mathrm{kg/s^2}$, and this happens because the added mass is much less than the hanging mass[412].

t^2 in s	Actual m_i in kg	$m_i\ t^2$ in kg s^2
45.024	0.5	22.5
21.7	1.0	21.7
14.82	1.5	22.2

Correspondingly we find a strong reduction of the acceleration $a \approx 0.11\ \mathrm{ms}^{-2}$, as the following table shows:

Actual m_i in kg	t^2 in s	$Ka = S/m_i t^2$ in m $\mathrm{kg}^{-1}\ \mathrm{s}^{-2}$
0.5	45.024	0.106
1.0	21.7	0.110
1.5	14.82	0.107

If we suppose that the role played by the sine of the angle on the inclined plane is now played by the factor m/M_T, obviously this relationship follows:

$$S = K\, m_i t^2/(M_T + m_i).$$

Knowing that $S/m_i t_i^2 \approx 2.384/22.5$ and that $M_T \approx 44$ kg, it follows that

$$K \approx 4.66.$$

412 Galileo had a water clock available to measure time, which for brief intervals of time had a precision of a tenth of a second and even more.

The result obtained leads us directly to write the motion equation as

$S(t) = 4.66\ [m_i/(M_t + m_i)]\ t^2.$

Galileo may easily have imagined that the case of free fall occurs when $M_T = 0$; so

$S = 4.66\ t^2$ (K expressed in metres/t^2),
$S = 8.46\ t^2$ (K expressed in *braccia*/t^2).

In 4 pulse beats ($t = 3.4$ s)[413], the space that is travelled is $S \approx 98$ *braccia.*
Again I recall the note inserted by Galileo in his copy[414] of the *Dialogo sopra i due Massimi Sistemi del Mondo*:

> SIMPLICIO: Please put it down to my lack of practice in the mathematical sciences if I say freely that your arguments, based upon "greater ratios" and "lesser proportions" and other terms which I do not sufficiently well understand, have not removed my doubt – or rather my incredulity – that a heavy ball of lead, weighing some 100 pounds [*libbre*], leaving its state of rest and being let fall from on high, must pass through every gradation of slowness when one may see it to have moved more than 100 yards [*braccia*] in 4 pulse beats.

It is certain that Galileo wrote this note between 1635 and 1636 when he could still see clearly and had a steady hand and so, therefore, he began his experiments with the pulley in these years, immediately obtaining a good value for g, which remained the best value until 1659, when Huygens found a way to measure g with incredible precision[415].

19.3 *Third experiment: conservation of momentum at the instant of wrenching (equal masses)*

Galileo described the experiment as follows[416]:

> SALVIATI: [...] Let us imagine making the first experiment by dropping from some length, say one *braccio*, a weight equal to the other, which we have placed on a [supporting] plane, these weights being tied to the opposite ends of the same rope. What shall we believe to be

---

413 I remind you that four pulse beats are less than four seconds.

414 G.G., Vol. VII, *Dialogo*, p. 54.

415 Huygens, in December 1659, discovered that in a second a sphere travelled 31.5 Rhine feet, that is to say 9.81 m, in free fall. Christiaan Huygens, *Oeuvres complètes*, The Hague, 1932, Vol. XVII, pp. 245-247 and 278-284.

416 G.G., Vol.VIII, *Discorsi*, pp. 333-334.

the effect of the pull of the falling weight, with regard to the moving and raising of the other, which was at rest? I should be glad to hear your opinion.

The opinions expressed by Sagredo and Aproino, as often happens in the course of his texts in dialogue form, are not satisfactory and Galileo is forced to frame the experiment that he has in mind better, clarifying what the question is: what happens to the velocity of the falling body at the moment of the *wrenching* (*strappata*)? The experiment is analogous to the experiment of the completely inelastic frontal collision between two equal spheres, one of which is stationary. Galileo later also gives his solution[417]:

SALVIATI: [...] But since we are considering the speed acquired by one of these weights in descent from some height while the other remains at rest, it will be good to determine what and how much must be the speed with which both would be moved after the [initial] fall of the one, this descending and the other ascending. From what is already demonstrated, we know that a heavy body which falls freely on departing from rest perpetually acquires a greater and greater degree of speed; hence in our case the greatest degree of speed of the heavy body, while it descends freely, is that which it is found to have at the point at which he commences to lift its companion. Now it is evident that this degree of speed will not go on increasing when its cause of increase is taken away, this being the weight of the descending body itself; for its weight no longer acts when its propensity to descend is taken away by the repugnance to rising of its companion of equal weight. Hence the maximum degree of speed will be conserved, and the motion will be converted from one of acceleration to uniform motion.
What the future speed will then be is manifest from the things demonstrated and seen in the [discussion of the] past days. That is, the future speed will be such that, in another time equal to that of [the initial free] descent, double the space of [free] fall would be passed.

To understand the statement in this long passage better we recall the theorem Galileo refers to[418]:

[...] If, after fall through some inclined plane, there follows motion through the horizontal plane, the time of fall through the inclined plane will be, to the time of motion through any horizontal line, as double the length of the inclined plane is to that horizontal line.

Galileo did not talk of measurements taken when the motion is uniform, much less of the final velocity arrived at by M_2 at the moment of wrenching, but he resolved the case theoretically, comparing the free fall motion of M_2 to the descent along an inclined plane and the inertial motion after the *wrenching* to the inertial motion on the horizontal plane. So, since the time in the two paths is the same, the relationship $S = 2h$ follows (where h is the space travelled by M_2 before the wrenching and S is the space travelled by the two united masses after the wrenching). Dividing the two paths by the same time, we obtain the relationship between the constant velocity

[417] G.G., Vol.VIII, *Discorsi*, p. 337.

[418] G.G. vol. VIII, *Discorsi*, p. 246, Proposition XXV, Theorem XVI.

$v' = S/t = 2h/t$ after the wrenching and the velocity v of M_2 at the moment of the wrenching: given that in accelerated motion the final velocity is $v = gt = (2gh)^{1/2}$ (since $h = gt^2/2$) we have $v' = 2h/t = 2gh/v = v^2/v = v$.

Obviously the result is wrong: we must have $v' = v/2$, because after the wrenching the mass is doubled. On the other hand, it is easy to measure the uniform velocity v' after the wrenching and so we must deduce that Galileo did not carry out the experiment: indeed, if he had measured v' with the water clock or with the pendulum in seconds, and if too, in the worst case hypothesis, he had used what follows from "100 *braccia* in 5 seconds" to calculate v, to calculate $v = (2gh)^{1/2}$ he would have found $v'/v \approx 1.4$.

Anyway, the experiment that he proposed is completely valid and if Viviani had let the text that Vincenzo Galileo had given him soon after his father's death be known, the experimenters of the *Accademia del Cimento* could have been the first to find the rules for completely inelastic collision. It is, indeed, an experiment which is not difficult to do.

The experiment is carried out as follows: the weight M_1 is lowered almost to the ground, so as to raise the weight M_2 until it comes into contact with the electromagnets. The electromagnets are activated. M_2 remains suspended. The weight M_2 is made safe by manually inserting the blocking lever (fig. 19.7). To raise M_1 a structure with a pulley was built (fig. 19.8). M_1 is raised to an appropriate height and below the weight a steel bench, built for the purpose, is inserted.

M_1 rests on the bench, which keeps it raised 26.6 cm from the point of departure, and the pulley is removed. The lever blocking weight M_2 is removed manually. The electromagnets are turned off, uncoupling the weight M_2, and the downward movement that is induced is ob-

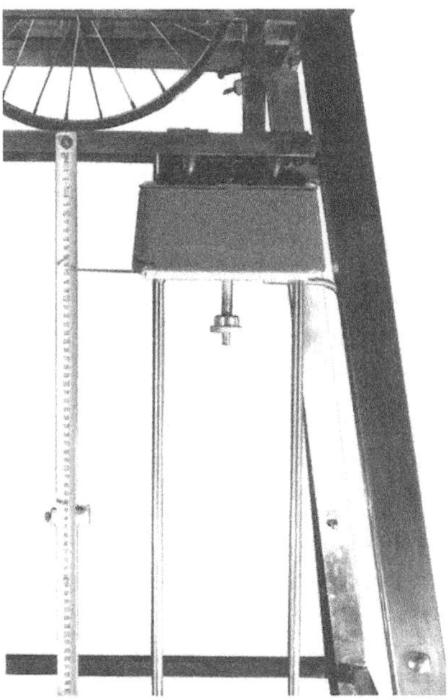

Fig. 19.7 Safety stop.

Fig. 19.8 Pulley and bench.

served[419]. The velocity v_f reached by M_2 at the moment immediately before the wrenching, after a free fall of 25.6 cm, when the cable tautens and M_1 begins to move, becomes v_c = constant, with the joint and uniform motion of M_1 and M_2.

Measurements

We took measurements of the fall time at constant velocity with a manual chronometer, but the water clock can be used with the same precision. The time of descent at constant velocity, travelling the remaining space that is 2.144 metres, after the fall of 0.256 m, (average of three measurements), is

$$T = (2.07 + 2.12 + 2.08 + 2.13 + 2.06)/5 = 2.09 \text{ s}$$

and the velocity is $v_c = 1.03 \text{ ms}^{-1}$.

The velocity acquired by M_2 in free fall from a height of 0.256 metres is $v_{2f} = [2gh + v_{2i}^2]^{1/2} = 2.24 \text{ ms}^{-1}$; where the velocity imparted at first by the electromagnet, $v_{2i} = 0.17 \text{ ms}^{-1}$, is negligible.

We find that the conservation of momentum is verified with good accuracy and that the velocity immediately after the wrenching is about half that immediately before the wrenching:

$$v_{2f}/2 = 1.06 \text{ ms}^{-1},$$
$$v_{T1} - 1.03 \text{ ms}^{-1}.$$

Could Galileo have done it?

Exactly as in the previous experiment, we know that Galileo had no difficulty in measuring the time: the accuracy of his equipment (the water clock) is not far from that we have today with our stopwatches, since, for experiments lasting only a few seconds, the variability of the measurements with one instrument or the other is also the same and only depends on the speed of the reflexes of the person measuring.

Galileo's mistaken statement about the final velocity suggests that he did not personally carry out the experiment at Arcetri. Unfortunately no notes remain referring to the machine and to his experiments on the force of percussion. He was then about 74 years old and was beginning to lose his sight; for this reason he had the *Giornata aggiunta* dedicated to percussion written by the priest Marco Ambrogetti, who stayed with him through 1637 and 1638.

He himself certainly could not do or repeat the experiments, which only needed a pulley and some equipment but required the movement of very large weights, and we do not know whether, in the final years of his life, there was anyone else at Arcetri who could do them for him, or as competently as he could have done. Only Ambrogetti could have done the experiments for him, together with his servant Pier Ferri and his son Vincenzo, but I do not believe it possible.

Galileo needed to give an evaluation of the final velocity and thought he could apply a theorem, which is not valid in this specific case, because the mass that descends with accelerated motion is half the mass that proceeds in uniform motion.

---

419 We have seen that the electromagnets impart an initial velocity of $v_{e.c.} = 0.17 \text{ ms}^{-1}$.

Setting aside any uncertain suppositions, what we can state with certainty today is that this experiment and the following one could easily have been done by the great scientist.

19.4 *Fourth experiment: conservation of momentum at the instant of wrenching (different masses)*

Galileo's text which introduces the experiment is[420]

> [...] An if we rest the first weight on the said plane that sustains it, we can use other weight of varying heaviness (though each of them less than the weight sustained at rest) to test what the force of different impact are. [This is made] by tying such weights to the end of the rope and then letting them fall from a given height, observing that happens at the other end to that great solid, that feels the pull of the falling weight, which pull will be to that large weight as a blow that would drive it upward

The previous experiment is repeated, adding a mass m to M_1 (fig. 19.9).
The motion now – after the *wrenching* – is uniformly delayed.

For the conservation of momentum to be verified, at the moment of the wrenching, it is necessary that immediately after the wrenching the velocity v_{Ti} of the coupled system of mass M_T verifies the relationship:

$$M_2 v_{2f} = M_{Ti}\, v_T \, .$$

v_{2f} is equal to the value obtained in the previous experiment, $v_{2f} = 2.24\ \mathrm{ms}^{-1}$.To measure v_{Ti} experimentally it is necessary to study the delayed motion with initial velocity v_{Ti}.

The relationship between the initial velocity of the system (and therefore of each of the two masses) after the wrenching and the space H travelled upwards by M_2 and downwards by M_1 is given by the relationship[421]

$$v_{Ti} = [2gHm/(m + M_T)]^{1/2} \, .$$

Let us compare the momentum immediately before the wrenching:

$$M_2 v_{2f} = 20.732 \times 2.2 = 46.4 \, ,$$

[420] G.G. Vol. VIII, *Discorsi*, pp. 333.

[421] The energy at the moment of wrenching is only kinetic $E = M_T v_{Ti}^2/2$. When the system is instantaneously still, with M_1 raised to S_d, the energy is only potential $E = mgH$. Equalising, we obtain $M_T v_{Ti}^2/2 = mgH$.

Fig. 19.9 Added mass m.

with the momentum immediately after the wrenching, for some values of m_i

$$M_T\, v_{Ti} = M_T\, [2gHm_i/(m_i + M_T)]^{1/2} = 44.7[19.632\, Hm_i/(m_i + 44.7)]^{1/2}.$$

These experiments were done with $m_1 = 1$ kg, $m_2 = 1.982$ kg and $m_3 = 3.944$ kg. The results were satisfactory, as the following table shows:

m in kg	H in m	Momentum "after" $M_T\, ([2gHm/(m + M_T)]^{1/2}$	Momentum before M_2v_{2f}
$m_1 = 1$	2.160	43.0	46.4
$m_2 = 1.982$	1.052	42.3	46.4
$m_3 = 3.944$	0.563	42.3	46.4

The comparison between the results in the last two columns shows that the conservation of the momentum holds even in the inelastic collision between unequal masses.

20. Marin Mersenne: A man who «wants to turn everything topsy-turvy»

Marin Mersenne (1588-1648), a theologian, a mathematician and above all a scholar of music and musical instruments, is well known for his correspondence with outstanding personalities of his day: Giovan Battista Baliani, Isaac Beeckman, René Descartes, Nicolas-Claude Fabri de Peiresc, Pierre de Fermat, Thomas Hobbes, Constantijn and Christiaan Huygens, Pierre Gassend, Etienne and Blaise Pascal, Gilles Personne de Roberval, Evangelista Torricelli and many more.

Educated by the Jesuit priests of the La Flèche college[422], in 1611, after attending the Sorbonne for two years, he entered the order of the Minims of St. Francis of Paola and in 1614 he was sent to teach philosophy to young monks at a monastery near Nevers; after having endured this unwelcome task for five years he returned to Paris in 1619, to a conventual life in the monastery of the Annunciation where he remained until his death. Before the publication of the *Dialogo sopra i due massimi sistemi del mondo* which would greatly influence his research, amongst the various interests that he cultivated[423] we find him dealing with the principles of motion, but inconsistently and with rather strange ideas, first stating that bodies slow as they fall, then claiming that they descend with constant velocity.

20.1 *The laws of motion (1628-1633)*

The first to discuss this question with him, rather contentiously it must be said, was Robert Cornier[424] who in a letter in March 1628 stated his conviction that the motion of stones ac-

[422] He entered the college in 1604, the year it opened, and stayed there until 1609. Descartes, instead, arrived in 1606 remaining until 1614. Despite the fact that the years they spent at the college overlapped it is believed that, because of the difference in age (8 years), they only met later, in 1623.

[423] The titles of his early publications already give an idea of his studies: *L'usage de la raison* (Paris, 1623), *Quaestiones celeberrimae in Genesim* (Paris, 1623), *L'impiété des Déistes* (Paris, 1624), *La vérité des Sciences* (Paris, 1625), *Synopsis mathematica* (Paris, 1626), *Traité de l'Harmonie Universelle* (Paris, 1627).

[424] *Correspondance du P. Marin Mersenne*, Paris, 1945, Vol II, p. 52. In his first letter to Mersenne (29 July 1625, p. 326) Cornier asked if the experiment mentioned in a book is true that a ball fired vertically from a rifle does not fall back, because the author of the book believes instead that it falls far away and Cornier thought of a third possibility, because he knew a man who assured him that the ball did fall back «although much later, after such a long time that he almost became bored». Hence his request from Descartes in May 1634 to carry out new experiments

quires force in falling, against Mersenne who gives the opposite opinion to his, that is to say that «the descent of a heavy body slows as the [*motion*] progresses».

The following year Isaac Beeckman (1588-1636) began corresponding regularly with him[425] and Mersenne fell under his spell from the first letter sent in March 1629. Beeckman raised his interest because he wrote to him that with weigh scales it was possible to locate the point after which the velocity of a body falling in air no longer grows, and after this point the body moves through the remaining space to Earth «equaliter», that is to say with constant velocity[426].

Mersenne in a (lost) letter dated 20 August 1629 disputed Beeckman's idea that the velocity increased in falling, and Beeckman reported a phrase that especially struck him in his *Journal*[427]:

> [...] So, if *Marinus Marcennus* had understood this [*the subject of the scales*] correctly, he would not have written to me on 20 August 1629: «But you suppose that the motion of a falling body, in the second foot moves faster than in the first and in the third [*more*] than in the second, which I judge to be false, supported both by my experience and by reason. Why, indeed – he asks – would it move more swiftly if everywhere it is of the same weight in any place or part of the path and always descends naturally. On the contrary – he adds – I believe rather that it moves more slowly the more it descends, although – he says – I am not able to prove it and perhaps it is false».

Note that here Mersenne refers to his experiments on falling and seems to attribute to Beeckman the idea that at the beginning of the motion the velocity increases in proportion to the space travelled. On the same day he wrote this note Beeckmann wrote to Mersenne[428]:

> I wonder, then, that you do not believe that the falling stone, before arriving at the point of *equality*, grows every moment in velocity [...] The attractive force [...] in the first moment attracted the stone that is at rest, then in the remaining ones it attracts, with forces equal to the first moment, the stone that is already in motion towards the Earth; so, in the second moment it moves partly with the motion acquired in the first moment and partly too with the new motion of the second moment and if there were no impediment the motion of

«because the author says that it has been experimented several times, without the ball falling back to the ground; which may seem unbelievable to many, but I do not judge it impossible and I believe that it is a thing very worthy of being examined». Mersenne carried out new experiments with the assistance of Pierre Petit which were inconclusive. In January 1626 Cornier put to him, together with other questions, the problem of the nature of gravity, whether it changed with the distance from the centre of the Earth, and in the following March he discussed the refraction of light and the cutting of lenses.

425 *Correspondance, op. cit.,* Vol. II, p. 219.

426 *Correspondance, op. cit.*, Vol. II, p. 223: «so take the lighter sphere therefore, to facilitate the experiment, suppose at most [*that it is*] of a size of 12 ounces, and that it strikes from above the other arm of the scales, you will see that 13 ounces will be lifted; falling from an even higher place it will raise 14 ounces *etc.*, until it arrives at a maximum height, beyond which it adds nothing to the weight».

427 The annotation can be found in *Journal tenu par Isaac Beeckman de 1604 à 1634 publié ... par C. De Waard,* The Hague, 1945, Vol. III, p. 134, dated 1 October 1629.

428 *Correspondance, op. cit.* Vol. II, pp. 280-281.

> the stone would grow unto the centre of the Earth, what you say would happen if it were perforated. And although I have never sought the point of equality with scales, these things have been taught to me fairly clearly by the slowness of the feather and of other things that fall in air or in water [...]

Descartes also began to correspond with Mersenne and in a letter in December 1629 he wrote that Beeckman's opinion that a body arrives at a constant velocity was false «although it is true that after a certain space this velocity increases so little that it can be believed imperceptible».

Mersenne later accepted Beeckman's ideas but he overturned them, proposing the constancy of the velocity from the start of the motion, as we can read[429] in a letter that Beeckman wrote to him in April 1630: «you say you have experimented that a stone, falling from 50 feet [16.33 metres], in the last 25 feet does not appear to move more swiftly than in the first 25».

At the end of April of that year Mersenne began a journey, going first to Brussels and then in Holland to The Hague, to Leiden and perhaps also to Amsterdam, finally reaching Beeckman in Dordrecht on 12 August, where he was able to take a look at what his host called his *Journal*.

As time passed Mersenne became ever more convinced that a body acquired a constant velocity almost at once and in a letter[430] dated 1 September 1631, addressed to Jean Rey who had sent him his *Essays*, he returned to the subject that he had already discussed with him: «you suppose in chapter V, that the motion of heavy things is faster towards the end than at the beginning. Experiment makes me see the opposite, because a cannon ball in the first twenty-five King's feet descends just as quickly as in the last twenty-five».

Mersenne still maintained the idea of fall at constant velocity in a later letter to Rey:

> Truly I am astounded that you doubt my experiment on the equal velocity of an iron ball and of a wooden ball: for I only have to make the many persons of quality that saw and carried out the experiment with me solemnly swear and they would bear true witness. And I know with absolute certainty that if from the window of a high chamber you let lead and coal drop down from your two hands at the same time, both the one and the other will go to the ground equally swiftly, and the same thing will happen if you drop a piece of one hundred pounds and a piece of the same kind of only a single ounce[431].

To appreciate the ideas that Mersenne maintained on motion, at the time of the publication of the *Dialogo sopra i due massimi sistemi del mondo*, one must read the letter[432] that Rey addressed to him on 1 January 1632:

> With regard to what you say, that *the experiment shows that a cannon ball descends just as fast through the first twenty five paces as through the last twenty five, and that a steel ball and a*

[429] *Correspondance, op. cit.*, Vol. II, p. 457.

[430] *Correspondance, op. cit.*, Vol. III, p. 188.

[431] *Correspondance, op. cit.*, Vol. III, pp. 274-275. The letter is dated 1 April 1632.

[432] *Correspondance, op. cit.*, Vol. III, p. 239.

wooden one of the same volume go downwards equally fast, although the iron weighs eight times more, and that a lump of coal and an equal piece of lead, falling from the same hands, go to earth with the same velocity, in other words that a body does not go downwards more swiftly although it is heavier, I would wish that ⟨*incomprehensible word*⟩ say so, because, without doubt, these experiments were performed badly by you, and I beg you to repeat them, but precisely and from a high place, binding myself on my honour if afterwards you do not change your language. For the descent of a cannon ball it is difficult to judge by eye if it goes faster in the last twenty-five feet than in the first twenty-five. But one can decide, dropping it once from a height of twenty five feet onto some soft ground, because it will sink a little, but not as much as if it fell from fifty. Now, this greater force comes either from the greater weight or from the greater velocity; not from itself, because it is the same ball, therefore from the latter, whatever one may say.

So Mersenne knew part of the truth, having tested that the weight and the material are not very relevant; but he seems not to have had the slightest suspicion that the velocity varies during the fall.

So we come to November 1632, when a copy of the *Dialogo* reached Mersenne and at once, already in the first day, he found the fundamental theorems on motion[433] that Galileo wanted to make known, together with an exhortation to the reader, which is also a promise[434]:

Content yourselves for now that I have removed your incredulity; but wait for the science another time, that is when you shall see the things demonstrated by our Academician on local motion: where you will find proved that in the time that one mobile falls the length of *CB*, the other descends along *CA* to point *T*, where the perpendicular drawn to it from point *B* falls.

[433] It is interesting to follow in the correspondence with Mersenne what Descartes thought of Galileo's ideas. Descartes wrote to Mersenne towards the end of 1632: «about what you send to me on the calculation that Galileo makes of the velocity with which descending bodies move, it has no confirmation in my philosophy … this leads me to believe that he cannot have arrived at the truth». In April 1634 Descartes was even more negative: «For the experiments of Galileo that you send I deny them all»; and in a letter in July 1634 he drew the trajectory of a projectile pointing out that he had not yet examined the nature of the line, which in the drawing however is shaped very differently from a parabola. Descartes, after reading the *Dialogo*, interpreted thus Galileo's law which he said was equal to that found by him (letter to Mersenne dated 14 August 1634): «if the ball takes three seconds to descend from *A* to *B*, it will take only one to descend from *B* to *C*». Note that in the drawing that accompanies the text $BC = AB$. At the end of 1635, in another letter to Mersenne, he put forward further doubts on Galileo's law: «… two or three totally false things are supposed: one is that the movement, as Galileo judges, grows by degrees from very slow …»; Descartes' explanation of the force of gravity as an effect of the vortices of thin matter makes him think that, from the very beginning, at the start of the motion, bodies have a definite velocity.

[434] G.G., Vol. VII, *Dialogo*, pp. 50-51. In the second day (G.G., Vol. VII, p. 248) Galileo reaffirms with Salviati: «Most purely mathematical, and not only of this, but of many other beautiful properties belonging to natural motions and to projectiles also, all of which have been discovered and proved by our friend. I have seen and studied them all, to my very great delight and amazement, seeing a whole new science arise around a subject on which hundreds of volumes have been written; yet not a single one of the infinite admirable conclusions within this science had been observed and understood by anyone before our friend».

This is the theorem that I discussed in chapters 2 and 13, accompanied in the printed text by a drawing (fig. 2.27) that differs only very slightly from the one in the Padua manuscript (fig. 13.1). But, as we shall see, the friar was not a man to be content and wait!

Proceeding in his reading of the *Dialogo* Mersenne came to the second day and learned, again for the first time[435], that «the acceleration of the straight motion of heavy bodies is done according to odd numbers *ab unitate* ... which in other words is the same as saying that ... the spaces passed through are to each other like the squares of the times» and, a little further on, he also found a quantitative result: «an iron ball of a hundred pounds ... by repeated experiments descends from the height of a hundred *braccia* in five seconds of an hour». There is also a clue that reveals the instrument Galileo used to verify the law of odd numbers, when he talked of the pendulum that: «makes its swings always in equal times, whether very long or very short».

Arriving at the end of the fourth day Mersenne read another fundamental property of the pendulum: «...the vibrations of such a pendulum occur with such necessity in such determined times, for it is completely impossible to make it do them in different times, except by lengthening or shortening the cord». Immediately afterwards he came across the theorem of chords, for which he did not find any demonstration but that, like the law of motion, it is possible to verify by direct experiments, which he did for both.

Mersenne's interest in the pendulum, in connection with his research into sound and the oscillations of the strings of musical instruments, dates back at least to 1629, because the question he asked about the oscillations of a weight as a function of the length of the cord it is tied to is from that year. In a letter[436], dated 8 October 1629, Descartes answered, proposing a strange relationship: if we choose as the unit of time the length T_1 of a simple oscillation of a pendulum with a length L_1 equal to a foot, then, another pendulum with a length which is an even multiple of L_1, *i.e.* $2L_1$, $4L_1$, $6L_1$, ... and in general, $L_n = 2(n-1)\, L_1$, has a period $T_n = (4/3)^n\, T_1$.

The relationship is a consequence of the deductive procedure followed by Descartes, to obtain the period as a function of the length of the pendulum: the mass of the pendulum, from the moment when it is released until when it reaches the lowest point – according to Descartes – takes a time equal to that necessary for it to travel the same difference in height vertically in free fall.

---

[435] Mersenne at first doubted the general validity of Galileo's law, perhaps taking into account what Descartes and Beeckman wrote to him on the opposing resistance of air: see *Question IV* of the *Questions theologiques, physiques, morales et mathematiques*, Paris, 1634 (Librairie A. Fayard edition) 1985, pp. 223-225, in which he states that a wooden or lead ball that falls through 12 feet in one second, will fall about 48 feet in two seconds, but «*il est difficile, et peut-estre impossible de determiner le peu qui s'en faut, et de sçavoir en que lieu la boule commence a garder une autre proportion dans son mouvement*». Bear in mind that Galileo was also clearly aware of the existence of a limit velocity in the *Discorsi* (G.G., Vol. VIII, p. 119) when he analysed the difference between motion in vacuum and in air, where in the long term «... the speed gets to such a point, and the resistance of the medium to such a magnitude that the two balance each other, prevent further acceleration and bring the moveable to an equal and uniform motion, in which it always [thereafter] continues to maintain itself».

[436] *Correspondance, op. cit.*, Vol II, pp. 304-306. The first known letter from Descartes to Mersenne is dated August 1629 (*Correspondance*, Vol. II, pp. 250-254); On 3 May 1632 Descartes confirmed to him the law of the sine for the inclined plane, which Mersenne already knew from the manuscript of Galileo's *Le Mechaniche*, which he had long since possessed.

In the following letter dated 13 November he explained to him the time that regulates the fall of heavy bodies: if a given path is divided into spaces, all equal to each other, his law assigns the following transit times with this rule: if, for example, the path S is divided into two equal parts A and B, ($S=A+B$) and the first part is travelled in three time units, then the second part will be travelled in one unit, so overall we find that in 4 time units the body descends double (*i.e.* it descends $S=A+B$) than the space it descends in three time units (*i.e.* when it descends $A=S/2$). If we double the path in such a way that it can be divided into 4 parts equal to A, $2S = A + B + C + D$, it is not difficult to see that the time necessary to travel $2S$ is $(4/3)^2$ the time necessary to travel A. The general law is that written for the pendulum: with T_A the time to travel the distance A, and with T_{2nA} indicating the time to travel the distance $2nA$, we obtain $T_{2nA} = (4/3)^n T_A$.

At the end of 1632 the situation was this: Mersenne and Descartes had very confused ideas about motion, while Beeckman was noting in his *Journal* a series of considerations and results that were on the whole correct, which he only in part conveyed to his two correspondents and which would become known with the complete publication of the manuscript in the years 1939-1945. Not even Beeckman, however, knew that the space passed through by falling bodies grows with the square of the time and none of the three of them carried out experiments measuring the fall time of a body.

20.2 *Experiments on motion and on the pendulum (1634-1644)*

During 1633, probably while he was translating *Le Mecaniche* into French[437], Mersenne decided to verify the statements that he had read in the *Dialogo* and after his first observations he immediately wrote a small treatise[438]. By that date he had already made some experiments on fall and he had found that a body fell from about 147 feet (48 metres) in 3.5 seconds, from 108 feet (35.27 metres) in 3 seconds and from 48 feet (15.68 metres) in 2 seconds; then his measure of g is $g = 7.84$ ms^{-2}. He measured the time with a pendulum which he believed he had adjusted so that each simple oscillation lasted a second.

[437] Mersenne had known *Le Mecaniche* for some time, at least since 1629, because as he wrote to Galileo on 1 February that year: «*Vidimus etiam tractatum Mechanicorum, quem a tua manu putant ortum, in cujus fine conaris vim ictus mallei aut alterius rei definire*». He had his translation, which is not very faithful to the original, reprinted with the title: *Les Mechaniques de Galilée Mathematicien* & *Ingenieur du Duc de Florence avec plusieurs additions rares,* & *nouvelles … traduit de l'Italien*, Paris 1634. Mersenne, towards the end, of the small treatise (pp. 73-82), presented and illustrated the theorems he had read in the *Dialogo*, introducing them as follows: «*il faut seulement icy ajouter quelques considerations touchant les mouvements; en attendant que nous en donnions plusieurs observations tres-exactes*» and he announced his *Traité des mouvements* with these words: «*comme je demonstreray dans un traité particulier*».

[438] *Traité des mouvemens et de la cheute des corps pesans et de la proportion de leurs differentes vitesses. Dans lequel l'on verra plusieurs experiences tres exactes. A Paris* …MDCXXXIIII. In the comment on Godefroid Wendelin's letter to Mersenne dated 15 June 1633, on pp. 430-441 of the III volume of the *Correspondance* there is a brief summary of this treatise, which is difficult to track down.

That is what he thought but it is not so because the pendulum that Mersenne used was 3.5 feet (1143 millimetres) long, an excessive length[439]. When he wrote of the pendulum 3.5 feet long, some times he specified that this measurement included the lead ball attached to the thread[440], other times he wrote that it was the length of the thread alone[441].

But before continuing with the description and discussion of his experiments we should stop and consider the events that led Mersenne, Descartes and above all Isaac Beeckman to concern themselves with pendulums.

It began in 1603 with the news[442] of a new instrument discovered by Santorio Santorio (1561-1636) and named by its inventor with the term *pulsilogium*, «with which anyone can measure in the most exact fashion, observe and keep firmly in mind the motion and the repose of the arteries and then compare it to the pulsations of the previous days». Nothing else is written in his book; a detailed description, accompanied by drawings only appeared in 1626[443].

It is known that in this period Santorio was practicing his profession as a doctor in Venice and that he knew Galileo; once he also treated him, and many believe that Santorio heard the pendulum spoken of from Galileo himself, or from someone amongst his acquaintances, and that therefore he did not discover the principle of the *pulsilogium* by himself, because his ideas on the pendulum are rather confused, even though the actual use he made of the instrument is clear, varying the length of the string to make it oscillate simultaneously with the pulse beats.

In 1618, at the beginning of July, Beeckman, who had studied medicine at university and who dedicated much space to medical subjects in his *Journal*, included a note[444] with the title *pulsilogium esse fabricandum* next to it:

> If anyone does not trust [*his*] practice and his experience in examining the pulsations and the speeding up and the slowing of respiration, let him first find what fraction of the natural day or of the hour is a single pulse or a single breath in a man of regular weight and let him make for himself a clock, or rather a *pulsilogium*, in which the single beats last exactly the time of a pulse and in this way he can examine the pulse with this instrument; let him build it rather so that he can lengthen or shorten the time of the beats and adapt the strokes to each natural beat, so that he can know by how much that pulse departs from normality.

---

[439] Remember that the exact distance is about 993 mm, measured between the centre of gravity of the body hanging from the thread and the point of suspension.

[440] On p. 221 of the *Harmonie Universelle*, Paris, 1636, Mersenne described an experiment similar to that of Galileo's sieve rolling in it a lead sphere with a diameter of one King's inch (27.2 millimetres), and then – as we shall see – he compared the times of its oscillations with those of a pendulum 3.5 feet long, a length that also included the sphere attached to it which had the same diameter as the sphere rolling in the sieve.

[441] On p. 135 of *Harmonie Universelle*: «it is easy to carry with one everywhere a thread or a fine rope three and a half feet in length, whose every swing backwards or forwards will mark exactly a second ... And if it is wished that every passage of the cord last only half a second only a quarter has to be taken, and this is very easy, folding it into four».

[442] *Methodi vitandorum errorum omnium qui in arte medica contingunt libri quindecim... Sanctorio Sanctorio...auctore*, Venice, 1603.

[443] *Commentaria in prima Fen primi libri Canonis Avicennae*, Venice, 1626.

[444] *Journal, op.cit.* Tome I, 1639, pp.196-197.

A few months later, in November of the same year, Beeckman observed that the vibrations of the strings of musical instruments occur in equal times independently of the amount by which the string is moved away from the position of rest, because the note produced does not depend on the amplitude of the vibration, and the same happens with a lamp hanging from a rope:

> No differently does it happen in chandeliers hanging from a rope: we see indeed that they move in intervals of equal time, with circular, but not conic, motion which has its centre fixed at the end of the rope that is tied to a rafter [...] I would say that the same chandelier, that hangs from a rope [*always*] of the same length, always conserves the same time, whatever part of that circle it travels, and this [*time*] is always equal, and the longer [*the ropes*] the greater the time they last, the shorter they are the lesser they last. This in fact I think I have proved in those objects that hang from long ropes: indeed if you move them with the slightest touch, much time will be needed for them to return to you. But the contrary happens in those that hang from a short rope: indeed, when touched they immediately return to you[445].

The description of what happens if a lamp is pushed when the cord is long or very short shows perspicacity and spirit of observation, even if the reasoning is only qualitative and there is not even an attempt to seek some kind of relationship between period and length.

There is nothing else in the *Journal* on the pendulum until February 1629, when Mersenne – through Rivet[446] – asked Beeckman, whom he did not yet know, some questions about his oscillations: a) if a weight is attached to a thread and is allowed to swing from a certain height, what height will it reach on the other side of the first oscillation? b) whether, if the pendulum continues to swing, the reductions will always keep the same proportion? c) if a pendulum completes half a simple oscillation in a pulse beat how much longer must the cord be for the same path to be travelled in two pulse beats?

It is strange that Mersenne did not seek the answers to his questions himself simply by watching a pendulum swing, but with him we frequently find this interesting and positive attitude of wanting to involve his correspondents in his research and in his doubts, indeed, this is the main reason that led him to write to so many people. We have already seen that it was Descartes who answered giving him an elaborate and mistaken relationship between period and length, while Beeckman avoided the questions, «because – he wrote – your pendulum moves in air and not in vacuum, and it is necessary to take into account whether it is shaped like a globe or a pyramid, if it is large or small, if it is made of wood or lead[447]».

Beeckman returned to considering the pendulum only three years later, at the beginning of 1631, and he very soon discovered other notable properties, including the length of the pendulum that beats a second, a length that he believed to be unchangeable and worthy of being chosen as a standard for a universal unit of length. This is how he determined it:

---

[445] *Journal, op. cit.*, Tome I, 1639, pp. 259-260.

[446] *Correspondance, op. cit.*, Vol. II, p. 206.

[447] *Correspondance, op. cit.*, Vol. II, p. 219.

> I counted how many beats my clock makes in a single hour and I found it was 4186 and 7/8 those that I valued with the eclipse of the Sun[448]. So therefore, having corrected the clock, that is to say having evaluated it with the shadow of the Sun for some days, I hung a great round weight from a thin thread and I ordered another person to count the going to and fro of the weight hanging from the thread; I instead counted the beats of my clock. If I heard 4186 beats just at the moment in which he counted 3600 swings to and fro, it was certain that the length of the cord had been found. If I counted more than 4186 I would have made the cord shorter, if fewer, longer.
> This then is more easily done if your clock makes 3600 beats in an hour, which can be done by a smith, with the teeth of the wheels proportionate to each other so that as many beats in an hour as I have said will be heard.

Beckman did not say in this note how long the thread was and how great the weight, but three years later, at the end of March 1634, he noted down in his *Journal*[449] the length of the pendulum with which he observed the eclipse that year: 3 Rhine feet and 4 inches, or 1046 millimetres. If the length included the ball and the ball had a diameter of 4 Rhine inches (104.6 mm), then the distance to the centre of gravity of the ball is 3 feet and two inches, or 993 mm, exactly the length that a pendulum that beats the second must have, but it would have been difficult for Beeckman to attach a lead ball weighing almost 7 kg to the thread. So even his pendulum, therefore, is not totally precise. And this is all that the most expert of the three knew about the pendulum.

Before discussing the experiments that Mersenne carried out on the fall of heavy bodies, which produced results very distant from the values indicated by Galileo, we should speak of another kind of experiment, that does not require the measurement of time. In this experiment Mersenne checked whether the ratio given by Galileo between the spaces that are travelled *in the same time* on the inclined plane and vertically was correct: from his experiments he again obtained results that are in clear contrast with Galileo's, so much so that he came to write this crude conclusion[450]:

---

[448] See his *Journal, op. cit.*, Vol. III, pp. 153-156, where he describes the observation of the eclipse of the Sun of 10 June 1630 – done with the help of students and friends – and the procedures he followed to correct his clock, which previously he had adjusted to the length of the 24 hours of the day. His notes also contain the detailed description of the gears of the clock, which is of course a traditional clock without a pendulum.

[449] *Journal, op. cit.*,Vol. III, p. 341.

[450] *Harmonie Universelle, op. cit.*, p. 112. The reaction of Raffaello Magiotti is not surprising. He wrote to Galileo from Rome on 25 April 1637: «… from Arcetri you informed me several times that you were very busy perfecting the work on the resistance of solids. I do not believe that these demonstrations have arrived in France with the other works, because Father P. Mersenne of the Minims, who had seen the book *de motu* with the other observations, makes no mention of these things; and yet it is true that he wished to turn everything topsy turvy. This friar prints many and large bad books, seeking to acquire reputation by displeasing others, and perhaps he will succeed with the riff-raff. The works of his that have been lent to me, most of them in French; and it is a pity not to be a master of it for I would send them so you could see them and in your time and place reach him with some lashing». The same day Magiotti wrote to Fabiano Michelini: «... the works *de motu* (as well as these demonstrations) have already been seen in Flanders and in France by his imitators, or rather examiners, indeed great enemies; amongst whom I count the Abbot Mersenio a Minorite in France, since having seen several works by this friar,

> I doubt that Mister Galileo has carried out experiments of falls on a plane, because he does not talk of it at all and because the proportion that he gives, often contradicts the experiment: & I wish that many may try the same thing on different planes with all the precautions they can imagine, to see if their experiments correspond to ours […]

And a little later he added another gibe against Galileo:

> Those who have seen our experiments and who have helped us know that it is not possible to proceed with more precision, both because of the plane which is very straight and well smoothed and which forces the mobile to descend straight, and because of the roundness and the heaviness of the balls and for the descents; from this one may conclude that the experiment is not capable of giving rise to a science and that one must not trust too much to reason alone, because it does not always correspond to the truth of appearances, from which it often distances itself: this will not prevent me from talking of the equally inclined plane, as it must be because heavy bodies compress it and weigh equally on each of its points. If anyone should wish to carry out more precise experiments he must use an inclined plane longer than ours, for example a plane of 48 feet [*15.59 metres*], on which the time of the descent will be much more perceptible and if one of a hundred or 200 feet were to be had, it would be even better […]

20.3 *The experiments with the inclined plane and with the sieve (1635-1636)*

But what experiment did Mersenne carry out? Let us listen to what he said:

> So having chosen a height of five King's feet [*1.633 m*] and having grooved and smoothed a plane, we gave to it many modes of inclination, so as to let a lead ball and a wooden ball, well rounded, roll along the plane, and this we did from many positions, different according to the different inclinations, while another ball of the same dimension and weight fell in air from the height of five feet; & we found that in the time that it fell from the height of five feet perpendicularly, [*the other*] descended only a foot on the plane inclined at fifteen degrees, while it should descend sixteen inches [*i.e. one and a third feet*].

I find that he has no other aim than to be displeased (even if at the end it will be to his own cost) by the noble thoughts, subtle inventions and demonstrations of a man of such great virtue». And again to Galileo on 16 May: «… That Father Mersenio boasts of having read the book *de motu*, is certain, since he informed Master Gio. Batista Doni of it, and I have read the letter. I do not yet know how this work has made its way there. That he tries in every way to gain honour with the work of others, I have no doubt, knowing him very well from his writings, on which, being most of them French, I have lost time unfortunately». The Magiotti letters are in G.G., Vol. XVII, pp. 63-64 and 80.

Mersenne changed the inclination of the plane and for every angle he measured the space L travelled by one of the two balls exactly in the time in which the other fell vertically from a height of five feet; or he kept the angle α fixed and changed the height of the fall H.

I have gathered together his results in a table and have added in the final column the value of $K = L/H \sin \alpha$:

H in inches	L in inches	α in degrees	$K = L/H \sin\alpha$
60	12	15	0.773
60	18	25	0.710
60	24	30	0.800
72	30	30	0.833
60	33	40	0.856
< 84	38.5	40	> 0.713
60	36	45	0.849
66	< 40	45	0.857
60	33	50	0.718
78	46	50	0.770
60	33~36	60~65	0.635–0.692
60	42	75	0.700

Mersenne's results clearly indicate that the sphere rolled on the plane touching at only one point and that, therefore, the groove that he had ordered to be made in order to ensure that the straight path was wider than the ball. When this happens we must have $K = 5/7 = 0.714$ and this theoretical value is fairly close to that in his results.

When the angle is increased sometimes K increases a little because the sphere begins to slip and therefore no longer rolls; Mersenne realised this after he arrived at 45°: «we can say – he wrote – that it happens because the movement of the ball is too violent at the inclination of 50 degrees and it cannot descend and roll on the plane, which often makes it jump». Soon afterwards he again referred to the experiment done with an inclination of 50°, for which he cannot decide whether the path is 33 or 36 inches long:

> [...] and this shows the great difficulty of the experiments, because it is very difficult to understand which of the two balls falls first, whether the ball falling perpendicularly or the ball on the inclined plane [...] The experiments give us nothing certain, especially at inclinations over 45°, because the path followed by the ball at this inclination is almost equal to the path followed on planes at 50°, 60° & 65°; and on a plane at 75° it travels only half a foot more[451].

[451] *Harmonie Universelle, op.cit.*, p. 112: «*ce qui monstre la grande difficulté des experiences; car il est tres-difficile*

If Mersenne had done his experiments with smaller angles, probably he would have noticed the constancy of the ratio $H/L = K = 5/7$.

Mersenne did not overlook another experiment, easy to verify: the experiment with a ball rolling in a "large box" (this is the term that Guidobaldo del Monte used for the container that forces the ball into a circular path) or a "sieve box" as Galileo preferred to call it in the fourth day of the *Dialogo*[452] describing his old experiment as follows:

> [...] take an arc made of a very smooth and polished concave hoop bending along the curvature of the circumference *ADB* [*in the text there is a drawing of a quarter of a circumference*], so that a well-rounded and smooth ball can run freely in it (the rim of a sieve is well suited for this experiment). Now I say that wherever you place the ball, whether near to or far from the ultimate limit *B* – placing it at the point *C*, or at *D*, or at *E* – and let it go, it will arrive at the point *B* in equal times.

Mersenne commented on the experiments with the large box in Proposition XXIII of the third book of the *Harmonie Universelle*[453], with the title: «Explaining several circumstances and properties of Motion, both natural and violent, whether oblique or perpendicular, in which we see an examination of Galileo's thoughts and experiments on this matter». Mersenne compared the oscillations of a ball going to and fro in a «*crible*» to those of weights attached to a cord[454] «these oscillations are similar in many things to those of weights attached to a cord going from one side to the other» and he observed that in the sieve «the ball ... takes as much time to rise as to descend ... but if we compare one of the last oscillations with one of the first ... we shall find that the former is made more quickly than the latter and the same also happens with the cord, for which the smaller oscillations are made more quickly than the greater ones».

We know that Mersenne was printing his treatise a bit at a time as he finished the various sections, and in the meantime he continued to carry out experiments, so that only when he had printed everything – as often happens – did he begin to write the General Preface which he followed by an extensive table of contents[455]. He included some observations in the preface and in particular he asked the reader to add the following experiment to the one with the sieve that he discussed on p. 222 of the treatise which was already printed:

---

d'appercevoir lequel tombe le premier de deux boulets, dont l'un tombe perpendiculairement, & l'autre sur le plan incliné ... Les experiences ne nous donnent rien d'asseuré, particulierement aux inclinations qui passent 45 degrez, parce que le chemin que fait le boulet à cette inclination, est quasi egal à celuy qu'il fait sur les plans de 50, 60, & 65; & sur celuy de 75 il ne fait que demi pied davantage».

452 The same subjects as in the letter are, indeed, discussed together in the *Dialogo ... sopra i due massimi sistemi*, G.G., Vol. VII, pp. 475-476: This passage is preceded by the discussion of the isochronicity of pendulums and is followed by the theory of chords, two other subjects in the letter to Guidobaldo which in the *Dialogo* are presented in the same detail.

453 *Harmonie Universelle op. cit.*, p. A ij.

454 *Harmonie Universelle, op.cit.*, p. 222,

455 The index alone is 44 pages long with independent numbering, and consists of the Table of Propositions of the XIX books of the *Harmonie Universelle.*

> So having rolled a lead ball in the semicircle *LBK*, which has a radius *AB* of 2 feet and 7 inches [*about* 0.84 m] and having hung another ball of the same weight from a string of equal length, this string with its ball makes 19 oscillations in the same time that the ball rolling in the aforesaid quarter of a circle makes only 18, so that the ball hung from a small rope always precedes the oscillations of the rolling by one of its oscillations; but while the latter only goes 9 times from *L* to *K* and returns rolling 9 times from *K* to *L* before stopping at point *E*, [*the other one*] goes at least 1500 times from *L* towards *K* and returns as many times from *K* towards *L* before stopping at *B*, when it is attached to the string *AB*, so it can be seen how much the wooden plane *LBK* hinders the oscillations of the ball that rolls along it: because if it were so perfectly round and smooth that the plane made no greater impediment than that which one imagines in the air, the ball would roll at least as many times again, and equally high, from one side to the other as it does when attached to a string. I said at least, because it would not have the obstacle of the cord, which delays and diminishes slightly the amplitude of the oscillations of the ball.

Mersenne assigned the difference in frequency between two oscillatory motions to friction; note then that there is no contradiction between the 18:19 = 0.947 ratio which refers to the number of "quarters of a circle", *i.e.* to half simple oscillations, and the fact that the ball in the sieve only performs 9 simple oscillations before stopping.

It is instead interesting to understand why Mersenne's result is not in contradiction with what I wrote about this experiment while commenting Galileo's letter to Guidobaldo in 1602, supposing that Galileo could have carried it out, and that is to say that the ratio between the two periods is $(5/7)^{1/2} = 0.845$. We know that every oscillation of the sphere in the sieve is delayed by this factor compared to one of *equal amplitude* of a pendulum as long as the radius of the sieve, but while the pendulum maintains its initial amplitude for many oscillations the oscillations in the sieve diminish rapidly in amplitude and duration, partly compensating for the delaying effect of the rolling: that is why the ratio is closer to unity. Mersenne knew (he even wrote it on page 222) that, as the oscillations became less wide, they are performed in ever less time. But he does not appear to set any importance on it. He recorded what he saw, but he did not comment on it and he never tried to link the results of the various experiments, for him it was enough to establish when and where his experiments did not agree with Galileo's.

In the second experiment, the one in which he was seeking the length of the pendulum that oscillates with the same frequency as the ball in the sieve, the situation is more favourable, because then he was looking at the first oscillations of the two spheres when they were still of the same amplitude:

> So, the cord that bears *B* suspended, being 3 and a half feet long, including the ball, makes each of its oscillations exactly in the same time that the other ball does for each of its rolls in the circle, which has a radius of 2 feet and 7 inches, that is to say that each of the oscillations of its rolling lasts a second: so that the radii of the circles of the rolling are proportional to the square of the times, as we have said of the small cords that support the balls.

The final numerical result reported by Mersenne shows the accuracy of his observations because the motion of a pendulum and of a sphere in the box are synchronous when the ratio between the radius of the box and the length of the pendulum is 5/7 = 0.714 and Mersenne found a quantity only slightly greater because, expressing the two lengths in inches, we obtain 31/42 = 0.738 with an error of just over 3%, which is an excellent result[456]. Mersenne did not realise that the same ratio existed in the experiment in which he compared the motion on the inclined plane and the motion in free fall.

20.4 *Experiments on vertical fall (1634-1644)*

It must be admitted that Mersenne had justifiable cause to doubt the truth of Galileo's experiments, above all after his experiments in 1634 on fall carried out from various heights, with results which were perceptibly different from Galileo's, Mersenne to be sure used two balls of different material and weight[457]:

> We have proved with great precision that a globe of lead weighing about half a pound [*about* 245 g] and one of wood weighing about an ounce [30.54 g] fall from 48 feet in 2″, from 108 in 3″ and from 147 in 3″ 1/2.

In reality, the extraordinary agreement with Galileo's law of falling is artificially constructed because the results that Mersenne had were slightly different; indeed he explained immediately afterwards:

> If satisfaction is to be found lacking this comes rather from the fact that we give too little space for this time rather than the opposite, because having dropped the weight from 110 feet [0.35926 *metres*] it fell in exactly 3″ but we take 108 to adjust the proportion, and men cannot observe the difference in the time taken to fall from 110 or from 108 feet. As for the height of 147 feet it is half a foot short and this expresses the quadratic relationship very exactly [...]

Mersenne believed that the few experiments that he had made were sufficient to confirm the quadratic dependence of the time discovered by Galileo; indeed they produced compatible results: $110/(3)^2 = 12.22$ feet and $146.5/\ (3.5)^2 = 11.96$ feet. From then on the friar would use the path of 12 feet in a second as the standard to calculate uniformly accelerated motion, which corresponds to an acceleration of $g = 7.84\ \text{ms}^{-2}$, a value that is 20% lower than the correct value $g \approx 9.81\ \text{ms}^{-2}$.

---

456 To be thorough and to take into account the position of the centre of gravity of the ball, one has to take away 1/2 inch which is its radius, and then the ratio between the two lengths becomes 31/41.5 = 0.747.

457 *Harmonie Universelle*, *op. cit.*, p. 87: «*Nous avons esprouvé tres-exactement qu'un globe de plomb pesant environ demie livre* [245 *g*] & *que celuy de bois pesant environ une once* [30.54 *g*] *tombent de* 48 *pieds en* 2″, *de* 108 *en* 3″, & *de* 147 *pieds en* 3″ 1/2 ... *s'il se trouve du mesconte, il vient plustost de ce que nous donnons trop peu d'espace ausdits temps, qu'au contraire, car ayant laissé cheoir le poids de* 110 *pieds, il est justement tombé en* 3″, *mais nous prenons* 108 *pour regler la proportion:* & *les hommes ne peuvent observer la difference du temps auquel il tombe de* 110, *ou de* 108 *pieds. Quant à la hauter de* 147 *pieds, il s'en falloit un demi-pied; ce qui rend la raison doublée tres-juste...*».

Mersenne was an excellent experimenter and he could count on a great deal of help[458], inside and outside the convent of the Annunciation in Paris and certainly the two spaces of fall – 110 feet and 146.5 feet – were measured with precision[459].

The wrong result cannot depend either on the length of the pendulum, which had simple oscillations that lasted longer than a second, because with this pendulum Mersenne evaluated the time taken as *less* than the time that really passed while instead the result tells us that *too much* time has passed. A pendulum 3.5 feet, (l = 1143 mm) long has a half period $T/2$ = 1.0725 s, and so 3 simple oscillations do not last 3 seconds but 3.22 s and in this time, neglecting the resistance of the air, the path travelled would be almost 50 metres, equal to 153 feet and not 110 feet.

So the error must depend on how the pendulum was used: maybe he did not release it exactly at the beginning of the motion, which happens at a distant point, and above all he cannot have succeeded in evaluating the position of the pendulum when the ball arrived and the time corresponding to this position. From the following analysis we shall find that the error he made is about half a second, because of the resistance of the air, which leads to the time depending not only on the acceleration g but also on the radius of the sphere.

Since the days of Newton, who developed the theory of motion in a resistive medium and compared it with the experiment, we know that the resistance of air is proportional to the square of the velocity and that there are two relationships to be used for the comparison with the experiment:

1) the limit velocity: $v_L = (8\rho Rg/3C\rho_{Air})^{1/2}$,
2) the equation of motion: $\cosh(gt/v_L) = \exp(gx/v_L^2)$.

Here ρ indicates the density of the material the sphere is made of, R its radius, $\rho_{Air} = 1184 \times 10^{-6}$ g cm^{-3} is the density of air and C the drag coefficient, which for a perfectly spherical body is 0.47 but it may be greater if the sphere is not perfectly smooth. Like Newton I chose the value C = 0.5 and I applied Newton's theory to Mersenne's results, obtained using a lead sphere weighing half a pound (0.245 kg) and a wooden sphere weighing an ounce (0.03059 kg).

For the calculations that follow we should remember the correspondence between our modern units of measure and those used in Paris in the XVII century[460]:

Livre (pound) = 0.4895068 kg (= 16 ounces),
Pied de Roi (King's foot) = 0.3266 m (= 12 *pouces* or inches = 144 *lignes* or lines),

[458] For example in the first observation, at the end of the "*Table de matieres*", he wrote: «as witnessed by the experiment, that I did from more than 14 *toises* [14 *toises* = 144 *pieds* = 46 m] of height in the presence of knowledgeable persons, who helped me, ...».

[459] *Harmonie Universelle, op. cit.*, p. 99. When, instead of measuring the times starting from the well measured distances, the distances are measured starting from the times, Mersenne observed: « ... it is easy to be in error by 3 or 4 feet, or *toises*, and more since between 108 & 147 feet there is but half a second of difference».

[460] After 1668 the old standard of length, which was the *toise du Châtelet* (equal to 6 *pieds de Roi*), was revised and became 1.949036 m and so the *pied de Roi* = 0.3248 m, while until that date the *pied de Roi* was worth 0.3266 m.

There is very little doubt about the density of lead , ρ_{Pb} = 11.34 g cm^{-3} and from the weight of the ball we can calculate its radius: R_{Pb} = 1.728 cm.

The density of wood is actually extremely variable:

density of ordinary wood: $\rho_{\text{Ordinary wood}}$ = 0.74 g cm^{-3} ,
density of olive wood: ρ_{Olive} = 0.86 g cm^{-3} ,
density of ebony[461]: ρ_{Ebony} = 1.26 g cm^{-3} .

However an observation of Mersenne's allows us to find the density of the wood it was made of. Indeed he wrote that a lead ball weighing a pound had the same diameter as a wooden ball weighing an ounce[462], and so $\rho_{\text{Wood}} = \rho_{Pb}/16 \approx 0.708$ g cm^3.

From these value for density and from the weight of the ball, 30.54 g, we find for the radius $R_{\text{Wood}} = [30.54(3/4\pi\rho_{\text{Wood}})]^{1/3} = 2.177$ cm.

It is obvious that Mersenne used ordinary wood and this result allows us to carry on our calculations and the comparison between theory and experiment, which can be done by looking at the results given in these tables:

Lead sphere R = 1.728 cm				
Height				
in m	in feet	v_{Limit} in ms^{-1}	$t_{\text{Theoretical}}$ in s	$t_{\text{Experimental}}$ in s
35.93	110	27.83	2.72	3.22
47.85	146.5	27.83	3.15	3.75

Wooden sphere R = 2.177				
Height				
in m	in feet	v_{Limit} in ms^{-1}	$t_{\text{Theoretical}}$ in s	$t_{\text{Experimental}}$ in s
35.93	110	26.09	2.95	3.22
47.85	146.5	26.09	3.49	3.75

We can see from the table that the error is of 5-6 tenths of a second for lead and less than 3 tenths for wood and my conviction that the inaccuracy is due to the way in which the experiment was organised has a confirmed by an even greater error repeated about ten years later.

461 An ebony sphere was used in an experiment on fall from the Leaning Tower of Pisa in 1993. Its diameter is on average 65.75 mm and it weighs 173.935 g. The density turned out to be ρ_{Ebony} = 1.1687 cm^3g.

462 *Harmonie Universelle, op.cit.*, p. 124: «*une boule de bois de mesme grosseur [de la boule de plomb d'une livre] ne pese aussi plus qu'une once*». In the case of a lead ball weighing 1/2 ounce the radius R_{Pb} must be $(2)^{1/2} R_{\text{Wood}}$.

Mersenne, on an uncertain date but certainly before 1644, realised that the pendulum that he was using for the second was too long. The new pendulum[463] now had a string 3 feet long [*i.e.* 0.98 *metres*], and so one simple oscillation lasted $T = \pi(0.9798/9.806)^{1/2} = 0.993$ s, with a precision of 7/1000 of a second. Mersenne had the opportunity of confirming the precision of the new pendulum with an experiment carried out on one of his journeys to Rome, between 1644 and 1646:

> [...] The observation that I made at Rome in the Basilica of St. Peter's, together with friends of renowned wit, will not be unwelcome and so it may be more easily understood, in the figure of prop. 15 of the *Balistica* let *AB* be [*the height of*] 50 toises of six feet, that is to say 300 feet [*about 98 metres*], which reproduces the height of the hemisphere or vault of St. Peter's, in French *dome*, in Italian *Cupola*.
> From the aforesaid observation it emerges that a rope firmly fixed to a point *A*, that is to say to the limit of the windows that shed light on the upper part of the hemisphere or lantern, and descending to point *B*, close to the floor of St. Peter's, to the end of which is closely joined a lead of 4 or 5 pounds, drawn out of its perpendicular *B*, towards *D*, for example at *H*, returns from *H* to *G*, that is to say it returns a single time, in the space of ten seconds: but a hundred experiments show that a rope of three feet passes a single time in the space of a second; so we see that the oscillations of the pendulum are in subduplicated [*are proportional to the square root*] ratio of the heights. However to have recollection of the circumstance, it seems to me that that rope of 300 feet passed half a second beyond the ten previous seconds; so that it was seen that lead globes dropped perpendicularly from the window A for 300 feet to the floor of St. Peter's, fell in the time of 5 and 1/2 seconds, while they should descend in 5 seconds in conformity with the quadratic ratio of the time, if the lead globe descends 12 feet in a second, agreeing with our observation.

We do not know either the diameter or the weight of the lead globes used in the experiment from the dome of St. Peter's but I do not think they would have been bigger than usual, if only because of the risk of damaging the furnishings of the church. With the radius $R = 17.3$ mm of the 1634 experiment I calculated the theoretical time, predicted by Newton's formula: the result is $t = 4.55$ s to be compared with the 5.5 oscillations observed by Mersenne. Once again the experimental result is excessive, and the error is now 20%; on the other hand, the distance of 98 metres that separates the ends of the path justifies the reduced precision. Obviously this assessment is questionable, because the size of the ball was not chosen in an objective way.

As for the oscillations of the remarkable pendulum of 99 metres, which theoretically has a period of 10 seconds, Mersenne, measuring the duration of one of its oscillations with a pendu-

[463] *F. Marini Mersenni minimi Cogitata Physico Mathematica*... Paris, 1644, pp. 37-44 and *Novarum observationum Physico-mathenaticarum F. Marini Mersenni Minimi*, tomus III, Paris, 1647. In the latter work, on p. 114 he wrote: «I wish to warn you that I have observed again and again the vibrations of any string of three feet that corresponds to a second, which must not be of 3 1/2 feet, as I had done *in harmonicis*, in which it is very easy to adjust everything to three feet». To reduce as much as possible the effect of the resistance of air, to determine the precise length of the pendulum that beats the second he made use of various types of suspension: waxed cords, hair, horsehair, thin iron or silver wires, *etc.*

lum which had a string 3 feet long, obtained 10.5 seconds, which is a good result. The difference between the two pendulums is 5% per oscillation.

Note that Mersenne changed the length of the pendulum beating the second, but he did not change the space (12 feet) that – according to him – a body in free fall travels in one oscillation, while applying Galileo's law to his last experiment in Rome, with a fall from a height of 300 feet in a time of 5.5 seconds, he would have had to reduce it to 9 feet and 11 inches per second, that is to say to $g \approx 6.5$ ms^{-1}, clearly worse compared to the 12 feet per s^{-2}.

The difficulties that have to be overcome when trying to verify Galileo's law by direct experiments on falling are very great and require adequate apparatus, as we shall soon see, and the difficulty Mersenne met with in arriving at precise results highlights the genius of Galileo who immediately abandoned direct experiments and who sought and found his law with the inclined plane. But his use of the inclined plane would not have been enough if he had not also found a way of making precise measurements of time with a pendulum, and I shall never tire of recalling that he found these instruments and this law before 1604, when Beekman, Mersenne and Descartes still had to go to school!

20.5 *Hauksbee's and Newton's experiment in St. Paul's church in London (1710)*

Francis Hauksbee is the author of an experiment that produced results which were used by Newton to verify his theory of motion with the resistance of air proportional to the square of the velocity. The experiment, published[464] with the title *Experiments concerning the Time required in the Descent of different Bodies, of different Magnitudes and Weights, in Common Air, from a certain Height*, begins at once with a description of an «apparatus to calculate exactly the time of the descent of bodies»:

> At the Height from which the Balls were to be dropt, I fix'd a contrivance in form of a Trough, in all about 4 Feet long, and the end of it, on which the balls were laid, was loose, swinging on 2 Pins at the extremity of it. This loose end was supported by a thin Piece of Board, which slid under it through a Groove from the other part of the Board: To this sliding Board was fix'd a String, which related to a small Wire that reach'd to the bottom of the Descent, where it (the Wire) had a Communication with a Contrivance, to give motion to a Pendulum which beat 1/2 Second: Now when this sliding Board (just mention'd) was drawn from under that part of the Trough on which the Balls were placed, the String thereby became so much shorten'd, as to move the Limb of that Contrivance at bottom, which dropt the Pendulum at the same instant of time, as the Balls began to Descend.

---

[464] Philosophical Transactions, Oct.-Dec. 1710, pp. 196-198. Francis Hauksbee (1666-1713), curator and experimenter for the Royal Society, a student of Robert Boyle's and collaborator of Newton's, is better known for his work in the field of the new born science of electricity. He collected his research in a book: *Physico-Mechanical experiments on various subjects containing an account of several surprizing phenomena touching light and electricity…* London, 1709.

EXPERIMENT I

The first Experiment I made, was with two Balls: One of them a thin glass Bubble, fill'd with Quicksilver; its Diameter 8 tenths of an Inch, and its Weight 840 Grains. The other Ball was a Cork, whose Diameter was 2 Inches two 10th, and its Weight 120 Grains. When these Balls were dropt, the Pendulum made 8 Vibrations, just as the Quicksilver Ball struck the Ground, and 8 more were repeated before the Cork arrived at the same place. The Pendulum vibrated 1/2 Seconds precisely

[*omissis*]

These Experiments where made from the top of the Cupola of *St. Paul's* Church, *London*, from whence to the Floor, on which the Balls were dropt, measured near 220 Feet. It is to be observ'd, that the Quicksilver Balls made no sensible Impression on the Floor on which they descended (which at that time was covered with Deal Boards) notwithstanding their Weight and Velocity of Descent.

Isaac Newton, as I have already said, inserted the results of Hauksbee's last experiment in the second edition of the *Philosophiae Naturalis Principia Matematica* (1713), without citing the author[465], to compare them with the original theory he had developed; in doing this he inserted some changes in the description of the apparatus, which should be known:

From the top of St. Paul's Church in London, in June, 1710, there were let fall together two glass globes, one full of quicksilver, the other of air; and in their fall they described a height of 220 English feet [*about* 67 *meters*]. A wooden table was suspended upon iron hinges on one side, and the other side of the table was supported by a wooden pin. The two globes lying upon this table were let fall together by pulling out the pin by means of an iron wire reaching thence down to the ground; so that, the pin being removed, the table, which had then no support but the iron hinges, fell downwards, and turning round upon the hinges, gave leave to the globes to drop off from it. At the same instant, with the same pull of the iron wire that took out the pin, a pendulum oscillating the second was let go, and began to oscillate. The diameters and weights of the globes, and their times of falling, are exhibited in the accompanying table[466].

[465] ISAAC NEWTON, *Philosophiae Naturalis Principia Mathematica*, 2nd ed. 1714, p. 325. *Mathematical Principles of Natural Philosophy*, translated by A. MOTTE, revised by F. CAJORI, *Encyclopaedia Britannica*, 1952, pp. 242. Newton was present, as president, at the two meetings of the Royal Society on 7 and 14 June 1710, at which Hauksbee presented all his experiments, some of which were later published in the article quoted, which came out at the end of that year. See the note to a letter from Cotes to Newton, in *Correspondence of Sir Isaac Newton and professor Cotes* ..., London, 1850, p. 43.

[466] ISAAC NEWTON, Latin ed. *op. cit.*, p. 326. English ed. on p. 243-244. The original editions of the *Philosophiae Naturalis Principia Mathematica* which cite Hauksbee's experiment were printed in London, in 1713 and 1726, respectively.

I have grouped the *Principia* results in two tables:

Glass spheres filled with mercury – Height from the ground: 220 feet = 67.056 m							
Weight in grains	Weight in g	Ø in inches	Ø in cm	Limit velocity v_L in ms^{-1}	Time measured in s	Theoretical time in s	Time difference in s
908	58.837	0.8	2.032	77.544	3.7	3.765	+ 0.065
983	63.697	0.8	2.032	80.683	3.7 (–)	3.760	+ 0.060
866	56.116	0.8	2.032	75.729	3.7	3.768	+ 0.068
747	40.406	0.75	1.905	75.026	3.7 (+)	3.770	+ 0.070
808	52.357	0.75	1.905	78.026	3.7	3.764	+ 0.064
784	50.802	0.75	1.905	76.851	3.7 (+)	3.766	+ 0.066

Glass spheres filled with air – Height from the ground: 220 feet = 67.056 m							
Weight in grains	Weight in g	Ø in inches	Ø in cm	Limit velocity v_L in ms^{-1}	Time measured in s	Theoretical time in s	Time difference in s
510	33.047	5.1	12.954	9.116	8.2	8.0	– 0.20
642	41.601	5.2	13.208	10.031	7.7	7.39	– 0.31
599	38.814	5.1	12.954	9.880	7.7	7.48	– 0.22
515	33.371	5.0	12.7	9.344	7.95	7.84	– 0.11
483	31.298	5.0	12.7	9.049	8.2	8.05	– 0.15
641t	41.536	5.2	13.208	10.023	7.7	7.4	– 0.30

I have added two columns to Newton's table, with the measurements in grams and in centimetres, a column for the limit velocity relative to each sphere, and then two more columns, one with the expected theoretical times and the other for the differences between the times measured (reduced by 0.3 s in accordance with the correction estimated by Newton) and the expected times.

Newton's solution was adopted in a recent edition (1993) of the experiment at Pisa, with the only addition that the weight of the board was calibrated so that the rotation was sufficiently fast so as not to be an obstacle.

The board rotates slowly and the globes do not descend exactly at the moment when the pendulum begins to move: there is a small delay, noted by Newton, but not mentioned in Hauksbee's publication: for this reason the times have to be reduced by 0.3 seconds:

> But the times observed must be corrected; for the globes of mercury (by Galileo's theory), in 4 seconds of time, will describe 257 English feet, and 220 feet in only 3 seconds 42 thirds. So that the wooden table, when the pin was taken out, did not turn upon his hinges so quickly as it ought to have done; and the slowness of that revolution hindered the descent of the globes at the beginning. For the globes lay about the middle of the table, and indeed were rather nearer to the axis upon which it turned than to the pin. And hence the times of falling were prolonged about 18 thirds (*i.e.* 18/60 = 0.3 s); and therefore ought to be corrected by subtracting that excess, especially in the larger globes, which, by reason of the largeness of their diameters, lay longer upon the revolving table than the others. This being done, the times in which the six larger globes fell will come forth 8 seconds 12 thirds, 7 seconds 42 thirds, 7 seconds 42 thirds, 7 seconds 57 thirds, 8 seconds 12 thirds, and 7 seconds 42 thirds.

Newton then went on to compare the results of Hauksbee's experiment with his theoretical prediction and chose for the comparison one of the glass balls full of air, to be precise the ball that weighed 483 grains. Since it is easier and more precise to observe differences in paths rather than differences in time, he decided to calculate the path predicted by the theory for this sphere and to compare it with the 220 feet actually travelled.

One of the most important parameters of the theoretical formula is the limit velocity of this sphere, $v_L = (16\rho Rg/3\rho_{Air})^{1/2}$, which for Newton was $v_L = 359.02$ inches s^{-1} or 29 feet 11 inches per second, (in metric units $v_L = 9.119$ ms^{-1}) while today the values of the constants lead to a slightly smaller value $v_L = 9.049$ ms^{-1}; naturally the difference is due to the constants g and ρ_{Air} to which today we give different values[467].

Newton's final formula is precisely the formula that results from a resistance proportional to the square of the velocity:

$$\exp(gx/v_L 2) = \cosh gt/v_L = (1/2)[\exp(gt/v_L) + \exp(-gt/v_L)] \,.$$

Newton does not seek the time taken, as in Mersenne's experiments, but expresses the space travelled x as a function of $t = 8.2$ s and of v_L and he succeeds, simplifying the expression, because one of the two exponentials is extremely small compared to the other:

$$\exp(-gt/v_L) = 0.00015 \ll \exp(gt/v_L) = 6771.$$

Neglecting the extremely small exponential, the equation becomes $(1/2)\exp(gt/v_L) = \exp(gx/v_L^2)$, or

$$gt/v_L = gx/v_L^2 + \ln 2$$

---

[467] It is instructive to see how the constants have changed: as for the value of the acceleration I observe that for Newton it varies from $g = 9.792$ ms^{-2} (257 English feet in 4 seconds) to $g = 9.821$ ms^{-2} (193 and 1/3 inches in a second) compared to the current value $g = 9.812$ ms^{-2} (obtained for the latitude of London from the formula for the rotating ellipsoidal Earth); while the value of the density of the air for Newton was $\rho_{Air} = 0.001166$ g cm^3 compared to the current value of $\rho_{Air} = 0.001184$ g cm^3.

I write the result in the form Newton gave it[468]:

$x = tv_L - (v_L^2/g)\ln 2 = tv_L - (16R(\rho + \rho_A)/\ 3\rho_{Air})\ \ln 2 = tv_L - (8R(\rho + \rho_A)/\ 3\rho_{Air})\ \ln 4.$

I introduce the Newtonian expression F and the data of the experiment:

$F = (8/3)\ R\ (\rho + \rho_{Air})/\ \rho_{Air} \approx 173\ 1/3$ inches ≈ 14 feet 5.5 inches,

$x = tv_L - F \ln 4 = tv_L - 1.3863F = tv_L -$ 20 feet 1/2 inch $= tv_L -$ 6.109 metres,

$t = 8.2$ s ,

$v_L = 359.02$ inches s^{-1} ,

$tv_L =$ 245 feet 4 inches,

$x =$ 225 feet .

Newton's conclusion is clear: between the distance actually travelled of 220 feet and the calculated value of 225 feet «*differentia insensibilis est*» (the difference is imperceptible).

Note that in the case of the spheres that only contain air the velocity very soon approximates to the limit velocity, and indeed dividing the whole path by the limit velocity we have a time of 7.4 seconds, in other words nearly all the space is travelled at an almost constant velocity, because, if we wish to be precise, the velocity always grows but with ever smaller values and it cannot reach its limit exactly in a finite time (Descartes, somehow, had guessed this!).

20.6 *Final comment*

This long chapter was written for two equally important reasons: the first one which we believe is immediately obvious to the reader, concerns the question of priority, put in doubt by many scholars to the benefit of their favourite authors. The documents that we have collected and carefully studied are sufficient to silence many untenable claims and to clarify many deceitful arguments; however, there is one more thing we would like to add. We have seen that Galileo had finished nearly all of his work on mechanics before his return to Florence in 1610. Until the publication of the *Dialogo* there are no scholars who had discovered anything of importance on motion, except for the reflections written from time to time in his *Journal* by Isaac Beeckman who was, however, more given to thoughts and judgements of a general nature than to the concrete application of the principles he believed in, not being as gifted as his friend Descartes

[468] Newton wrote $\rho + \rho_A$ in the formulae because for him ρ was the density in vacuum of the falling material: for this reason he added the density of the air.

with geometrical ability, which Galileo also had to a supreme degree, much less with the latter's extraordinary experimental capacity. The superficial observations on the motion of a body hanging from a wire made by Cardano raised nobody's interest, not even when Santorio, who did not cite his illustrious predecessor in the medical arts and above all did not mention Galileo, made his cryptic hint in 1603, without returning to the subject however until after the death of Gian Francesco Sagredo (1620). In 1613 Sagredo, a sincere friend and zealous defender of Galileo's discoveries, had already disputed Santorio's invention of the thermometer, naturally after having consulted Galileo who had confirmed that he was the *primo auttore et inventore* (first author and inventor) of this instrument. To know what Sagredo thought of Santorio's ability to explain how the instruments functioned , we just have to read what the Venetian aristocrat wrote to Galileo in his letter dated 15 March 1615[469]:

> He who claims to be inventor of these instruments is little able, so as not to say totally unfit, to instruct me in accordance with my need and desire, as I in vain have strained to make him understand the reason for the effects that can be seen in some of my instruments, (as I shall say) composite and multiplied.

Galileo never publicly claimed paternity of the instruments he invented throughout his life (except for the compass because forced to so by Capra) and he was wise to do so, especially with regard to the pendulum, because he thus avoided drawing attention to an instrument which measured time so precisely and which was so easy to construct. Indeed Beeckman only had to read Santorio's hint about the *pulsilogium* to discover isochronicity immediately, comparing the oscillations of the pendulum to those of the strings of musical instruments, however he never thought of using it to study motion, which for him was an assumption of purely theoretical interest. Not even Mersenne, who was interested in it for reasons associated with music, recognised its practical usefulness until the clash between Galileo and Scheiner on the time necessary for a heavy body to reach Earth from the lunar concave drove him to seek the length of the pendulum with oscillations that lasted an exact second. The ease of finding the relationship between period and length, due to the possibility of comparing the oscillations of two pendulums at the same time, should be a sufficient argument to discredit the opinion of those who claim Galileo became aware of it after Mersenne, or even learnt of it from him: as if it would take Galileo, who was so interested in the properties of the pendulum, 45 years to arrive where the scrupulous friar had arrived in a short time.

And here we arrive at the second, less obvious, motive which gave rise to the whole chapter: Mersenne began to concern himself with motion from an experimental point of view above all in order to assess the accuracy of Galileo's statements, carrying out experiments in ways that were a direct application of Galileo's text, without ever showing any original critical spirit.

In his nevertheless accurate reconstructions he never asked himself why things were not working so well, and he accused Galileo of not having done the experiments and he was the first to see him as an unscrupulous theoretician, who created mental experiments and used them as the basis of his theory: «I doubt that Mister Galileo carried out the experiments of fall on the

[469] G.G., Vol. XII, pp. 156-158. I wrote about the relationship between Galileo and Santorio in *Galileo e Pisa*, Pisa, 2004, pp. 29-34.

plane» – and then he added – «one may conclude that the experiment is not capable of giving rise to a science and that one must not trust too much to reason alone, because it does not always correspond to the truth of appearances, from which it often distances itself», but instead it is he who fills the sheets of the *Harmonie Universelle* with a quantity of measurements, without being able to separate the essential from the futile.

The inclined plane that he had built was certainly rather short, more suitable for his role as verifier than for developing research. In his experimental activities he did not have the attitude of one who wants to try and construct an organic complex of results in order to arrive at a theory on motion, rather each experiment is disconnected from the others, random, an aim in itself, precisely because he was being towed by the ideas of others, he was more a checker than a scientist, and in addition he had for Galileo mixed feelings of admiration for the scientist's intelligence and caution towards the Italian's involvement in theological questions that brought him to trial and prison.

I want to give a single example of Mersenne's inability to perceive the importance of results that were in contradiction of each other, between rolling and sliding without friction, which blocked Galileo for 30 years. The subject he dealt with in proposition VIII on p. 113 of his *Harmonie*, where he proposed to describe an inclined plane, on which a weight could descend to the centre of the Earth in such a way as always to weigh equally, is an example of his tendency towards abstraction but also of his lack of physical sensitivity. This plane had to be equally inclined with respect to the horizon, something that does not happen along all the points of a normal inclined plane, «so that it happens that it is very easy to make errors in treatises on Mechanics, that suppose inclined planes: because, although the difference of the inclinations and of their different parts is not very great, even so it can be an impediment to the truth of demonstrations that consist of the indivisible; & if the planes are very long, then the error would become perceptible & the weight that was borne in one of its points, could roll or slide on the others». After profound study of how the weight of a body on a straight plane tangent to the Earth changes when it moves away from the point of tangency he reverted to talking of a plane with constant inclination, which «should cut all the lines originating at the centre according to a same angle, and which forms a kind of helix similar to that made by a vessel sailing always according to the same course and that cuts all the meridians according to a same angle», and just as a vessel following the rhumb line can never arrive at the Pole, so the weight following this curve could never arrive at the centre of the Earth. Mersenne dedicated 6 pages to this discussion, and then continued with the next proposition, little different from the first and then goes on to describe the curve made by the point of the sphere touching the plane which according to him «describes a semi ellipse at every rotation [*in reality it traces a cycloid*]».

Let us ignore the details to concentrate on what he wrote on p. 120 in answer to a question he had asked: whether the rolling of a ball on an inclined plane is faster than its slipping or sliding:

> It is very difficult to solve and it is not easy to make an experiment of it, because we would need a perfectly smooth plane and so hard that it would not yield because of the mobile, which in turn should have the same qualities: so it is probable that the slipping would be as fast as the rolling [*sic!*]; but since one never finds a plane without pores, which are an impediment to the mobile, and that the rolling mobile does not touch almost but in a single point, we cannot have rolling that is not faster than sliding: but it is not easy to know how much the one is faster than the other.

And a little later on p. 124

> One could perhaps explain why the ball that rolls on the inclined plane goes less swiftly than when it falls perpendicularly, by the previous demonstration, saying that the part of the ball borne by the plane is a kind of counterweight, which hinders the fall of the ball as much as it can, that rolls the slower the more it is supported, as I have shown in the other propositions. Where it must be noted that it is not the same thing that the weight is weakened by the said counterweight, or that it is of a lighter material: for example, if the weight of a lead ball of one pound is so diminished by the support of the plane, that does not weigh more than an ounce, that is to say 16 times less, & that a wooden ball of the same size weighs only an ounce, it does not follow that the wooden ball does not descend perpendicularly faster than the lead one does obliquely, because it has no counterweight, or plane that hampers it, or that deviates from its straight path. But it is sufficient to consider here whether the impediment of the plane is perpetually analogous and proportional to the slowness or the velocity of the oblique fall of the ball that rolls or slides.

For me this example is sufficient to show how Mersenne was verbose, futile, imprecise, uncertain. How can anyone who credits Mersenne with inventing and first carrying out the many experiments Galileo spoke of or implied be credible? For me this is the best proof that one can give of Galileo's discoveries, I just have to think: if Mersenne did it...

21. Conclusion

Now that I have reached the end and I have done everything possible to reconstruct and follow Galileo's intellectual progress over time, assigning a probable date to the onset of his more important ideas, reflecting on what he wrote and considering it as a whole, I see that I have penetrated quite some way into the contents of Galileo's research into the laws of local motion; it has been a long journey, perhaps rather rambling, that I would like to conclude with a concise summary.

Before 1590. He made his greatest discovery, which made everything else possible: the isochronicity of the motion of a pendulum. For three centuries the oscillations of a pendulum have formed the basis of every device to measure time with accuracy. Initially Galileo became interested in the pendulum in order to examine the motion of bodies subject to gravity in a situation with minimal friction but he immediately realised that the period does not depend much on the amplitude and that it could therefore be useful to measure time in a much more precise way than any other instrument then known. He attributed the slowing-down that he observed as the amplitude increased to the friction of air: this justification is not correct but the differences have no influence on his experiments which lasted only a few seconds.

For isochronicity it is necessary for the mass of the pendulum to travel the arc of a cycloid; Huygens discovered this but he could only do so because Galileo, sixty years earlier, had found the laws of motion with a pendulum, otherwise Huygens' correction would not have existed. Clockmakers, too, followed Galileo and not the Dutchman when they built their clocks, making them ever more sophisticated in controlling the amplitude and friction. It is only after Galileo that scientists began to talk of seconds; and we cannot ignore the precision of the water clock, which he claimed to be of one tenth of a second and completely ignored by everyone.

Around 1590. In his *De motu* Galileo formulated his first law concerning local motion: the principle of inertia. Galileo's greatness lies in having insisted throughout his life that this principle is only locally valid, because gravity, inevitably present in our world, is directed towards the centre[470]. For him the principle valid on a large scale is the principle of the conservation of circular motion, which was held against him as a grave error, while it is actually the recognition of another law of nature, the conservation of angular momentum.

[470] Just as Einstein did with his principle of equivalence.

Around 1590. While studying the motion of wax spheres weighed down in water with lead filings he discovered the properties of surface tension, adhesion and the phenomenon of wettability. With spheres of specific weight barely greater than that of water he studied the properties of motion at constant velocity.

Around 1590. Again in the *De motu*, Galileo began to talk about the inclined plane and about the experiments that can be carried out with this apparatus, having shown that the effective force varies with the sine of the angle of inclination. At the same time he discovered the theorem of chords, which proved essential for the study of motion on the inclined plane.

Between 1592 and 1600. He enunciated the «Principle of the centre of gravity» and found experimentally that the times of descent along planes of the same height are inversely proportional to their lengths. Thus a new concept of velocity was born, different from the Aristotelian one.

Before 1604. By experimenting with the pendulum Galileo had already found, the law of the fall of heavy bodies: «So the distances from the beginning of the motion are as the squares of the times and, dividing the spaces passed in equal times, are like odd numbers *ab unitate*».

Before 1607. Galileo studied the motion of a body launched transversally and discovered the parabolic trajectory and, as he would then explain in the *Discorsi*, the law of composition of velocities: «supposing, that is to say that the transversal motion always stays uniform, and that the natural *deorsum* equally keeps its course, proceeding always accelerating according to the doubled proportion of the times, and that such motions and their velocities, as they mix together, do not alter, perturb and impede, so that finally the line of the projected body does not, as the motion continues, degenerate into other kinds ». *Velocity became a vector.*

Before 1610. In his experiments Galileo used the relationship, valid for any path, between the final velocity of a body that descends from stationary and the vertical height from which it comes: it is a special case of conservation of mechanical energy.

At an uncertain date but probably while still at Padua. Galileo invented the «constant-flux chronograph», an apparatus that allowed short periods of time to be measured with the extraordinary accuracy of a few fractions of a second.

1628-1632. He wrote and published the «Dialogo sopra i due massimi sistemi del mondo». He thus made the most important principles of his mechanics universally known.

1634-1638. «He wrote and published the «Discorsi intorni a due nuove scienze». The long period of reflection, during which Galileo confronted the contradictions he had met with, comes to its conclusion; he resumed writing his treatise concerning «Mechanics & Local Movements» which he had kept in abeyance for twenty years; he rediscovered his interest in research giving birth to the *third* new science, the science of collisions, and so he arrived at his final discoveries. The instruments that he believed to be most suitable for this new research were two new machines, one with a pulley suspended vertically and the other with a pulley applied to an inclined plane. The use of these two machines led inevitably to other remarkable results, of which he left some traces:

a) the confirmation of the principle of inertia in motion in arbitrary directions, when the resultant of the forces acting on the system is zero,

b) the different contribution of inertial mass and of gravitational mass to motion,

c) the more precise determination of the acceleration constant *g*,

d) the study of completely inelastic collisions between equal masses and between different masses.

I conclude by inviting you to bear in mind the distance that separates the time when Galileo obtained his laws of motion (at Pisa from 1589 to 1692 and at Padua from 1593 to 1610) from the time when the scholars who followed in his footsteps were active; it is sufficient to list their names with their dates of birth: Marin Mersenne (1588) - Isaac Beeckman (1588) - Pierre Gassendi (1592) - Renée Descartes (1596) - Pierre de Fermat (1601) - Gilles Roberval (1602) - Blaise Pascal (1623) - Christiaan Huygens (1629).

Appendix A: Solution to Newton's equation for motion with resistance proportional to velocity

For a sphere the equation of motion with resistance proportional to velocity is

$$[(4/3)\,\pi\, r^3\rho]\; dv/dt = (4/3)\,\pi\, r^3(\rho - \rho_0)g - 6\,\pi\eta\, rv.$$

The second member forces are: gravity $F_G = (4/3)\pi r^3\rho g$, buoyancy $F_A = (4/3)\pi r^3\rho_0 g$ and the resistance of the fluid $F_{Re} = 6\,\pi\eta\, rv$, with

ρ = density of the sphere,
ρ_0 = density of the fluid,
r = radius of the sphere,
g - 9.806 ms^{-2} ,
η = viscosity of the fluid which for water is $\eta = 0.81\cdot 10^{-3}$ Nsm^{-2} at 25°C.

The acceleration is

$$dv/dt = (\rho - \rho_0)\, g/\rho - (9/2\rho r^2)\,\eta\, v.$$

If we introduce the expressions

$$v_L = 2r^2 g(\rho - \rho_0)/\,9\eta,$$
$$\tau = 2r^2\rho/\,9\eta,$$

the equation takes the simplified form

$$dv/dt = (v_L - v)/\tau\,.$$

By integrating the equation $(v_L - v)^{-1}\, d(v - v_L) = d(t/\tau)$ once, supposing the initial velocity to be zero, we obtain the velocity as a function of time,

$$v(t) = v_L\,[1 - \exp(-t/\tau)].$$

We see that for $t \rightarrow \infty$, $v(\infty) = v_L$. Integrating again we arrive at

$$s(t) = v_L\,[t + \tau\exp(-t/\tau) - \tau].$$

If $t/\tau << 1$, the exponential can be developed in series stopping at the quadratic term:

$$x(t) = x(t_0) + v_L\{t + \tau[1 - t/\tau + (t/\tau)^2/2 - \ldots] - \tau\} = (v_L/2\,\tau)\, t^2 - \ldots$$

In this case motion in water can be treated as a uniformly accelerated motion with acceleration

$$\alpha^T = v_L/\tau = g(\rho - \rho_{water})/\rho.$$

To compare the velocities of two spheres, for example the velocities of A and B, it is necessary to compare the spaces travelled in the same time Δt after letting a time t_C pass so that the velocity of the spheres is not too far from their limit velocity v_L.

$$\begin{aligned} v_A/v_B &= [s_A(t_C + \Delta t) - s_A(t_C)]/[s_B(t_C + \Delta t) - s_B(t_C)] = \alpha_A^T / \alpha_B^T \\ &= [(\rho_A - \rho_{water})/(\rho_B - \rho_{water})]\ \rho_B/\rho_A \\ &\approx (\rho_A - \rho_{water})/(\rho_B - \rho_{water}). \end{aligned}$$

Appendix B: The theory of violent motion according to Galileo

This is how Galileo illustrated his theory of impressed force[471]:

> Since, then, a heavy mobile [...] in going down is moved more slowly at the beginning, it is therefore necessary that it be less heavy at the beginning of its motion than in the middle or at the end; for we know with certainty, from the things demonstrated in the first book, that speed and slowness follow heaviness and lightness. If, then, it is found out how and why a mobile is less heavy at the beginning, the cause for which it goes down more slowly will certainly have been found. But the natural and intrinsic heaviness of the mobile is certainly not diminished, since neither its size nor its density is diminished: it remains, therefore, that that diminution of heaviness is against nature and accidental.
>
> Hence if we have found in what way the heaviness of the mobile is diminished against nature and extrinsically, what we need will surely have been found. But that heaviness is not diminished by the heaviness of the medium, for the medium is the same at the beginning of motion as at the middle: it remains, therefore, that the heaviness of the mobile is diminished by some violence that is extrinsic and comes from outside (for it is only in these two ways that a mobile gets to be light by accident).
>
> If then, again, we find out how a mobile could be lifted by an extrinsic force, the cause of slowness, again, will have been found. Now the force impressed by a thrower not only at times diminishes the heaviness of a heavy thing, but it often even renders it so light that it flies upward with great speed: hence let us see and search attentively, whether perhaps this force is the cause of the diminishing of the heaviness of the mobile at the beginning of its motion.
>
> And, I say, it certainly is that force impressed by the thrower which renders natural motion weaker at the beginning: so let us hasten to make clear by what method it is able to accomplish this.
>
> For a heavy mobile to be able to be moved upward violently, an impelling force greater than the resisting heaviness[472] is necessary; otherwise the resisting heaviness would not be able to be overcome, and, consequently, the heavy thing would not be able to be carried upward. Hence, the mobile is carried upward, provided the motive impressed force is greater than

---

[471] G.G., Vol. I, *De motu*, pp. 318-320.

[472] *I.e.*, greater than its weight.

> the resisting heaviness.. Now since this force, as has been demonstrated[473] – , is continuously diminished, it will finally become so diminished that it will no longer overcome the heaviness of the mobile, and then it will not impel the mobile any further: but that impressed force will not therefore have been annihilated at the end of the violent motion, but it will only be diminished to the point that it no longer surpasses the heaviness of the mobile, but it will be equal to it; and, to put it in a word, the impelling force, which is lightness[474], will no longer dominate in the mobile, but will have been reduced to parity with the heaviness of the mobile: and then, at the ultimate point of the violent motion, the mobile will be neither heavy nor light. But, moreover, as the impressed force diminishes in its own way, the heaviness of the mobile begins to predominate; and hence the mobile starts to go down. But since at the beginning of such a descent a great deal of force that impels the body upward, which is lightness, still remains (even though it is no longer greater than the heaviness of the mobile), it comes about that the proper heaviness of the mobile is diminished by this lightness, and, consequently, that the motion at the beginning is slower. And, moreover, since that extrinsic force is further weakened, the heaviness of the mobile is increased by having less resistance, and the mobile is moved still faster. And I believe this to be the true cause of the acceleration of the motion.

A little later he also analysed the case in which there is no violent motion at the beginning, examining the situation of a stone dropped from stationary[475].

> I say, then, that it is for the same reason that motions, which a violent motion does not precede, are also moved more slowly at the beginning. For even in motions which a violent [motion] does not precede, the mobile begins to be moved, from a state of rest, and not from a violent motion. Thus a stone projected upward, when it begins to be moved downward from that extreme point at which there is equality between the impelling force and the resisting heaviness, which is a state of rest, begins to go down; this is the same thing as if it were falling from someone's hand. For even when the stone falls from someone's hand, with no force impelling it upward having been impressed on it, it leaves with a quantity of impressed force equal to its heaviness. For when the stone is at rest in someone's hand, one must not say that in that case he who holds it impresses no force on the stone: for since the stone exerts pressure downward by its heaviness, it is necessary that it be impelled upward by the hand with an equal quantity of force, neither larger nor smaller[476]. For if the force, by which the hand impels the stone upward, was greater than the heaviness of the stone, the resisting stone would be raised by the hand; and it would not be at rest, as we are presupposing: but, on the other hand, if the stone exerted more weight than the hand lifted, the stone would proceed downwards; now we are presupposing that the stone is at rest in the hand: hence

---

473 The demonstration follows a few lines later.

474 Later, on p. 332, Galileo explained: «Indeed from now on we shall call the impressed virtue lightness».

475 G.G., Vol. I, *De motu*, p. 320.

476 Here *the principle of action and reaction* is affirmed in the special and evident case of contact forces.

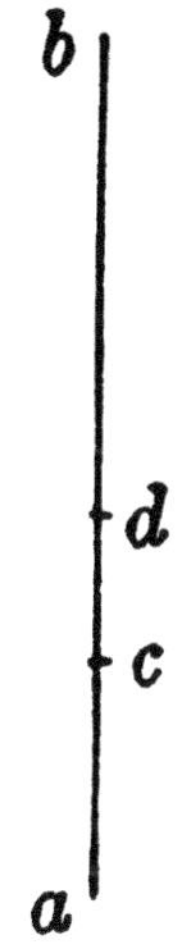

Fig. B.1

there is impressed in the stone, by the hand or by whatever else by which it is controlled, as much force impelling upward as there is heaviness of the stone tending downward; nevertheless the stone is not raised, because, as we have said, that impelling force cannot surpass the resisting heaviness, since it is not greater than that heaviness. It is thus evident how, when the stone comes out of the hand, it leaves with a quantity of impressed force equal to its heaviness: which is not different from what happens when the stone starts to proceed downward, having completed its upward motion; for in that case too, when it recedes from the state of rest, it leaves with a quantity of force equal to its heaviness: hence for the same reason it is moved more slowly at the beginning in the case of that motion, just as in the case of this one.

The accelerated motion must end however in a uniform motion; the first argument concerns the continuous reduction of velocity in upward motion[477]:

[...] since this is so, and since violent motion is not without end, it necessarily follows that that force, impressed by the thrower, is continuously weakened in the projectile; and that there cannot be given in that motion two points of time in which the motive force is the same and is not weakened. In order that this may be even more clearly apparent, I shall use this demonstration: by first presupposing that the same mobile, in the same medium and along the same line, is moved by the same force with the same speed.
This having been presupposed, let the line on which the motion takes place be line ab; and let the motion take place from a to b; and, if it can be done, let there be found on line ab two points at which the impelling force is the same, and let them be *c,d* (fig.B.1). Since, then, at *c* and at *d* the motive force is the same, the medium is the same, the mobile is the same, and the line along which the motion takes place is the same, therefore the mobile will be moved

[477] G.G., Vol. I, *De motu*, p. 315. See how he treats the same subject on p. 390 and on pp. 405-406.

> from point *d* at the same speed as it has been moved from point *c*: but from point *c* it has been moved so as to be carried from point *c* to *d* always at the same speed, and the force has not ended up to be weaker. Therefore from point *d* also it will be moved at the same speed along a line equal to *cd*, the impressed force having stayed the same. For there is no greater reason why the force should stay the same from *c* to *d*, but not from *d* along a line toward *b* equal to line *cd*, since the force is the same, the mobile is the same, the medium is the same, and the line of motion is the same. For there is no greater reason why the force should stay the same from *c* to *d*, but not from *d* along a line toward *b* equal to line *cd*, since the force is the same, the mobile is the same, the medium is the same, and the line of motion is the same. Hence, repeating the same argumentation, it will be demonstrated that violent motion is never weakened, but is carried always at the same speed and without end, with the motive force always staying the same: which is truly very absurd: hence it is not true that in violent motion two points can be assigned in which the impelling force stays the same.

So the velocity of a stone thrown upwards is always reduced until it arrives at a maximum height when the impressed force and the gravity are equal, it is the inflection point where the mobile cannot remain at rest for a finite time however small, because if it did it would remain there for ever but must descend immediately with a velocity that increases with the same progression with which the impressed force decreased. So once the impressed force is exhausted bodies move naturally towards the centre of the Earth with constant velocity. The dissipation of the impressed force is continuous – *continue remittitur* – he wrote: so once again his considerations would have led him to discuss how velocity must change with time, but Galileo stopped here, he was not able to tackle the subject, he did not have a quantitative rule to describe the hypothetical transitory phase which, in experiments in air, never seemed to end.
Galileo went as far as to say also that he had carried out experiments[478]:

> For since the mobile is accelerated because the contrary force weakens continuously, and the natural heaviness is being acquired, it will stand to reason that all the contrary force will finally be lost, and that the natural heaviness will be resumed, and that, therefore, the cause having been removed, the acceleration will cease. [...]For, in the first place, if we look at something that is not at all heavy coming from on high, a ball of wool or a feather or some such thing, we will see that it is moved more slowly at the beginning, but that nevertheless, a little later, it will observe a uniform motion. Now the reason why this appears more manifest in things that are less heavy is that, when these things begin to be moved, since they have an amount of the contrary force equal to their proper heaviness, and they themselves are not very heavy, hence, the contrary impressed force will also be small, and thus it will be consumed more swiftly; when it has been consumed, these things will be moved with a uniform motion: and since they are moved slowly, it will be easier to observe the uniformity of such a motion in them than in the case of those that go down very swiftly. Now in the case of heavier things, since a great amount of contrary force must be consumed in their descent, a greater time will be required for it to be consumed; in which time, since they are carried

[478] G.G., Vol. I, *De motu*, pp. 328-329.

> swiftly, they will descend a great distance: since we cannot avail ourselves of such great distances from which to release heavy things, it is not astonishing if the stone, released from merely the height of a tower, will seem to accelerate all the way to the ground; for this short distance and short time of motion are not sufficient to destroy the whole contrary force.

The argument is presented almost in the same way in the third treatise, in which Domenico and Alessandro discuss with each other[479]:

> ALESSANDRO: That this is opposed to the opinion of many, is of no concern to me, so long as it is coherent with reason and experience, even though sometimes experience points rather to the contrary. For if a stone goes down from a high tower, its swiftness seems always to be increased: yet this happens because the stone, in comparison with the medium through which it is carried, namely air, is very heavy; and since it goes away with an amount of impressed force as great as its heaviness, it assuredly goes away with a great impressed force, which the motion from the height of a tower is not sufficient to consume, so that the swiftness is always intensified all through the height of a single tower. Now if we were to take a certain heavy thing, whose heaviness would not so very far surpass the heaviness of air, assuredly we would then see with our own eyes that this thing, a little after the beginning of its motion, would always be moved uniformly, provided however that the air was very calm. And we would observe the same thing happen in the case of a stone, if it were let down from a very high place, and we were so placed as always to observe the line of motion according to the same disposition. For even our position hinders us from apprehending the uniformity of the motion.

[479] G.G., Vol. I, *De motu*, pp. 406-407.

Appendix C: A body is faster than another when it travels the same space in less time

So far we have seen the importance Galileo attributed to the second Aristotelian definition of velocity but the first definition of velocity also played a significant role, above all in the study of situations when the times of paths travelled that are equal to each other in length, but arranged differently, have to be compared, which is the situation discussed in theorem IV of the third day of the *Discorsi*:

> The times of motions on planes that are equal but inclined differently, are to each other just as the square root of the inverse ratio between the heights of those planes[480].

In fig. C.1 there are two inclined planes, *AC* and *AD*, of equal height. The circumference of radius *AE* marks on the inclined plane *AC* point *G* so that $AG = AE$.
From the first definition of velocity:

«a body is faster than another when it travels the same space in less time »

we obtain that the ratio between the (constant) velocities on the two planes *AD* and *AC* is given by the ratio between the times necessary to travel the spaces *AG* and *AE*, equal to each other.

$V_{AD}/V_{AC} = V_{AE}/V_{AG} = t_{AG}/t_{AE}$ (first definition of velocity).

Note that for the fundamental theorem of the inclined plane the chords *AE* and *AF* are travelled in the same time, which is greater than the time necessary to travel $AG < AF$.
From the second definition of velocity:

«a body is faster than another when it travels more space in the same time»

we obtain that *AE* and *AF* are travelled in the same time, and we have seen that the ratio between the velocities on the two planes *AD* and *AC* is given by the inverse ratio of their lengths:

$V_{AD}/V_{AC} = AC/AD.$

---

[480] G.G., Vol. VIII, *Discorsi*, p. 219: «*Tempora lationum super planis aequalibus, sed inequaliter inclinatos, sunt inter se in subdupla ratione elevationum eorumdem planorum permutatim accepta*».

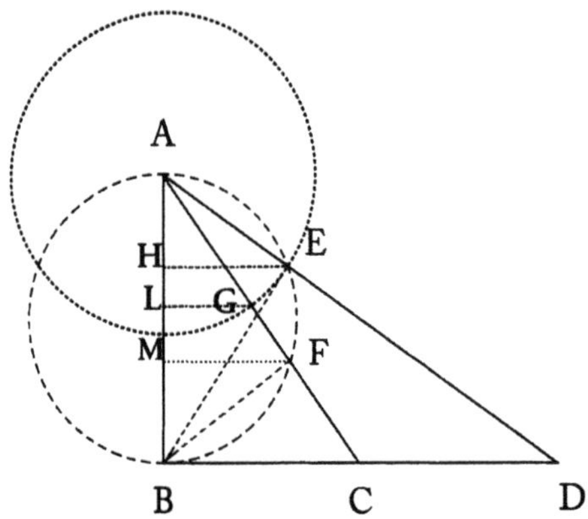

Fig. C.1

I am concerned by the criticism, often made when formulas are introduced, that it seems that by doing so we anticipate thoughts and formalisms that would appear much later; so I shall carefully try to avoid the risk of appearing anachronistic. In order to proceed writing more compactly I shall make use of the following convention, in which the symbol $\Psi(t)$ is not a function but replaces systematically the writing next to it:

$AE = (AB/AD)\ \Psi(t_{AE})$ is the space travelled in the time t_{AE} on a plane inclined at an angle with sine AB/AD,
$AG = (AB/AC)\ \Psi(t_{AG})$ is the space travelled in the time t_{AG} on a plane inclined at an angle with sine AB/AC,
$AF = (AB/AC)\ \Psi(t_{AF})$ is the space travelled in the time t_{AF} on a plane inclined at an angle with sine AB/AC.

With this convention I can write

$\Psi(t_{AE}) = [AE \otimes AD]/AB$ which is the space travelled in the time t_{AE} multiplied by AD/AB,
$\Psi(t_{AG}) = [AG \otimes AC]/AB$ which is the space travelled in the time t_{AG} multiplied by AC/AB,
$\Psi(t_{AF}) = [AF \otimes AC]/AB$ which is the space travelled in the time t_{AF} multiplied by AC/AB.

The ratio $\Psi(t_{AE})/\ \Psi(t_{AG})$ is given by

$$\Psi(t_{AE})/\ \Psi(t_{AG}) = \{[AE \otimes AD]/AB\}\ /\ \{[AG \otimes AC]/AB\} = \{AE \otimes AD\}\ /\ \{AG \otimes AC\}.$$

But $AE = AG$ and so

$$\Psi(t_{AE})/\ \Psi(t_{AG}) = AD/\ AC = AL/AH.$$

This relationship may be useful if one wishes to find the quantity $\Psi(t)$ and it has been understood that a pendulum can be used to divide time in equal parts.

Consider fig. C.1, in which *AG* is the hypotenuse of the right-angled triangle of which *AL* is a cathetus. Let us suppose that we have found the distance *AL* on the vertical such that a ball, starting from rest from *A*, travels the distance *AG* on the plane *AC* in the time of one oscillation of the pendulum. Now let us increase the inclination of the plane, seeking the height *AH* for which the ball departing from rest from *A*, travels the distance *AE* = *AG* (in fig. C.1 *AE* is the hypotenuse of the right angled triangle of which *AH* is a cathetus) on the plane *AD* exactly in two oscillations: we will find that the ratio of the heights is *AH*:*AL* = 1:4.
Repeating these experiments for different inclinations and varying the number of oscillations of the pendulum, the results suggest consistently that the quantity $\Psi(t)$ is proportional to the square of the time.

I just wish to stress that the experiment was thought of strictly in the context of Aristotelian physics which, in cases in which differences of time and instantaneous values of velocity are not involved, leads to correct results: it is a physics of integral equations, unlike Newtonian physics which is a physics of differential equations. The *integral* definition of the velocity allows the motion of two bodies to be compared correctly, within the limits that have been indicated, as long as one accepts that the sine of the angle of inclination is a multiplying factor.

If we introduce the correct temporal dependence explicitly, we obtain from $\Psi(t_{AE})/\Psi(t_{AG}) = t_{AE}^2/t_{AG}^2$ a remarkable result:

$$t_{AE}/t_{AG} = [AL/AH]^{1/2},$$

which is the enunciation of theorem IV of the third day of the *Discorsi*:
The ratio $\Psi(t_{AE})/\Psi(t_{AF})$ also follows an interesting relationship:

$$\Psi(t_{AE})/\Psi(t_{AF}) = \{[AE\otimes AD]/AB\} / \{[AF\otimes AC]/AB\} = [AE\otimes AD] / [AF\otimes AC] = [AE/AF]\otimes[AD/AC].$$

Since the triangles *ADB* and *AEH* are similar we have *AD*/*AE* = *AB*/*AH*.
The triangles *ACB* and *AFM* are also similar and so *AC*/*AF* = *AB*/*AM*.
But, therefore, *AD*/*AC* = (*AE*/*AF*)(*AM*/*AH*) and by substitution we obtain

$$\Psi(t_{AE})/\Psi(t_{AF}) = [AE/AF]^2 [AM/AH].$$

If we set $\Psi(t_{AE}) = k\, t_{AE}^{\,2}$ and $\Psi(t_{AG}) = k\, t_{AG}^{\,2}$, we obtain

$$t_{AE} / t_{AG} = [AE/AF]\, [AM/AD]^{1/2},$$

which is theorem V of the third day of the *Discorsi*.

> The ratio of the times of descent on inclined planes, with different inclinations and lengths, and also different heights, consists of the ratio of the lengths of the same planes and of the square root of the inverse ratio of their heights[481].

[481] G.G., Vol. VIII, *Discorsi*, p. 220: «*Ratio temporum descensum super planis, quorum diversae sint inclinationes et longitudines, nec non elevationes inaequales, componitur ex ratione longitudinum ipsorum planorum et ex ratione subdupla elevationum eorumdem permutatim accepta*».

In conclusion, part of the structure of the third day of the *Discorsi* can be traced back to the two Aristotelian definitions of velocity, because only geometrical considerations are present in its theorems. Galileo only needed to determine how the space travelled depended on time: all his research in his first few years at Padua would be dedicated to the determination of $\Psi(t)$, which he would arrive at when he managed to find the right experiment which could give him the answer he wanted.

Appendix D: Study of the effect of rolling along a guide channel

Let the following be (fig. D1):
m: mass of the ball,
r: radius of the ball,
G: the ball's centre of gravity,
v: translation velocity of the ball's centre of mass,
$I = (2/5)mr^2$: moment of inertia of the ball with regard to G,
c: width of the groove,
d: diameter of the ball,
α: angle of inclination of the plane,
$\sin \alpha$ = height of the plane/length of the plane = H/L,
g: acceleration of gravity,
g_A: deceleration by static friction.

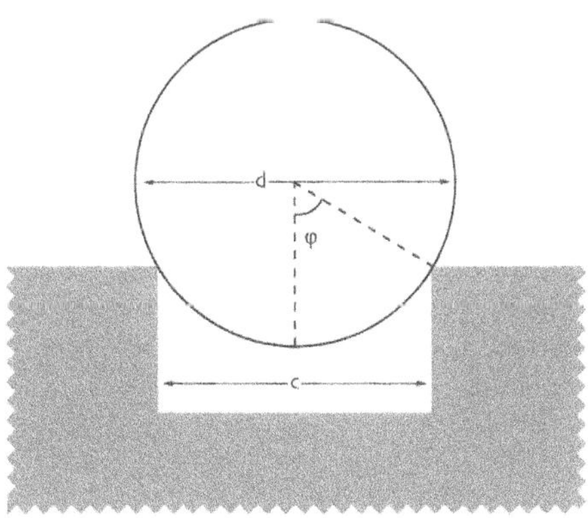

Fig. D.1

A simple way of obtaining the acceleration along the inclined plane is to write that the increment in kinetic energy of translation and rotation must be equal to the work of the external forces. Given that the force of friction f does not carry out work when the ball rolls without sliding on the plane from the point of departure to distance x, we must have

$$[m\, v^2 + I\, \omega^2]\ /2 = x\, m\, (g \sin \alpha - g_A).$$

The distance between the axis passing through the two points of contact and the centre of the sphere is $r \cos \varphi$.

Let us introduce into the equation the relationship between the angular velocity and the translation velocity of the ball:

$$\omega = v/(r \cos \varphi),$$

and the moment of inertia of the sphere

$$I = (2/5)mr^2;$$

we have

$$1/2m\, v^2\, [1 + 2/(5 \cos^2 \varphi)] = x\, m\, (g \sin \alpha - g_A)$$

$$v^2 = 2x\, (g \sin \alpha - g_A) \cos^2\varphi / [\cos^2 \varphi + 2/5].$$

Given that $\sin \varphi = c/d$, we have: $\cos^2\varphi = 1 - (c/d)^2$ and the equation is written as

$$v^2 = 2Kx\, (g \sin \alpha - g_A)$$

with $K = [1 - (c/d)^2]\, [7/5 - (c/d)^2]^{-1}$.

Deriving with respect to time

$$a = [g \sin \alpha - g_A]\, K,$$

$$a = [g(h/L) - g_A]\, K.$$

Making $c = 0$, we obtain the well-known relationship for the space travelled $s(t)$:

$$s(t) = (5/14)\, [g(h/L) - g_A]\, t^2.$$

Acknowledgements and thanks

I owe the gift of the large inclined plane and the inclined plane with the pulley to the generosity of Alessandro Tantussi who agreed to have the wooden parts constructed at his company's expense, entrusting them to the skills of Francesco Ferrante who built them. The great weigh scales for the study of percussion were built by the firm «Antolini Bilance s.r.l.» and was a personal gift for which I am extremely grateful to Mario and Gabriele Antolini.

Stefano Gennai created the metal part of the two inclined planes and completed the scales; he also built the marvellous Galilei's Machine, the apparatus for proving isochronicity with wooden and bronze pendulums and the pulsilogium and other equipment for the *Laboratorio di Galileo Galilei.* Mario Montanari built the water clock. The electronic apparatus for the inclined planes and for Galileo's machine were designed and built by Alessandro Masetti. Alberto Di Lieto designed and created the software interfaces of the electronic controls, projected the electronic schemes and I turned to him for the statistical analyses of the measurements regarding Folio 107v. I discussed some results with Riccardo Mannella and I also owe to him the analysis of an experiment for measuring *K*, carried out with the plane in a horizontal position, an analysis that showed the inconsistency of the results and thus led to the elimination of the experiment from this book. Maurizio Meliani took the photographs of the equipment and of the details and produced the photograph of Galilei's machine, Beatrice Rapisarda produced the other photographs.

Finally, Stefano Gennai and Maurizio Meliani, helped me in acquiring the data of some experiments. My grateful thanks go to all those worked with me.

The Department of Physics "Enrico Fermi" of Università di Pisa, the INFN – Istituto Nazionale di Fisica Nucleare – Sezione di Pisa, and the Fondazione Galileo Galilei, Pisa, have contributed as institutions with their support to the realization of the experimental apparata and of the experiments.

It is a great sadness to me that Prof. G.F. Bassani is no more with us and cannot see the completion of this volume, that he suggested some years ago that I should write. To him go my affectionate memories.

Finally I would like to thank Christine Pennison for her excellent and faithful translation in which she succeeded in conveying unchanged my way of expressing myself, and Angela Oleandri for her accurate editing which she carried out with an acute spirit of observation and great scientific knowledge.

Grants for reproductions

The illustrations in the figures listed below are reproduced by kind permission of *Ministero per i Beni e le Attività Culturali della Repubblica Italiana / Biblioteca Nazionale Centrale di Firenze*; any reuse, reproduction by any means or storage in data banks is not allowed without the previous written permission of *Biblioteca Nazionale Centrale di Firenze.*

p. 18: Ms. Gal. 74, f. 16r
p. 68: Fig. 2.18, Ms. Gal. 71, f. 27; Fig. 2.19, Ms. Gal. 71, f. 31
p. 69: Fig. 2.20 a, b, Ms. Gal. 71, f. 29 and f. 97; Fig. 2.21, Ms. Gal. 71, f. 49
p. 93: Fig. 2.26, Ms. Gal. 71, f. 95v
p. 103: Fig. 2.30, Ms. Gal. 72, f. 151r
p. 138: Fig. 6.1, Ms. Gal. 72, f. 128r
p. 142: Fig. 7.1, Ms. Gal. 72, f. 107v
p. 160: Fig. 8.4, Ms. Gal. 72, f. 164v
p. 170: Fig. 10.1, Ms. Gal. 72, f. 116v, upper part
p. 171: Fig. 10.2, Ms. Gal. 72, f. 116v, lower part
p. 176: Fig. 11.1, Ms. Gal. 72, f. 114v
p. 183: Fig. 12.1, Ms. Gal. 72, f. 163v
p. 184: Fig. 12.2, Ms. Gal. 72, part of f. 174r
p. 191: Fig. 13.1, Ms. Gal. 72, f. 147v
p. 192: Fig. 13.2, Ms. Gal. 72, f. 147v (corner).

Quotations of the *De motu* on the following pages:

p. 21 [G.G., Vol. I, *De motu*, p. 335]
p. 22 [G.G, Vol. I, *De motu*, p. 413]
p. 30, footnote [G.G., Vol. I, *De motu*, p. 263]
p. 31 [G.G., Vol. I, *De Motu*, p. 380]
p. 32 [G.G., Vol. I, *De Motu*, p. 281]
p. 32 [G.G., Vol. I, *De motu*, pp. 406-407]
pp. 32-33 [G.G., Vol. I, *De motu*, p. 272]
p. 33 [G.G., Vol. I, *De motu*, pp. 272-273]
p. 33-34 [G.G., Vol. I, *De motu*, pp. 402-403]
p. 34 [G.G., Vol. I, *De motu*, p. 403]

pp. 34-35 [G.G., Vol. I, *De motu*, p. 404]
p. 35 [G.G., Vol. I, *De motu*, p. 273]
p. 35 [G.G., Vol. I, *De motu*, p. 380]
p. 36 [G.G., Vol. I, *De motu*, p. 264]
p. 39 [G.G., Vol. I, *De Motu*, p. 379.]
pp. 39-40 [G.G., Vol. I, *De Motu*, p. 379]
p. 52 [G.G., Vol. I, *De motu*, p. 264]
pp. 52-53 [G.G., Vol. I, *De motu*, p. 265]
p. 60 [G.G., Vol. I, *De motu*, p. 414] repeated on p. 73 [G.G., Vol. I, *De motu*, p. 414]
p. 78 [G.G., Vol. I, *De motu*, p. 314]
pp. 78-79 [G.G., Vol. I, *De motu*, p. 266]
p. 87[G.G., Vol. I, *De motu*, pp. 252-253]
p. 88 [G.G.,Vol. I, *De motu*, a) p. 388, b) p. 413]
p. 89 [G.G., Vol. I, *De motu*, pp. 311-312]
p. 89 [G.G., Vol. I, *De motu*, pp. 374]
pp. 90-91 [G.G., Vol. I, *De motu*, pp. 336-337]
p. 91 [G.G., Vol. I, *De motu*, pp. 334-335]
p. 94 [G.G., Vol. I, *De motu*, p. 297]
p. 94 [G.G., Vol. I, *De motu*, p. 297]
p. 94 [G.G., Vol. I, *De motu*, p. 296]
p. 99 [G.G., Vol. I, *De motu*, p. 301]
p. 100 [G.G., Vol. I, *De motu*, pp. 301-302]
p. 104-105 [G.G., Vol. I, *De motu*, pp. 298-299]
p. 106 [G.G., Vol. I, *De motu*, pp. 300-301]
p. 107 [G.G., Vol. I, *De motu*, p. 274]
p. 108 [G.G., Vol. I, *De motu*, p. 297]
p. 119, footnote [G.G., Vol. I, *De motu*, p. 412]
p. 120 [G.G., Vol. I, *De motu*, p. 398]
pp. 279-280 [G.G., Vol. I, *De motu*, pp. 318-319]
pp. 280-281 [G.G., Vol. I, *De motu*, p. 320]
pp. 281-282 [G.G., Vol. I, *De motu*, p. 315]
pp. 282-283 [G.G., Vol. I, *De motu*, pp. 328-329]
p. 283 [G.G., Vol. I, *De motu*, pp. 406-407]

are reproduced from the translation by Raymond Fredette
that is freely available on the internet at

http://archimedes.mpiwg-berlin.mpg.de/cgi-bin/toc/toc.cgi

http://archimedes.mpiwgberlin.mpg.de/cgibin/toc/
toc.cgi?dir=galil_demot_094_en_2000;step=textonly

Quotations of the *Dialogo* on the following pages:

p. 48 [G.G., Vol. VII, p. 275]:
p. 98 [G.G., vol. VII, *Dialogo*, p. 50]:
pp. 157-158 [G.G., Vol VII, p. 249]
p. 159 G.G., Vol. VII, p. 248]
p. 205 [G.G., Vol. VII, p. 69]
p. 206 [G.G., Vol. VII, pp. 50-51]
p. 206 [G.G., Vol. VII, p. 225]
pp. 206-207 [G.G., Vol. VII, , p. 248]:
p. 207 [G.G., Vol. VII, p. 52]
p. 207 [G.G., Vol. VII, p. 252]
p. 207-208 [G.G., Vol. VII, p. 47]
p. 217 e 240 [G.G., vol. VII, p. 54]
p. 218 [G.G. Vol. VII, p. 46]
pp. 222-223 [G.G., Vol. VII, pp. 260-261]
p. 223 [G.G., Vol. VII, pp. 270-271]
p. 228 [G.G., Vol. VII, p. 240]
p. 250 [G.G., Vol. VII, pp. 50-51]
p. 250, footnote [G.G., Vol. VII, p. 248]

are reproduced by permission from
GALILEO GALILEI, *Dialogue Concerning the Two Chief World Systems, Ptolemaic and Copernican,* Second Revised Edition, translated and edited by Stillman Drake. © 1962, 1967, Regents of the University of California. Published by the University of California Press.

Quotations of the *Discorsi* on the following pages:

p. 8, footnote [G.G., Vol. VIII, pp. 323-325]
p. 9 [G.G.,Vol VIII, p. 343-344]
pp. 12-13, footnote [G.G., Vol. VIII, p. 345]
p. 25 [G.G., Vol.VIII, pp. 128-129]
p. 100 [G.G., Vol.VIII, *Discorsi*, pp. 221-223]
p. 101, footnote [G.G., Vol. VIII, p. 286]
p. 103, footnote [G.G., Vol. VIII, p. 216]
p. 153 [G.G., Vol. VIII, pp. 212-213]
p. 200 [G.G., Vol. VIII, pp. 212-213]
p. 155 [G.G., Vol.VIII, pp.185-186]
p. 164, footnote [G.G., Vol.VIII, pp. 86-87]
p. 173 [G.G., Vol. VIII, *Discorsi*, p. 294]
p. 181 [G.G., Vol. VIII, *Discorsi*, p. 205]
p. 182 [G.G., Vol. VIII, p. 215], p. 182 [G.G., Vol. VIII, p. 219]
p. 190,footnote [G.G., Vol. VIII, p. 128]

p. 206 [G.G., Vol. VIII, p. 198]
p. 207 [G.G., Vol. VIII, *Discorsi*, p. 209]
p. 207 [G.G., Vol. VIII, p. 208]
p. 208 [G.G., Vol. VIII, cit., p. 205]
pp. 221-222 [G.G., Vol. VIII, *Discorsi*, p. 344]
p. 224 [G.G., Vol. VIII, *Giornata aggiunta*, p. 345]
p. 224-225 [G.G., Vol. VIII, *Discorsi*, pp. 200-201]
p. 227 [G.G., Vol. VIII, *Discorsi*, p. 108]
p. 233 [G.G., Vol. VIII, pp. 332-333]
p. 233 [G.G., Vol. VIII, pp. 336-337]
p. 235 [G.G., Vol. VIII, p. 334]
p. 236 [G.G., Vol. VIII, p. 333]
p. 236 [G.G., Vol. VIII, p. 335]
p. 240-241 [G.G., Vol.VIII, *Discorsi*, pp. 333-334]
p. 241 [G.G., Vol.VIII, *Discorsi*, pp. 337]
p. 241 [G.G., Vol. VIII, pp. 246]
p. 244 [G.G., Vol. VIII, *Discorsi*, pp. 333]
p. 251, footnote [G.G., Vol. VIII, p. 119]

are reproduced by permission of the University of Wisconsin Press from
DRAKE STILLMAN, *Galileo Galilei , Two New Sciences*. © 1974 by the Board of Regents of the University of Wisconsin System.

Quotations of *Le Galleggianti* on the following pages:

p. 36, footnote [G.G., Vol. IV, p. 83]
p. 37, footnote [G.G., Vol. IV, pp. 88-89]
p. 38, footnote [G.G., Vol. IV, p. 89]
pp. 58-59 [G.G., Vol. IV, p. 98-99 and 107]
p. 64 [G.G., Vol.IV, p. 64]
pp. 73-74 [G.G., Vol. IV, pp. 93-94]
p. 74 [G.G., Vol. IV, p. 101-102]
p. 77 [G.G., Vol. IV, p. 122]
p. 77 [G.G., Vol. IV, pp. 120-121]
pp. 79-80 [G.G., Vol. IV, p. 121-122]

are reproduced by permission from
DRAKE STILLMAN, *Cause Experiment and Science – A Galilean dialogue incorporating a new English translation of Galileo's "Bodies that Stay atop Water or Move in It"*. © 1981, University of Chicago Press.

Quotations of *Le Mecaniche* on the following pages:

p. 11 [G.G., Vol. II, pp. 189-190]
p. 110 [G.G., Vol II, pp. 159-160]
pp. 110-111 [G.G., Vol.II, *Le Mecaniche*, p. 180]
p. 112 [G.G., Vol. II, p. 183]
pp. 112-113 [G.G., Vol. II, pp. 185-186]
pp. 113-114 [G.G., Vol. II, pp. 185-186]
p. 118 [G.G., Vol. II, p. 188]

are reproduced by permission of the University of Wisconsin Press from
DRABKIN I. E., *Galileo Galilei.* © 1960 by the Board of Regents of the University of Wisconsin System.

Quotations of *Il Saggiatore* on the following pages:

p. 84 [G.G., Vol. VI, p. 322]
pp. 84-85 [G.G., Vol. VI, pp. 322-323]
pp. 85-86 [G.G., Vol. VI, p. 323]

are reproduced by permission from
DRAKE STILLMAN and O' MALLEY C. D., *The Controversy on the Comets of 1618.*
© 1960, University of Pennsylvania Press.

Finito di stampare
nel mese di Settembre 2009
Compositori Ind. Grafiche - Bologna

www.ingramcontent.com/pod-product-compliance
Ingram Content Group UK Ltd.
Pitfield, Milton Keynes, MK11 3LW, UK
UKHW020242290926
15470UKWH00002B/694
9783642043529